THE FAMILIES OF FLOWERING PLANTS

I. DICOTYLEDONS

MACMILLAN AND CO., Limited
LONDON · BOMBAY · CALCUTTA · MADRAS
MELBOURNE

THE MACMILLAN COMPANY
NEW YORK · BOSTON · CHICAGO
DALLAS · SAN FRANCISCO

THE MACMILLAN CO. OF CANADA, Ltd.
TORONTO

THE FAMILIES OF
FLOWERING PLANTS

I. DICOTYLEDONS

ARRANGED ACCORDING TO A NEW SYSTEM
BASED ON THEIR PROBABLE PHYLOGENY

BY

J. HUTCHINSON, F.L.S.

ASSISTANT IN THE HERBARIUM, ROYAL BOTANIC GARDENS, KEW

ILLUSTRATIONS BY
W. E. TREVITHICK AND THE AUTHOR

MACMILLAN AND CO., LIMITED
ST. MARTIN'S STREET, LONDON
1926

COPYRIGHT

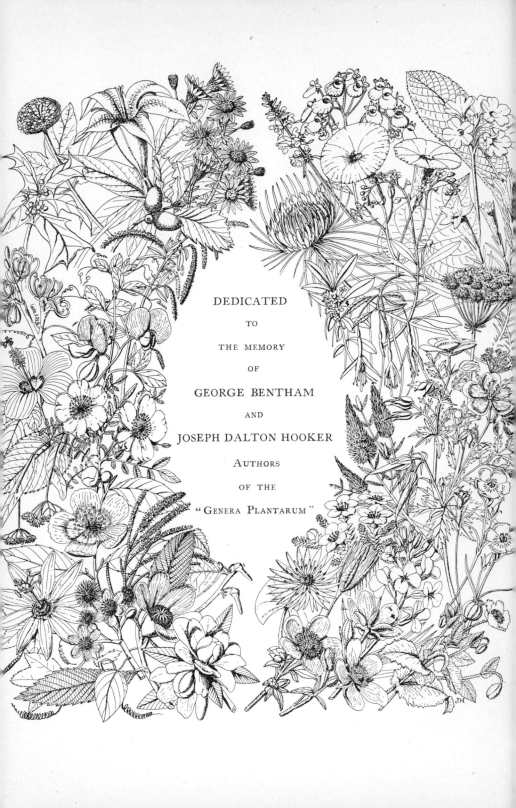

DEDICATED

TO

THE MEMORY

OF

GEORGE BENTHAM

AND

JOSEPH DALTON HOOKER

AUTHORS

OF THE

"GENERA PLANTARUM"

FOREWORD

THE production of a new work on the Families of Flowering Plants on phylogenetic lines, by a member of the Herbarium Staff of the Royal Botanic Gardens, is singularly appropriate, since the *Genera Plantarum* was prepared under the same roof. Mr. Hutchinson, in recognition of this fact, and also of his indebtedness to this classic work, very rightly dedicates his work to the memory of George Bentham and Joseph Dalton Hooker.

With our ever-increasing knowledge of the past and present distribution of plants a great need has been felt for a re-examination, and possibly a re-arrangement, of the families of the *Angiosperms*, with the object of discovering possible relationships, and also of throwing new light on the problems of plant distribution.

Of the various attempts towards a phylogenetic arrangement the system of Engler and Prantl has deservedly commanded universal attention. Their system has been widely accepted, though in recent years it has been subjected to some criticism. It is generally admitted that many anomalies in the older arrangements were adjusted and that great contributions were made to our knowledge of Taxonomic Botany ; but it has been felt that in some directions the deductions advanced in the *Pflanzenfamilien* were not always in accordance with generally accepted ideas, more particularly in Great Britain and America ; thus, for example, in regarding the *Amentiferae* as primitive, and by giving precedence to the *Monocotyledons*. The system of Engler and Prantl has been thought by some to have been built up on erroneous and illogical foundations.

Mr. Hutchinson has ventured to express his dissent from Engler and Prantl's views in this book and has returned, wisely as I think, to the position adopted by the authors of the *Genera Plantarum*, since he regards the *Ranales* on the one hand and the *Magnoliales* on the other as the starting-points of his phylogenetic arrangement.

His separation of the various families into two groups depending on their tendency to be herbaceous or arborescent is interesting and suggestive. In the charming and original frontispiece which he has designed and drawn with his facile pen, his views are graphically represented. With Engler and Prantl he is in some accord in his distribution of the apetalous families amongst the petaloid ones to which they appear to be most nearly related, though it will be found, from his careful consideration of the available facts, that his arrangement in many cases differs from that of the authors of the *Pflanzenfamilien.*

Mr. Hutchinson's contribution to the problem of plant phylogeny is of additional interest and value to botanists in general since he has studied the evidence afforded by fossil plants, and he draws attention to the important bearing of the fossil records in questions of plant relationships and plant distribution.

There is one feature of the book which will be of great practical value, and that is the artificial key to the families. This will, I feel sure, be welcomed by botanists, foresters, and all who are interested in the determination of plants, and it will be especially useful to workers in tropical countries.

Whether Mr. Hutchinson's new system be fully accepted or not, it will, I think, be readily conceded that this clear and admirably illustrated exposition of his views marks a distinct and noteworthy advance in our conception of the inter-relationships of the *Dicotyledons*, and forms a very valuable contribution to the study of the probable development and evolution of plant life.

"Diruit, aedificat, mutat quadrata rotundis" (HORACE, *Ep.* Bk. i. 1).

ARTHUR W. HILL.

ROYAL BOTANIC GARDENS,
    KEW.

AUTHOR'S PREFACE

THE book here presented is partly the outcome of a larger task the author has set himself in his leisure hours, towards which contributions have already been published in the *Kew Bulletin* during the last few years. The need for a small *Handbook of the Families of Flowering Plants* has long been felt by teachers, students, gardeners, travellers, and lovers of plants in general. The difference in the concept of plant families shown in the *Genera Plantarum* of Bentham and Hooker and in the latest edition of Engler and Gilg's *Syllabus* is very considerable, and students are apt to be confused by this divergence of treatment. The families of DICOTYLEDONS are therefore described according to more modern practice, *i.e.* they are smaller and in better defined groups, which are more easily fitted into the new phylogenetic scheme of classification here presented in complete form for the first time. In compiling these descriptions the fullest use has been made of the *Genera Plantarum*. A second volume will be devoted to the *Monocotyledons*, which the author intends to study specially before venturing to propose a new arrangement.

An *artificial analytical key* to these families, based on easily observed characters, would be useful it is thought to teacher and student alike, and by the use of this key and a pocket lens it should not be impossible for an intelligent person with only a slight knowledge of botany to allocate to their families most of the plants which he may meet with in any part of the world. A key based on the families as defined in Bentham and Hooker's *Genera Plantarum* was published by F. Thonner [1] in 1895, but has for a long time been out of print and unobtainable. The key here presented has been made entirely independently of that by Thonner and on somewhat different lines.

It is regrettable that the classical *Genera Plantarum* of Bentham and Hooker, perhaps the greatest pioneer botanical work of modern times, has never been made available to English readers in a popular form. The general sequence, however, appeared in a translation from the French work of Le Maout and Decaisne, edited by Hooker, and now long out of print. Had those distinguished authors seen fit to issue an English translation illustrated by their gifted botanical artist, Walter Fitch, it is probable that their work would still have held the field. As it is, it has largely been superseded by the great German work by Engler and Prantl, *Die natürliche Pflanzenfamilien*, published in German and copiously illustrated. Whilst the *Genera Plantarum* was based on the De Candolle system, which did not claim to be a phylogenetic system, the German work did make this claim. It is interesting to know what Hooker thought of the new system, and we may learn this from his *Life and Letters* by L. Huxley, vol. ii. p. 22. Writing to Arber he says : " With regard to your queries respecting the primitive type of Angiospermous plants, that subject

---

[1] F. Thonner, *Analytical Key to the Natural Orders of Flowering Plants*, London, 1895.

has never been far from my mind for upwards of half a century, during which period I have failed to grasp a feature in the Morphology, Physiology, or Geographical distribution of Angiosperms that gave much colour to whatever speculations I may have indulged in respecting it. I do not share Engler's views as expressed in his classification and writings. The classification is neither better nor worse in the abstract than De Candolle's (so-called), and is far more troublesome to apply for practical purposes. I hold to Robert Brown's view of the orders being reticulately not lineally related."

The supposition that the unisexual flower of the *Amentiferae*, or catkin group of plants, is primitive has been too readily accepted, and during recent years this theory has been frequently questioned. There is now a considerable body of opinion [1] in favour of the view that the whole of the *Dicotyledons* and *Monocotyledons* have been evolved from one common stock, and that that stock has at the present day its most primitive living representatives exhibited in the *Magnoliaceae* and *Ranunculaceae* and allied families, and that from such primitive types as these all other flowers have been derived by specialisation or reduction. In these early families we find the following characters associated :

(1) Free sepals and petals, (2) free and numerous hypogynous stamens, (3) free and numerous carpels, (4) small straight embryo in abundant uniform endosperm.

Furthermore, we believe that in flowering plants the arboreal or *woody* habit is generally more ancient than the herbaceous ; that only in some cases herbs have been derived from shrubs and trees. There are some very obvious examples. For instance, the *Papilionaceae*, largely herbaceous, are clearly derived from the more woody *Caesalpiniaceae* ; but *Clematis* (softly woody) is derived from *Anemone* (herbaceous). Perhaps it may be contended that in the present arrangement of families I have laid too much stress on the difference between the *woody* and the *herbaceous* habit. By separating these two types on very broad lines as a beginning, however, it becomes possible to establish more natural groups of closely allied families. Thus families such as the *Flacourtiaceae* (woody) and the *Violaceae* (mostly herbaceous), which have been closely associated on account of a single character, the *parietal placentation*, are now more widely separated. It is, too, significant that many of the primitive families are either *entirely woody* or *entirely herbaceous*. Examples that are wholly woody are *Magnoliaceae*, *Anonaceae*, etc. ; herbaceous, *Ranunculaceae*, *Papaveraceae*, *Crassulaceae*, *Saxifragaceae* (*sensu stricto*), *Caryophyllaceae* ; and often this habit character has persisted right to the end of a phylum, such as in *Lauraceae* (woody) and *Cruciferae* (herbaceous). In the primitive groups this difference in habit is often closely associated with a marked difference in the structure of the stomata of the leaves. In the woody group the guard cells are usually accompanied by special subsidiary cells parallel to the pore, whilst in the early herbaceous groups the guard-cells have no special subsidiary cells.[2] Of course in the case of more advanced families which show a mixed habit and which may have recruited their members from both groups on account of

---

[1] The student who wishes to read up the literature which deals with this subject should consult the following papers : C. E. Bessey in *Botanical Gazette*, 24. 145-178 (1897) ; Arber and Parkin in *Journ. Linn. Soc., Bot.* 38. 29-80 (1907) ; C. E. Bessey, " The Phylogenetic Taxonomy of Flowering Plants ", in *Ann. Missouri Bot. Gard.* 2. 109-164 (1915) ; Hutchinson in *Kew Bull.*, 1923.

[2] Parkin has independently been impressed with this stomatal difference. See his note in *Annals of Botany*, 38. 795 (1924).

convergence and parallel development, one would expect to find both types of stomata. This is well shown in the *Rosaceae*, amongst which the remarkably distinct woody tribe *Chrysobalaneae* is distinguished from the remainder of the family by having special subsidiary cells to the stomata.[1]

A phylogenetic classification is not necessarily one by which all plants may be readily determined ; rather the reverse. In the past too little regard to general affinity and too much notice of *Key* characters and *Floral Diagrams* has apparently been taken in working out systems of classification. For key characters are not always the characters of greatest phylogenetic importance. Very often a key is of necessity considerably artificial. It depends on the group ; the more natural the group, the more artificial the key. *A key mostly emphasises the differences amongst plants.* A truly natural and phylogenetic classification, however, should rather emphasise their *resemblances,* by which alone their true affinities may be ascertained. This I have attempted to do in the pages of this book.

I am particularly indebted to Mr. W. E. Trevithick, Temporary Assistant in the Herbarium, Kew, who has devoted much of his leisure time to the execution of many of the drawings in the following pages. The remainder are my own work, and our respective initials are inserted merely to distinguish them. A few only of these drawings are original, the remainder being adapted from other works (and they have lost nothing under his skilful pen). Their origin is always indicated. They are intended to give the student some idea of the general structure of each family, and they will probably be welcomed as a change from the continued repetition of the same drawings found in most text-books.

I am also very much indebted to my colleague, Mr. C. H. Wright, F.R.M.S., for reading the proofs ; to Dr. J. Burtt Davy for helpful suggestions and for testing the key with his *Flora of the Transvaal* ; to various other colleagues who have from time to time tested the key and assisted in other ways, including Dr. J. M. Dalziel, Mr. V. S. Summerhayes, Mr. P. G. Greenway ; and to Mr. H. A. G. Alston and Dr. W. Robyns (Brussels), who have also worked out a few of the maps.

I should also here make grateful acknowledgment of the kind help and encouragement extended by Dr. A. W. Hill, F.R.S., Director of the Royal Botanic Gardens, Kew, and to Mr. A. D. Cotton, F.L.S., Keeper of the Herbarium and Library, for facilities in the use of the unrivalled collections of specimens and drawings.

I shall welcome suggestions which will help to improve the system ; these will be gratefully acknowledged in the final work.

[1] See Solereder, *Systematic Anatomy of the Dicotyledons,* Engl. ed. 1. 301 (1908).

KEW, *May* 1925.

CONTENTS

SIGNS AND ABBREVIATIONS

♂ = male flower.   ♀ = female flower.   ⚥ = hermaphrodite (bisexual) flower.
B.H. = Bentham and Hooker, *Genera Plantarum.*
E.P. = Engler and Prantl, *Die natürliche Pflanzenfamilien.*
E.P.N. = Engler and Prantl, *Nachträge.*

INTRODUCTION

PERHAPS no subject is of more general interest to the younger generation of botanists of the present decade than the problem of the early race-history or *phylogeny* of plant life, and especially during recent years of flowering or seed-plants. The study of phylogeny, combined with that of the past and present distribution of plants, tends to awaken a new interest in Taxonomic Botany, and it should furnish important evidence in regard to the question of former land connections between areas now separated by wide oceans, a subject which has repeatedly attracted the attention of biologists. Especially is this the case where marked similarity in the floras of far-distant regions is clearly evident, such, for example, as those of (1) the Eastern United States and Eastern Asia, (2) the flora of the West African rain forest with that of the eastern coast of Brazil, (3) the Mascarene flora and that of Southern India, (4) the South African and West Australian floras, (5) the New Zealand and South-West American floras, and nearer home (6) the South-West British and Lusitanian floras.

Whether these areas were at one time connected by intervening land bridges, where now are deep oceans, or whether they were actually once contiguous areas which have now become separated, will for long remain a debatable question.[1] Certainly the comparatively new theory of the origin of continents, *i.e.* by displacement and gradual divergence one from another, would easily explain many of the problems of plant distribution. Though this subject cannot be dealt with here, it seems significant that with few exceptions these floral affinities of distant areas are entirely in an east and west direction and hardly ever north and south. I disregard for the moment the supposed affinity between the Mediterranean and South African floras, which may be due to parallel evolution in the two hemispheres and to similarity of climate and environment in these areas.

The distribution of the filmy fern, *Hymenophyllum ferrugineum*, of Juan Fernandez, Chile, and New Zealand, cannot easily be explained otherwise than by a former land connection, especially when we consider also the distribution of *Galaxias attenuata*,[2] a freshwater fish, which occurs in South-East Australia, Tasmania, New Zealand, and subantarctic South America. A further parallel is the distinct genus *Eucryphia* (see map, p. 188). I merely quote these examples from among several others to show that the phylogeny of plants is intimately connected with many interesting biological problems

[1] See A. Wegener, " The Origin of Continents and Oceans ", in *Discovery* 3 : 114-118, Figs. 1-3 (1922), and his recent book.
[2] See Cockayne, " The Vegetation of New Zealand ", in Engl. and Drude, *Die Veg. der Erde* 14 : 326 (1921).

and should not be neglected, and a phylogenetic system of classification should be the ultimate aim of taxonomy. In fact the description of every new genus, every new species or form of plant, may be regarded as a contribution towards this end.

SYSTEMS OF CLASSIFICATION

The number of systems of classification is now very considerable. There is not space here to consider them, but for an excellent account of the earlier systems the reader is referred to Lindley's *Vegetable Kingdom* (Introduction), and for later schemes to Rendle's *Classification of Flowering Plants* (vol. i., *Monocotyledons*, Historical Introduction). Since Lindley's time, however, only two great treatises have appeared which have commanded universal attention— (1) the *Genera Plantarum* of Bentham and Hooker, published in 1862–1883, which elaborated the De Candolle System, and (2) *Die natürliche Pflanzenfamilien* of Engler and Prantl (1887–1909). From a phylogenetic standpoint both these works have been subjected to a considerable amount of criticism, especially that of Bentham and Hooker. And in recent years the Englerian System has been assailed by certain North American [1] and British [2] botanists who have devoted special attention to the subject. Opinion in America in particular seems to have changed from an almost universal acceptance of the German system in favour of a modification of the arrangement of Bentham and Hooker. This criticism referred especially to the question of the relative primitiveness of the various groups from which a start should be made, such, for example, as the position of the " Amentiferae " and other apetalous groups, and of the Monocotyledons.

BENTHAM AND HOOKER'S " GENERA PLANTARUM "

The system of Bentham and Hooker was never intended to express a complete phylogenetic scheme of classification, for it is but a more extended arrangement of Jussieu's work elaborated as long ago as 1779, and further expounded by De Candolle in 1818, when botanists were still imbued with the idea of the fixity of species, and long before they had the aid of the Darwinian theory of descent as their guide. Perhaps Jussieu should be reckoned second only to Linnaeus in that he was the first botanist to co-ordinate the genera of plants into families more or less as we now know them. Although a few of the names of his groups are unfamiliar to present-day botanists, nearly all are still in use in a slightly modified form. Bentham and Hooker's work was primarily concerned with a practical handbook to the genera of plants arranged in such a manner as best to facilitate their determination. For the moment, however, we may assume that Bentham and Hooker's *Genera Plantarum* was intended to express a more or less natural system, and proceed to examine the arrangement of their main groups. They began with the *Polypetalae*, their first order (cohort) being the *Ranales*, composed of the well-known *Ranunculaceae* and allied families, characterised by apocarpy and hypogyny of the

---

[1] See especially C. E. Bessey, " The Phylogeny and Taxonomy of Angiosperms ", *Bot. Gaz.* 24 : 145-178 (1897); and *Ann. Missouri Bot. Gard.* 2 : 109-164 (1915).

[2] E. A. N. Arber and J. Parkin, " The Origin of Angiosperms ", *Journ. Linn. Soc. Bot.* 38 : 29 (1907). See also H. F. Wernham's suggestive papers on "Floral Evolution " in *New Phytologist*, 10 : 73 *et seq.*

flower. From these they proceeded to a discifloral series and finally (in the *Polypetalae*) to the calycifloral perigynous and epigynous types of flower. After these the *Gamopetalae* were enumerated, then the *Monochlamydeae* (*Apetalae*) and *Gymnosperms*, and finally the *Monocotyledons*. In elaborating their system, the *Monochlamydeae* were unfortunately retained as a group apart from the *Polypetalae*, and it is to this point and also to the anomalous position of the *Gymnosperms* that most criticism has been directed in the past. I use the word retained, for these distinguished authors were well aware of the true affinities of the families which are included in these two unnatural groups. This is clearly seen by reference to the notes on relationships at the end of each family description, wherein they point out quite clearly their affinities with families in the *Polypetalae*.

THE SYSTEM OF ENGLER AND PRANTL

The chief difference between this system and that of Bentham and Hooker is the amalgamation of Jussieu's groups *Polypetalae* and *Monochlamydeae* under the single group *Archichlamydeae*, and in the *Monocotyledons* taking precedence of the *Dicotyledons*. But in Engler's *Archichlamydeae* those apetalous families composing the so-called group *Amentiferae* or catkin bearers (*Betulaceae*, etc.) are regarded as being the most primitive and precede such petaliferous families as *Ranunculaceae* and *Magnoliaceae*. Bessey[1] has contended, however, and many botanists will agree with him, that polypetaly was earlier and that one of the first modifications of it was probably in the direction of apetaly, a condition reached by many plants in the earlier geological periods, but by relatively smaller numbers at the present day.

C. Robertson[2] has ably discussed the question of the primitive or non-primitive character of the " Amentiferae " group of *Apetalae*, on which the acceptance of Engler's views so much depends. He offers the theory that primitive Angiosperms were already entomophilous and that anemophilous types are metamorphosed entomophilous flowers resulting from reduction and degradation, and are not at all primitive. Probably too much importance has been attributed to the anemophily of the *Amentiferae*, on the false analogy of the Gymnosperms. It seems very probable that extreme reduction of the perianth and consequent loss of attractiveness to insects would result in the adoption of another mode of pollen transference, by the wind, *which in this case would not be a primitive condition* as it undoubtedly is in *Gymnosperms*. In my opinion the universally accepted theory[3] of the foliar origin of the carpel *is fatal to the assumption that the " Amentiferae " are primitive.* Many of the *Amentiferae* have an ovary composed of the *union of two or more carpels*, which must be the result of cohesion and reduction from older groups *which originally had free carpels.*

Regarding the origin of *Ranunculaceae* and allied families, after a careful examination of these groups, I find myself unable to accept Hallier's view[4]

[1] Bessey, *Bot. Gaz.* 24 : 151 (1897).
[2] C. Robertson, " The Structure of the Flowers and the Mode of Pollination of the Primitive Angiosperms ", *Bot. Gaz.* 37 : 294-298 (1904).
[3] See Arber and Parkin in *Journ. Linn. Soc. Bot.* 38 : 47 (1907).
[4] H. Hallier, " Provisional Scheme of the Natural (Phylogenetic) System of Flowering Plants ", in *New Phytologist*, 4 : 151-162 (1905) ; see especially p. 157.

that the *Ranunculaceae* and *Nymphaeaceae* have descended from the *Magnoliaceae* through the *Schizandraceae, Lardizabalaceae*, and *Berberidaceae*. It is a far cry indeed from a Buttercup to a Magnolia. To my mind the floral structure of *Berberidaceae* and *Lardizabalaceae* suggests evolution in entirely the opposite direction, *i.e.* from the *Ranunculaceae*. There are many connecting links between the *Ranunculaceae* and the *Berberidaceae*, and the latter appear to be the reduced and more recent forms. The relative antiquity of woody and herbaceous plants has been the subject of most interesting and instructive papers by Sinnott and Bailey,[1] whose researches go to show that in the flowering plants herbs, as a rule, have been derived from woody plants. However probable this may be, I do not think it can account for the origin of *Ranunculaceae* from any existing woody group. That herbs have been derived from ligneous types in certain families seems clear from some of the examples they quote, but it seems to me that the theory should be applied with considerable caution, for it is reasonable to suppose that the reverse may have frequently occurred, and that an herbaceous group may have evolved woody or semi-woody types. The study of this subject from both standpoints might be productive of interesting results. The type of wood peculiar to *Clematis, Berberis*, and the *Menispermaceae* generally, may owe its peculiarity to derivation from *herbaceous* ancestors. From a consideration of floral structure and wide distribution the genus *Clematis* with its woody habit, opposite leaves, its induplicate-valvate sepals and apetalous condition, in conjunction with this view regarding the origin of woody structure, may be traced back through the intermediate genus *Clematopsis* (*Kew Bull.*, 1920, 12-22) to the herbaceous and more primitive genus *Anemone*, by way of *Anemone*, § *Pulsatilla*. There are wide gaps in the relationships of the genera of *Berberidaceae*, but the genus *Berberis* may be similarly traced through *Mahonia*, and some lost type of plant related to *Epimedium*, which is itself a highly evolved member of the family. And similar reasoning may be put forward regarding the origin of the *Menispermaceae* and *Aristolochiaceae*, where in the case of the latter family complete suppression of the inner perianth has been carried out, as in *Clematis*. It is significant that the production of peculiar woody structure in these groups should be accompanied by reduction and degradation of the flowers. For instance all the New Zealand species of *Clematis* are dioecious.

CONSIDERATIONS FOR THE DELIMITATION OF GROUPS OF FAMILIES

With the exception of the primary division into DICOTYLEDONS and MONOCOTYLEDONS, large groups are usually artificial, especially if the characteristic fixed upon to distinguish them is a *general tendency* and founded on a *single* character. Examples are the De Candollean artificial groups *Thalamiflorae, Disciflorae, Calyciflorae, Inferae*, and to a less extent the *Parietales, Centrospermae*, and *Amentiferae*. The special characteristics indicated by the names of some of these groups are *general tendencies* in many families of flowering plants. Although it is still very convenient to recognise two main groups of Dicotyledons as *Archichlamydeae* (Polypetalae + Monochlamydeae) and *Metachlamydeae* (Gamopetalae, Sympetalae, etc.), a phylogenetic classification would be better attained if the gamopetalous character were regarded in

[1] E. W. Sinnott and J. W. Bailey, " The Origin and Dispersal of Herbaceous Angiosperms ", in *Ann. Bot.* 28 : 547-600 (1914).

its true light, *i.e.* as a *general tendency*, for gamopetaly is quite a common feature in many so-called polypetalous families.[1] It is perhaps too early to suggest so revolutionary a change. The result, however, would be the closer approximation of such clearly related families as the *Anonaceae* and *Sapotaceae* ; *Caryophyllaceae, Primulaceae*, and *Gentianaceae* ; the *Rhamnaceae* and *Myrsinaceae*, etc. But, on the other hand, it would be very difficult to place conveniently the long phylum shown in the present arrangement of families beginning with the *Gentianaceae* and ending with the *Labiatae*. In a new classification, therefore, smaller groups must be recognised, which are bound together by a *combination of characters*, and which allow the association of the general tendencies of floral development such, at any rate, as *perigyny, epigyny*, and *apetaly*. For this reason I have proposed (*Kew Bull.*, 1921, 185-191) the establishment of the order *Magnoliales* as distinct from *Ranales*, because I consider that they may have been evolved from separate primitive stocks and have been developed on parallel lines, *i.e.* with strobilus-like, hypogynous, polycarpellary flowers. The ultimate development of the more primitive families of these two groups, the *Magnoliaceae* and *Ranunculaceae* respectively, is entirely dissimilar, the one remaining arboreal, the other mainly herbaceous. Of course these two main phyla have often converged on similar lines and are associated in the same family, as is probably the case in *Rosaceae*.

CONSIDERATIONS FOR THE DELIMITATION OF FAMILIES

A great divergence of opinion is evident in the two principal systems of classification in regard to the delimitation of families. Thus the number of families of flowering plants, including the Gymnosperms, in the *Genera Plantarum* is 200, in the *Pflanzenfamilien* 280, whilst the number is further increased in Engler and Gilg's *Syllabus*. There is much to be said in favour of reducing the size of families wherever reasonably possible, and I am in favour of going slightly further even than Engler. For instance, to include in the *Magnoliaceae* such distinct families as the *Winteraceae, Schizandraceae, Trochodendraceae, Himantandraceae*, and *Cercidiphyllaceae* is decidedly incongruous. If these latter families are excluded, the *Magnoliaceae* proper is a homogeneous group, the characters of which are easily grasped. A similar argument may be advanced for the segregation of *Papaveraceae* and *Fumariaceae*, the *Guttiferae* and *Quiinaceae*, the *Theaceae* (*Ternstroemiaceae*), *Marcgraviaceae*, and *Caryocaraceae*, and many other families, even the *Leguminosae* into the *Caesalpiniaceae, Mimosaceae*, and *Papilionaceae* (*Fabaceae*). On the other hand I should consider it going too far to divide the *Compositae* into the *Asteraceae, Vernoniaceae, Eupatoriaceae*, etc., whilst the wisdom of separating the *Rosaceae* into several families is rather doubtful. If more than one family be recognised in *Rosaceae*, then at least ten will have to be segregated. I am not in favour of this undue multiplication. All this goes to prove that the delimitation of families, of genera, and of species is sometimes very much a matter of taste and personal idiosyncrasy. I should also add of judgment and experience ! And it is on this account that the work of Bentham and Hooker carries perhaps more weight, from being the production of a single pair of minds, than that of Engler and Prantl, who enlisted the services of a large number of botanists to carry out

[1] For example, *Anonaceae, Meliaceae, Rutaceae*, etc.

the work, resulting in a great diversity of treatment, especially as regards the genera.

I give below the general principles of classification which I have adopted in arranging the groups (orders) and families in the general scheme here presented.

General Principles adopted for the Classification of Flowering Plants [1]

Other things being equal, it may be stated that :

1. Evolution is both (1) upwards and (2) downwards, the latter involving degradation and degeneration ; examples : (1) the gamopetalous condition ; epigyny ; (2) the apetalous state of many flowers ; unisexuality in flowering plants.

2. Evolution does not necessarily involve all organs of the plant at the same time, and one organ or set of organs may be advancing whilst another set is stationary or retrograding.

3. Evolution has generally been consistent, and when a particular progression or retrogression has set in, it is persisted in to the end of the phylum ; examples : the strong tendency to zygomorphy of the corolla coupled with the reduction in the number of stamens in the hypogynous *Metachlamydeae* ; the great tendency to perigyny and epigyny in the *Archichlamydeae* and *Metachlamydeae*, as exhibited in the families *Umbelliferae* and *Rubiaceae* respectively.

Relating to the General Habit of Plants

4. In certain groups, trees and shrubs are probably more primitive than herbs ; examples : *Mimosaceae* and *Caesalpiniaceae* (trees and shrubs) as compared with the derived family *Papilionaceae* (*Fabaceae*) (mostly herbaceous).

5. Trees and shrubs are older than climbers, the latter habit having been acquired through particular environment.

6. Perennials are older than biennials, and from them annuals have been derived ; note the extraordinarily few annuals in the primitive family *Ranunculaceae* ; the great number in the more advanced and natural family *Cruciferae*.

7. Aquatic Phanerogams are as a rule more recent than terrestrial (at any rate in the members of the same family or genus), and the same may be said of epiphytes, saprophytes, and parasites.

Relating to the General Structure of Flowering Plants

8. Plants with collateral vascular bundles arranged in a cylinder (Dicotyledons) are more primitive in origin than those with scattered

[1] The reader is referred here to a second essay by Bessey, " Phylogenetic Taxonomy ", published in the *Annals of the Missouri Botanic Garden*, vol. ii. 112. The present writer cannot accept all Bessey's generalisations nor the system he proposed, but his principles are given above together with some additional observations.

bundles (Monocotyledons), though it does not necessarily follow that the latter have been directly derived from the former.

9. The spiral arrangement of leaves on the stem and of the floral leaves precedes that of the opposite whorled type.

10. As a rule simple leaves precede compound leaves.

Relating to the Flowers and Fruits of Plants

11. Bisexual (hermaphrodite) preceded unisexual flowers, and the dioecious is probably more recent than the monoecious condition.

12. The solitary flower is more primitive than the inflorescence, the highest forms of the latter being the umbel and capitulum ; examples of the latter : *Umbelliferae, Compositae.*

13. Spirally imbricate floral parts are more primitive than whorled and valvate ; examples : *Magnolia* and *Clematis.*

14. Many-parted flowers (polymerous) precede, and the type with few parts (oligomerous) follows from it, being accompanied by a progressive sterilisation of reproductive parts (sporophylls) ; examples : *Magnolia* and Wallflower.

15. Petaliferous flowers precede apetalous ones, the latter being the result of reduction.

16. Free petals (polypetaly) are more primitive than connate petals (gamopetaly).

17. Actinomorphy (regularity) of the flower is an earlier type than zygomorphy (irregularity) ; examples : *Caltha* and *Delphinium.*

18. Hypogyny is the primitive structure, and from it perigyny and epigyny were derived later.

19. Free carpels (apocarpy) are more primitive and from them connate carpels resulted ; sometimes, however, when the carpels have remained loosely united during evolution they may again become quite free ; example : *Asclepiadaceae.*

20. Many carpels (polycarpy) preceded few carpels (oligocarpy) ; examples : *Ranunculus* and *Nigella.*

21. The endospermic seed with small embryo is primitive and the non-endospermic seed higher ; example : *Ranunculaceae* and *Rosaceae.*

22. In the primitive flowers there are many stamens, in the higher flowers few stamens : *Ranunculus* and *Cheiranthus.* This condition may, however, be reversed in response to the needs of insect life within the confines of a single family like *Papaveraceae,* where bees feed on the pollen.

23. Separate stamens preceded connate stamens ; examples : *Tiliaceae* and *Malvaceae* ; *Campanulaceae* and *Lobeliaceae.*

24. Aggregate [1] fruits are more recent than single fruits, and as a rule the capsule precedes the drupe or berry.

---

[1] *I.e.* fruits formed from several separate flowers, as in *Morinda* (Rubiaceae).

The following table summarises the fundamental differences between the systems of (1) Bentham and Hooker, (2) Engler and Prantl, and (3) the system proposed in these pages :—

Bentham and Hooker, *Genera Plantarum.*	Engler and Prantl, *Die natürliche Pflanzenfamilien.*	System here proposed.
Flowering plants divided into a few large groups based mainly on single and mostly artificial characters. Closely allied families often widely separated in consequence. This was never claimed to be a phylogenetic system, but for practical purposes has served a very useful term. Based on the earlier De Candolle System (1818), itself an elaboration and slight modification of Jussieu's arrangement proposed as early as 1779. This system was therefore conceived under the influence of the old dogma of the fixity of species, and long before the theory of descent was propounded. As a *Genera Plantarum*, will ever remain a classic.	A phylogenetic system proposed subsequent to the acceptance of the theory of descent. Based on Eichler's System, and on the assumption that in flowering plants the *absence of a perianth* is a *primitive* feature. Thus families such as *Casuarinaceae, Piperaceae, Salicaceae, Betulaceae, Fagaceae, Urticaceae,* etc. are regarded as primitive and are placed before families such as *Magnoliaceae* and *Ranunculaceae.* Disregards the fact that many of these families without a perianth are characterised by having a gynaecium composed of the union of two or more carpels, a condition at variance with the universally accepted theory that the carpel is a modified leaf. With such an accepted view as to the origin of the carpel, a *syncarpous* ovary could hardly have preceded an *apocarpous* one. Moreover a syncarpous ovary is characteristic of nearly all the *highly placed* of Engler's *Archichlamydeae* and of *Metachlamydeae* (Gamopetalae), the later group accepted by all authors as being the most highly evolved of the *Dicotyledons.* *Monocotyledons* precede the *Dicotyledons.* Recent work on the fossil records gives little support to this system.	A phylogenetic system based on the assumption that plants *with sepals and petals,* associated with other floral and anatomical characters regarded as also primitive, are *more ancient phylogenetically* than plants without sepals or petals. This seems a logical interpretation of the theory that the parts of an angiospermous flower are modified leaves. *Free parts* are regarded as *primitive,* and *connate* or *adnate* parts as *more recent.* The *spiral* arrangement of parts is more primitive than the *cyclic* (whorled), and *numerous free* stamens are earlier than the *few* or connate. Also the hermaphrodite precedes the unisexual flower. In this system the groups (orders or cohorts) are smaller, and families are associated which show close general relationship. *Resemblances* emphasised rather than *differences.* The *Monochlamydeae* of Bentham and Hooker are distributed amongst the *Polypetalae as reduced forms* and are regarded as being more recent. The *Monocotyledons* are placed after the *Dicotyledons,* from which they were derived at an early stage, the point of origin being the *Ranales* and perhaps other groups. Recent work on the fossil records strongly supports these theories.

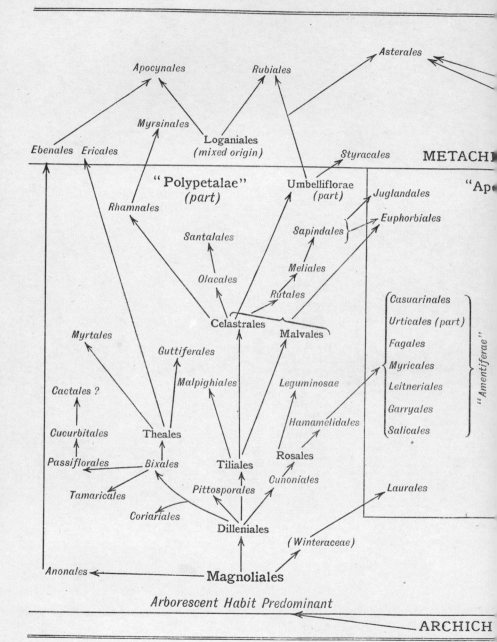

Diagram showing the probable course of evolution of the **Dicotyledons.** This group is theoretically divided int⸱
respectively. From these parallel basic stocks an attempt is made to show the probable path of developm⸱

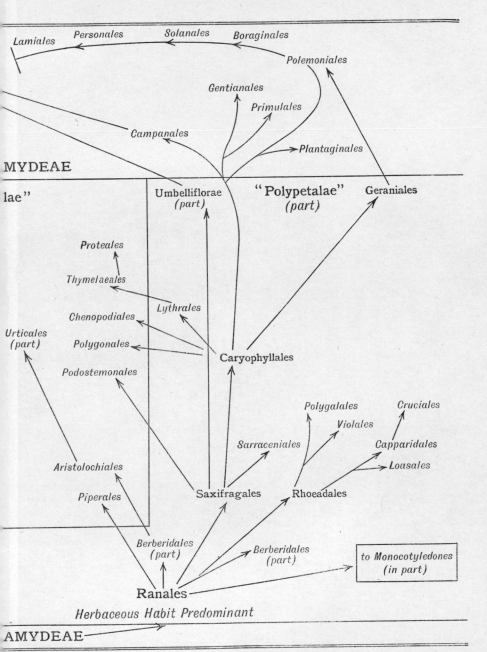

Lamiales   Personales   Solanales   Boraginales

Polemoniales

Gentianales
Primulales

Campanales

Plantaginales

MYDEAE

lae"   Umbelliflorae   "Polypetalae"   Geraniales
              (part)   (part)

Proteales

Thymelaeales
                        Lythrales
Chenopodiales

Urticales
(part)   Polygonales

Podostemonales
                                              Polygalales   Cruciales
                                                      Violales
                                    Sarraceniales   Capparidales

Aristolochiales   Loasales

Piperales   Saxifragales   Rhoeadales

                 Berberidales   Berberidales   to Monocotyledones
                 (part)   (part)   (in part)

Ranales

Herbaceous Habit Predominant

AMYDEAE

wo main phyla, the one mostly *woody*, the other mostly *herbaceous*, starting with the *Magnoliales* and *Ranales*
t of the principal groups, those groups in roman type being regarded as the main centres of development.

CONSPECTUS OF PRINCIPAL LIVING GROUPS OF FLOWERING PLANTS

PHYLUM I. GYMNOSPERMAE.[1]—Ovules naked, not enclosed by an ovary, receiving the pollen-grains (microspores), mainly borne by the wind, directly on the micropyle ; embryo-sac enclosed in the nucellus and filled with tissue (rudimentary prothallus) before fertilisation and containing two or more egg-cells (archegonia), the latter usually consisting of a large egg-cell and a short neck ; pollen-grains (microspores) spherical or oval, often with a bladder-like extension of the outer coat (extine), containing a prothallus of two or more cells, one of which produces two non-motile or rarely motile male cells. Cotyledons two or several, very rarely one by suppression. Wood (except in *Gnetaceae*) with no true vessels. Trees and shrubs with usually evergreen xerophilous, needle-like or fern-like foliage and unisexual " flowers ", mainly found in the mountainous and cool temperate regions of the world, extending to the limits of phanerogamic ligneous vegetation on high mountains and towards the poles. A comparatively small but very ancient phylum of plants, abundant in past ages, but now represented only by the Cycads, Yews, Pine-trees, etc., very numerous in individuals and yielding many valuable timber trees, but no food plants of any importance.

PHYLUM II. ANGIOSPERMAE.—Ovules enclosed in an ovary usually crowned by a style and stigma, the latter receiving the pollen-grains (microspores) mainly through the agency of insects, becoming wind-pollinated when much reduced. Wood when present consisting of true vessels.[2] A more recently evolved phylum than the *Gymnospermae*, and constituting the bulk of the present world vegetation, yielding valuable timbers and practically all food, forage and medicinal plants.

SUBPHYLUM I. DICOTYLEDONES.—Embryonic plant with 2 seed-leaves (cotyledons). Vascular bundles of the stem usually arranged in a circle (except in a few genera of the lower herbaceous families [3] (*q.v.*) which have scattered bundles). Leaves typically net-veined, opposite or alternate. Flowers usually pentamerous or tetramerous.

Division I. ARCHICHLAMYDEAE.[4]—Petals free from each other or absent (very rarely united at the base).

Division II. METACHLAMYDEAE.[5]—Petals united into a tube.

SUBPHYLUM II. MONOCOTYLEDONES.—Embryonic plant with only 1 seed leaf. Vascular bundles of the stem closed and scattered. Leaves typically parallel-nerved, alternate. Flowers usually trimerous.

This book deals only with the Subphylum DICOTYLEDONES.

[1] For convenience I include in this conspectus the Gymnosperms, though not, strictly speaking, true flowering plants.

[2] Except in some *Winteraceae* (*Drimys*, etc.).

[3] Cf. *Ranunculaceae*, p. 94.

[4] From ἀρχή (beginning) and χλαμύς (cloak), referring to the perianth ; includes *Polypetalae* and *Monochlamydeae* (*Apetalae*).

[5] Probably the most suitable name for *Gamopetalae* or *Sympetalae*, from μετά (implying change) and χλαμύς (cloak). These two divisions are convenient, but more or less artificial, being founded only on a *single* character.

[TABLE

Subphylum DICOTYLEDONES
Division I. ARCHICHLAMYDEAE

Notes on Affinity (Origin and further Development).	Sequence of Orders (Cohorts) [1] and Families.[2] A cross-line indicates the end of a group.	General Characters and Tendencies [3] of Orders (Cohorts).
	1. MAGNOLIALES	
Entirely woody groups, probably the most ancient type of existing Dicotyledons and indicating ancestry of the following also predominantly woody groups beginning respectively with *Dilleniales,Cunoniales,Tiliales.*	1. *Magnoliaceae*, p. 81. 2. *Winteraceae*, p. 81. 3. *Schizandraceae*, p. 83. 4. *Himantandraceae*, p. 84. 5. *Lactoridaceae*, p. 85. 6. *Trochodendraceae*, p. 85. 7. *Cercidiphyllaceae*, p. 86.	Hypogynous; becoming ♂♀ with reduction; acyclic to cyclic; apocarpous; petals present; stamens ∞, free or rarely in a mass; endosperm copious, not ruminate; embryo minute.
	2. ANONALES	
More or less fixed types clearly related to but more advanced than the above; probably little further evolution from this type; tropical distribution.	8. *Anonaceae*, p. 87. 9. *Eupomatiaceae*, p. 88.	Hypogynous to rarely perigynous; ♂; apocarpous to very rarely syncarpous with parietal placentation; petals present; occasionally gamopetalous; stamens ∞,free; endosperm copious, markedly ruminate.
	3. LAURALES	
Reductions from the *Magnoliales*, approaching most nearly the *Winteraceae*; higher types perigynous; mainly tropics.	10. *Monimiaceae*, p. 89. 11. *Lauraceae*, p. 90. 12. *Gomortegaceae*, p. 91. 13. *Hernandiaceae*, p. 92. 14. *Myristicaceae*, p. 93.	Hypogynous to perigynous; ♂ or ♂ ♀; cyclic; apocarpous to monocarpellary; no petals; stamens definite, free; endosperm copious, uniform or rarely ruminate or absent; embryo minute.

---

[1] The Orders (Cohorts) here recognised are much smaller conceptions than those of either Bentham and Hooker or of Engler, and correspond more with the Suborders (Unterreihe) of the latter. So far as possible nomenclature according to priority is used for these groups.

[2] Family names, mainly as in Bentham and Hooker, *Genera Plantarum*, but with many additional segregate families; where Englerian names differ they appear in brackets.

[3] The characteristics given here are quite general and do not account for exceptions, which occur in several of the orders.

The above list (excluding *Metachlamydeae*) was published by the author in the *Kew Bulletin*, 1923.

Notes on Affinity (Origin and further Development).	Sequence of Orders (Cohorts) and Families. A cross-line indicates the end of a group.	General Characters and Tendencies of Orders (Cohorts).

4. RANALES

Herbaceous (often with scattered vascular bundles) to softly woody groups (wood of special type probably derived from herbaceous), from which may have been derived the following herbaceous progressive groups beginning with *Rhoeadales*, *Saxifragales*, herbaceous *Rosaceae* and *Umbelliflorae*, and the reduced and degraded *Aristolochiales* and *Piperales*. — Considerable affinity with Monocotyledons, particularly with apocarpous families such as *Alismaceae*.

15. *Ranunculaceae*, p. 94.
16. *Cabombaceae*, p. 95.
17. *Ceratophyllaceae*, p. 95.
18. *Nymphaeaceae*, p. 96.

Hypogynous to rarely perigynous; ☿; hemicyclic to rarely cyclic; apocarpous; petals present; stamens ∞, free; endosperm copious, uniform, very rarely absent; embryo minute.

5. BERBERIDALES

19. *Berberidaceae*, p. 97.
20. *Circaeasteraceae*, p. 98.
21. *Lardizabalaceae*, p. 99.
22. *Sargentadoxaceae*, p. 100.
23. *Menispermaceae*, p. 101.

Hypogynous; ♂ to ♂ ♀; cyclic; one or few free carpels; petals present, small; stamens definite, free; endosperm copious, sometimes ruminate; embryo small to large; herbaceous to low woody or climbing habit; wood often with broad medullary rays.

6. ARISTOLOCHIALES

See note under *Ranales*; probably reduced *Berberidales* by way of *Menispermaceae* and with very similar wood; accompanying the reduction is the parasitic habit.

24. *Aristolochiaceae*, p. 102.
25. *Cytinaceae*, p. 102.
26. *Hydnoraceae*, p. 103.
27. *Nepenthaceae*, p. 104.

Hypogynous to epigynous; apetalous; ovary superior, half-inferior to inferior; stamens ∞ to few; parietal to axile placentation; endosperm present or absent; small to large embryo; herbaceous to climbing habit with wood as in *Berberidales*; some parasites with reduction of leaves.

7. PIPERALES

Reduced types from the *Ranales*, often with scattered vascular bundles as in *Monocotyledons*.

28. *Piperaceae*, p. 106.
29. *Saururaceae*, p. 106.
30. *Chloranthaceae*, p. 107.
31. *Lacistemaceae*, p. 108.

No perianth (usually); ovary mostly superior; placentas parietal to subaxile; endosperm copious; embryo minute.

Notes on Affinity (Origin and further Development).	Sequence of Orders (Cohorts) and Families. A cross-line indicates the end of a group.	General Characters and Tendencies of Orders (Cohorts).
	8. RHOEADALES	
	32. *Papaveraceae*, p. 109. 33. *Fumariaceae*, p. 110.	Hypogynous to rarely subperigynous; ☿; cyclic (except sometimes the stamens); petals present; syncarpous; parietal placentation; stamens ∞ and free, to definite; endosperm copious, uniform; embryo minute; flowers actinomorphic to zygomorphic.
Herbaceous to more or less woody groups, most of which have developed into fixed types and have not given rise to further evolution; gradual increasing zygomorphy of the flower with reduction of stamens and ovules.	**9. LOASALES** 34. *Turneraceae*, p. 110. 35. *Loasaceae*, p. 111.	Hypogynous to epigynous; stamens numerous and sometimes in bundles, to few; syncarpous with parietal placentation; endosperm copious; embryo straight; seeds often strophiolate; flowers actinomorphic.
	10. CAPPARIDALES 36. *Capparidaceae*, p. 112. 37. *Moringaceae*, p. 113. 38. *Tovariaceae*, p. 113.	Hypogynous or subperigynous; ☿; petals present; syncarpous with parietal placentation; carpels 2; stamens numerous to few, mostly equal; endosperm absent; embryo variously folded; flowers actinomorphic to zygomorphic.
	11. CRUCIALES 39. *Cruciferae*, p. 114.	More or less as above, but stamens 6, tetradynamous; petals 4; ovary usually divided by a false septum.

Notes on Affinity (Origin and further Development).	Sequence of Orders (Cohorts) and Families. A cross-line indicates the end of a group.	General Characters and Tendencies of Orders (Cohorts).
	12. VIOLALES	
Herbaceous to more or less woody groups, most of which have developed into fixed types and have not given rise to further evolution; gradual increasing zygomorphy of the flower with reduction of stamens and ovules.	40. *Violaceae*, p. 115. 41. *Resedaceae*, p. 116.	Hypogynous to perigynous; ☿ rarely ♀ ♂; petals present; syncarpous with parietal placentation; stamens several to few; endosperm present or absent; embryo straight or curved; flowers mostly zygomorphic.
	13. POLYGALALES	
	42. *Polygalaceae*, p. 117. 43. *Trigoniaceae*, p. 119. 44. *Vochysiaceae*, p. 119.	More or less as in preceding, but axile or apical placentation; stamens 8 or less with some infertility and cohesion.
	14. SAXIFRAGALES	
	45. *Crassulaceae*, p. 120. 46. *Cephalotaceae*, p. 121. 47. *Saxifragaceae* (*sensu stricto*), p. 123.	More or less perigynous to rarely epigynous; ☿; cyclic; apocarpous to syncarpous with axile placentation; stamens definite, free; endosperm copious; embryo small, straight.
Herbaceous groups closely connected with the *Ranales* (*sensu stricto*) but slightly more advanced; several small groups given off showing very special leaf morphology and habitat.	**15. SARRACENIALES**	
	48. *Droseraceae*, p. 123. 49. *Sarraceniaceae*, p. 124.	More or less as in *Saxifragales*, but plants mostly insectivorous; syncarpous; placentation parietal to axile; stamens numerous to few.
	16. PODOSTEMONALES	
	50. *Podostemonaceae*, p. 125. 51. *Hydrostachyaceae*, p. 125.	Possibly very much reduced apetalous types of *Saxifragales*, with peculiar habit, but position altogether problematical.

Notes on Affinity (Origin and further Development).	Sequence of Orders (Cohorts) and Families. A cross-line indicates the end of a group.	General Characters and Tendencies of Orders (Cohorts).

17. CARYOPHYLLALES

A prolific herbaceous group which has given rise to apetalous hypogynous groups such as *Polygonales, Chenopodiales*, perigynous petaliferous groups as *Lythrales*, perigynous apetalous groups as *Thymelaeales* and part of *Metachlamydeae* (*Gamopetalae*).

52. *Elatinaceae*, p. 126.
53. *Caryophyllaceae*, p. 127.
54. *Molluginaceae*, p. 128.
55. *Ficoidaceae* (*Aizoaceae*), p. 129.
56. *Portulacaceae*, p. 130.

Hypogynous to perigynous; ☿; cyclic; syncarpous; axile to free-central placentation; stamens mostly definite; endosperm copious; embryo curved.

18. POLYGONALES

Reduced degraded types of *Caryophyllales*.

57. *Polygonaceae*, p. 130.
58. *Illecebraceae*, p. 130.

More or less as in *Caryophyllales* but apetalous; ovary 1-celled, 1-ovuled; embryo straight to curved; endosperm copious; stipules often sheathing, intrapetiolar, membranous or scarious.

19. CHENOPODIALES

59. *Phytolaccaceae*, p. 132.
60. *Cynocrambaceae*, p. 133.
61. *Chenopodiaceae*, p. 134.
62. *Batidaceae*, p. 134.
63. *Amarantaceae*, p. 135.
64. *Basellaceae*, p. 136.

As in *Polygonales*, but stipules absent or very small; carpels numerous to solitary, free or connate; embryo curved.

20. GERANIALES

Here regarded as advanced more or less fixed types from *Caryophyllales*; considerable gap between the two groups, but affinity evident through *Limnanthaceae* especially.

65. *Linaceae*, p. 138.
66. *Zygophyllaceae*, p. 138.
67. *Geraniaceae*, p. 138.
68. *Limnanthaceae*, p. 140.
69. *Oxalidaceae*, p. 140.
70. *Tropaeolaceae*, p. 142.
71. *Balsaminaceae*, p. 143.

Hypogynous; ☿; ovary entire to lobed, syncarpous; ovules mostly 1-2 in each cell; stamens definite; disk-glands often present; no endosperm; leaves frequently much divided, stipulate; higher types have zygomorphic flowers and tendency to syngenesious anthers.

Notes on Affinity (Origin and further Development).	Sequence of Orders (Cohorts) and Families. A cross-line indicates the end of a group.	General Characters and Tendencies of Orders (Cohorts).

21. LYTHRALES

Herbaceous becoming woody; probably advanced type of *Caryophyllales* through subfamily *Sileneae*.	72. *Lythraceae*, p. 144. 73. *Crypteroniaceae*, p. 145. 74. *Sonneratiaceae*, p. 145. 75. *Punicaceae*, p. 146. 76. *Oliniaceae*, p. 147. 77. *Onagraceae*, p. 148. 78. *Halorrhagaceae*, p. 148. 79. *Callitrichiaceae*, p. 150.	Actinomorphic; perigynous to epigynous; calyx tubular, valvate; petals present; stamens as many or twice as many as petals; ovules numerous to solitary; placentation axile; no endosperm, several aquatic forms.

22. THYMELAEALES

Increasingly woody apetalous relations of *Lythrales*.	80. *Geissolomataceae*, p. 150. 81. *Thymelaeaceae*, p. 151. 82. *Penaeaceae*, p. 152. 83. *Nyctaginaceae*, p. 152.	More or less as in *Lythrales* but apetalous, often monocarpellary; ovules few to solitary; flowers often capitate; endosperm present or absent; calyx imbricate or valvate.

23. PROTEALES

Origin problematical, but probably allied to *Thymelaeaceae*; evidently a southern type, with no parallel in the Northern Hemisphere except a few representatives due to migration.	84. *Proteaceae*, p. 153.	Perigynous; actinomorphic or zygomorphic; calyx valvate, often split down one side; stamens equal and opposite the sepals; ovary superior, 1-celled; no endosperm.

24. DILLENIALES

Woody to herbaceous somewhat basal group rather remotely allied to the *Magnoliales* and perhaps indicating the origin of the *Pittosporales*, *Bixales*, *Theales*, *Guttiferales*, and woody *Rosales*.	85. *Dilleniaceae*, p. 154. 86. *Crossosomataceae*, p. 155.	Hypogynous; ⚥; apocarpous; petaliferous; stamens ∞, rarely definite, free; endosperm copious, plain; embryo minute to fairly large; seeds often arillate; leaves alternate, with strong pinnate nervation.

Notes on Affinity (Origin and further Development).	Sequence of Orders (Cohorts) and Families. A cross-line indicates the end of a group.	General Characters and Tendencies of Orders (Cohorts).

25. CORIARIALES

Rather doubtfully placed here.	87. *Coriariaceae*, p. 156.	More or less as above, but stamens 10, with large anthers; seeds with thin endosperm, not arillate; leaves opposite or verticillate; petals accrescent.

26. PITTOSPORALES

Might be equally well placed after *Cunoniales*, Order No. 39.	88. *Pittosporaceae*, p. 157. 89. *Byblidaceae*, p. 157. 90. *Tremandraceae*, p. 158.	Hypogynous; rarely ♂ ♀; syncarpous with parietal to axile placentation; stamens definite, free; petals imbricate to induplicate-valvate; endosperm copious; embryo minute.

27. BIXALES

Woody to rarely subherbaceous group in which syncarpy with parietal placentation has remained a fixed character; probably the *Passiflorales* and its allies, *Theales*, *Guttiferales* and *Tiliales*, find their origin by way of this group.	91. *Bixaceae*, p. 159. 92. *Cochlospermaceae*, p. 160. 93. *Flacourtiaceae*, p. 161. 94. *Samydaceae*, p. 162. 95. *Canellaceae*, p. 163. 96. *Cistaceae*, p. 164.	Hypogynous to perigynous; ♂ to ♂ ♀; syncarpous with parietal placentation; increasing unisexuality of flowers and some perigyny; stamens numerous to few; seeds with copious endosperm and small embryo.

28. TAMARICALES

Somewhat doubtfully placed here, but probably most nearly related to *Bixales*.	97. *Frankeniaceae*, p. 164. 98. *Tamaricaceae*, p. 164. 99. *Fouquieraceae*, p. 165.	Hypogynous; syncarpous, with parietal placentation; tendency to catkinlike inflorescences, small flowers; petals free to connate; stamens mostly definite; seeds often hairy, endosperm present or absent.

Notes on Affinity (Origin and further Development).	Sequence of Orders (Cohorts) and Families. A cross-line indicates the end of a group.	General Characters and Tendencies of Orders (Cohorts).

29. PASSIFLORALES

Mostly climbing types related to the *Bixales* and becoming herbaceous ; probably some of these also derived from the Papaverian groups.

100. *Malesherbiaceae*, p. 165.
101. *Passifloraceae*, p. 166.
102. *Achariaceae*, p. 167.

More or less as in *Bixales*, but no endosperm and corona often present ; fruit often stipitate ; habit mostly climbing and more herbaceous.

30. CUCURBITALES

Undoubtedly closely related to *Passifloraceae*, and better placed here than in the *Metachlamydeae* to which Engler assigned the *Cucurbitaceae*, but wherein they have probably no real relations.

103. *Cucurbitaceae*, p. 168.
104. *Begoniaceae*, p. 168.
105. *Datiscaceae*, p. 170.
106. *Caricaceae*, p. 171.

Constantly unisexual; ovary inferior with parietal placentation ; endosperm scanty or often absent ; corolla sometimes gamopetalous.

31. CACTALES

Position rather a problem, but perhaps best placed here ; some grounds also for placing next to *Ficoidaceae*, No. 55.

107. *Cactaceae*, p. 172.

Succulent or woody ; sepals, petals and stamens mostly numerous and in several series on a tubular axis ; ovary inferior, 1-celled with parietal placentas.

---

32. THEALES

Related to *Dilleniales* and *Bixales* and probably the direct syncarpous line developed from these groups. Discifloral groups such as the *Celastrales* perhaps also closely connected, but more advanced.

108. *Theaceae* (*Ternstroemiaceae*), p. 173.
109. *Medusagynaceae*, p. 174.
110. *Marcgraviaceae*, p. 174.
111. *Caryocaraceae*, p. 174.
112. *Actinidiaceae*, p. 177.
113. *Saurauiaceae*, p. 177.
114. *Ochnaceae*, p. 178.
115. *Ancistrocladaceae*, p. 178.
116. *Dipterocarpaceae*, p. 179.
117. *Chlaenaceae*, p. 180.

Hypogynous to rarely subperigynous ; mostly ⚥ ; syncarpous with axile placentation; stamens ∞, often in several series, free or shortly connate ; seeds with scanty or no endosperm ; embryo large, straight or curved, rarely spiral ; leaves usually alternate ; fruits becoming winged and 1-seeded.

33. MYRTALES

Probably epigynous representatives of the *Theales* and some *Tiliales* with leaves becoming opposite.

118. *Myrtaceae*, p. 181.
119. *Lecythidaceae*, p. 182.
120. *Melastomaceae*, p. 183.
121. *Combretaceae*, p. 184.
122. *Rhizophoraceae*, p. 185.

Mostly quite perigynous representatives of preceding group ; mostly gland-dotted, opposite leaves ; often specialised stamens and characteristic habitats ; calyx becoming valvate.

C

Notes on Affinity (Origin and further Development).	Sequence of Orders (Cohorts) and Families. A cross-line indicates the end of a group.	General Characters and Tendencies of Orders (Cohorts).

34. GUTTIFERALES

| Related to *Theales* and showing the same tendency as in the *Malvales*, *i.e.* stamens gathered into bundles. | 123. *Hypericaceae*, p. 186.
 124. *Eucryphiaceae*, p. 186.
 125. *Quiinaceae*, p. 189.
 126. *Guttiferae*, p. 189. | Advanced hypogynous types of the *Theales* with opposite leaves often glanddotted or lined; stamens uniting into bundles (phalanges); no endosperm; sepals always imbricate. |

35. TILIALES

| A fairly advanced group whence considerable evolution is evident, *i.e.* to *Celastrales*, *Rhamnales* (petaliferous, disciform types) and the bulk of *Euphorbiaceae* (apetalous types). *Tiliales* show affinities backwards with *Dilleniales* and *Bixales*. | 127. *Scytopetalaceae*, p. 191.
 128. *Tiliaceae*, p. 192.
 129. *Gonystylaceae*, p. 193.
 130. *Sterculiaceae*, p. 193.
 131. *Bombacaceae*, p. 194. | Hypogynous, actinomorphic; ♀ or ♂♀; cyclic; syncarpous with axile placentation; stamens ∞, rarely few and opposite the petals, free to partially united; anthers 2-1-celled; endosperm copious, rarely 0, embryo fairly large, straight or curved; calyx mostly valvate; leaves alternate, stipulate; indumentum often stellate. — Trees or shrubs. |

36. MALVALES

| A very natural group representing a fixed type of the *Tiliales*, and whence little or no further evolution has proceeded. | 132. *Malvaceae*, p. 195. | Mostly as above, but mainly herbaceous or softly woody; calyx always valvate; anthers 1-celled. |

37. MALPIGHIALES

| Advanced and specialised groups from the *Tiliales*, with special types of indumentum, fruits, etc. | 133. *Malpighiaceae*, p. 196.
 134. *Humiriaceae*, p. 196.
 135. *Erythroxylaceae*, p. 198. | Hypogynous; actinomorphic to subzygomorphic; ♀; syncarpous with subapical placentation; ovules few; stamens usually definite; endosperm mostly absent. —Often climbers with opposite leaves. |

Notes on Affinity (Origin and further Development).	Sequence of Orders (Cohorts) and Families. A cross-line indicates the end of a group.	General Characters and Tendencies of Orders (Cohorts).

38. EUPHORBIALES

A composite family probably derived from several sources such as *Bixales*, *Tiliales*, *Malvales*, *Celastrales*, and perhaps *Sapindales*.	136. *Euphorbiaceae*, p. 199.	Hypogynous; ♂ ♀; actinomorphic; petals usually absent; syncarpous with 1-2 ovules pendulous from inner angle; stamens various; endosperm mostly copious.

39. CUNONIALES

Woody to herbaceous (rare) groups allied to the early *Dilleniales* phylum and *Celastrales* and showing prolific evolution; origin through *Rosales* of the *Hamamelidales* and the so-called "*Amentiferae*".	137. *Cunoniaceae*, p. 200. 138. *Brunelliaceae*, p. 201. 139. *Escalloniaceae*, p. 201. 140. *Greyiaceae*, p. 202. 141. *Grossulariaceae*, p. 204. 142. *Hydrangeaceae*, p. 204.	Perigynous to epigynous; cyclic, mostly ♀; apocarpous to syncarpous, with central or parietal placentation; endosperm copious, embryo mostly small; leaves simple or compound.

40. ROSALES

	143. *Rosaceae*, p. 206. 144. *Chailletiaceae*, p. 206. 145. *Calycanthaceae*, p. 207.	As above, but without endosperm; rarely acyclic; embryo large.

41. LEGUMINOSAE

Prolific and highly successful group derived from the *Rosales* through the *Mimosaceae* and *Caesalpiniaceae*, and ending in the very natural family *Papilionaceae*.	146. *Caesalpiniaceae*, p. 208. 147. *Mimosaceae*, p. 209. 148. *Papilionaceae*, p. 210.	Progressive Rosalean group with increasing zygomorphy of the flower; free to monadelphous or diadelphous stamens; carpel solitary; no endosperm; embryo large.

42. HAMAMELIDALES

Closely allied to the *Rosales* with increasing reduction and unisexuality and specialisation of the inflorescence leading up to the "*Amentiferae*".	149. *Bruniaceae*, p. 212. 150. *Stachyuraceae*, p. 212. 151. *Hamamelidaceae*, p. 213. 152. *Eucommiaceae*, p. 214. 153. *Myrothamnaceae*, p. 215. 154. *Buxaceae*, p. 216. 155. *Platanaceae*, p. 217.	More or less as in *Rosales*, but the flowers often crowded into heads or catkins; increased unisexuality; ovary often bicarpellary; tendency to apetaly; leaves alternate, mostly stipulate.

Notes on Affinity (Origin and further Development).	Sequence of Orders (Cohorts) and Families. A cross-line indicates the end of a group.	General Characters and Tendencies of Orders (Cohorts).
	43. SALICALES	
Probably *Salicaceae* finds its true affinity here and not with *Tamaricaceae* or *Flacourtiaceae* as has often been suggested. Resemblance to these two families probably due to parallelism.	156. *Salicaceae*, p. 217.	As above, but flowers always in catkins and wind-pollinated; placentation parietal; no endosperm; leaves alternate, mostly stipulate.
	44. GARRYALES	
	157. *Garryaceae*, p. 218.	Dioecious; flowers in catkins; ovary superior, syncarpous, bicarpellary, 1-celled with apical placentation; endosperm copious; embryo minute; leaves opposite; no stipules.
	45. LEITNERIALES	
Reductions from the *Rosales* through *Hamamelidales*. These groups and the preceding group formerly known as the "*Amentiferae*".	158. *Leitneriaceae*, p. 219.	As above, but catkins erect; perianth 0 or rudimentary; ovary superior, 1-celled; placenta parietal; endosperm thin; embryo large; leaves alternate; no stipules.
	46. MYRICALES	
	159. *Myricaceae*, p. 220.	More or less as in preceding, but leaves aromatic and gland-dotted; placenta basal.
	47. BALANOPSIDALES	
	160. *Balanopsidaceae*, p. 221.	Resembling the preceding, but with two parietal placentas.
	48. FAGALES	
	161. *Betulaceae*, p. 222. 162. *Corylaceae*, p. 223. 163. *Fagaceae*, p. 224.	Perianth small or none; ovary inferior or nude, 2-6-celled; cells 1-2-ovuled; endosperm absent; flowers in catkins or spikes, ♂ ♀.

Notes on Affinity (Origin and further Development).	Sequence of Orders (Cohorts) and Families. A cross-line indicates the end of a group.	General Characters and Tendencies of Orders (Cohorts).

49. CASUARINALES

| Here regarded as an extreme reduction of the " *Amentiferae* ", adapted to dry climatal conditions. | 164. *Casuarinaceae*, p. 224. | ♂ ♀; male flowers spicate, female capitate ; no perianth ; male with 1 stamen ; seed solitary ; no endosperm ; leaves completely reduced. |

50. URTICALES

| Probably a mixed degraded group derived from several of the preceding groups ; *Urticaceae* proper almost entirely herbaceous. | 165. *Ulmaceae*, p. 226.
166. *Barbeyaceae*, p. 227.
167. *Moraceae*, p. 228.
168. *Scyphostegiaceae*, p. 229.
169. *Urticaceae*, p. 229.
170. *Cannabinaceae*, p. 230. | ♀ or more usually ♂ ♀; ovary rarely 2-celled; ovule solitary, erect or pendulous ; endosperm present or absent ; leaves stipulate. |

51. CELASTRALES

| Perhaps discoid types descended from the *Tiliales* and *Theales* ; considerable affinity with *Escalloniaceae*, No. 139. | 171. *Aquifoliaceae*, p. 231.
172. *Empetraceae*, p. 232.
173. *Celastraceae*, p. 233.
174. *Corynocarpaceae*, p. 234.
175. *Cyrillaceae*, p. 234.
176. *Cneoraceae*, p. 234.
177. *Pandaceae*, p. 235.
178. *Hippocrateaceae*, p. 236.
179. *Icacinaceae*, p. 237.
180. *Salvadoraceae*, p. 237.
181. *Stackhousiaceae*, p. 238. | More or less perigynous ; disk present, adnate to the base of the calyx-tube or lining it ; stamens definite, alternate with the petals ; petals mostly imbricate ; ovules 1-2, erect ; placentas mostly axile ; endosperm present ; leaves simple, without glands. |

52. OLACALES

| More advanced types of the preceding group. | 182. *Olacaceae*, p. 238.
183. *Opiliaceae*, p. 238. | As above, but petals mostly valvate; ovules pendulous. |

53. SANTALALES

| Mostly parasitic representatives of the preceding groups, some of rather doubtful affinity. | 184. *Octoknemataceae*, p. 240.
185. *Loranthaceae*, p. 241.
186. *Santalaceae*, p. 241.
187. *Grubbiaceae*, p. 242.
188. *Myzodendraceae*, p. 242.
189. *Balanophoraceae*, p. 244. | Epigynous ; calyx valvate or open ; stamens opposite to the corolla - lobes when latter present ; endosperm present ; embryo straight. |

Notes on Affinity (Origin and further Development).	Sequence of Orders (Cohorts) and Families. A cross-line indicates the end of a group.	General Characters and Tendencies of Orders (Cohorts).
	54. RHAMNALES	
Closely allied to the *Celastrales*; probably also the origin of *Myrsinaceae* in *Metachlamydeae*.	190. *Rhamnaceae*, p. 244. 191. *Elaeagnaceae*, p. 245. 192. *Heteropyxidaceae*, p. 245. 193. *Ampelidaceae* (*Vitaceae*), p. 247.	More or less as in *Celastrales*, but often of climbing habit, and the stamens always opposite the petals; leaves simple to compound; petals imbricate or valvate; endosperm often scanty or ruminate.
	55. RUTALES	
	194. *Rutaceae*, p. 248. 195. *Simarubaceae*, p. 249. 196. *Burseraceae*, p. 250.	Hypogynous to slightly perigynous; ☿ or ♂ ♀; apocarpous to syncarpous with axile, basal or apical placentation; ovules mostly few; stamens definite, free; petals contorted to valvate; disk mostly conspicuous; leaves often gland - dotted; endosperm present or absent.
A large, mainly tropical subphylum often spoken of as the "*Pinnatae*", characterised by mostly pinnately or rarely palmately compound leaves; origin and early affinities not very evident; *Sapindaceae* and *Anacardiaceae* especially related to some *Euphorbiaceae*, from some of which part of the latter may have arisen.	**56. MELIALES** 197. *Meliaceae*, p. 250.	More or less as in preceding group, but leaves usually not gland-dotted and stamens connate into a tube.
	57. SAPINDALES 198. *Sapindaceae*, p. 252. 199. *Akaniaceae*, p. 253. 200. *Aceraceae*, p. 253. 201. *Sabiaceae*, p. 254. 202. *Melianthaceae*, p. 255. 203. *Didiereaceae*, p. 255. 204. *Staphyleaceae*, p. 255. 205. *Anacardiaceae*, p. 257. 206. *Connaraceae*, p. 258.	Often zygomorphic and ♂ ♀; petals mostly present; stamens more or less perigynous; ovules 1-2 in each ovary cell; endosperm mostly 0; embryo curved or crumpled.—Trees or shrubs.
	58. JUGLANDALES 207. *Juglandaceae*, p. 258. 208. *Julianiaceae*, p. 259.	Flowers in catkins; apetalous; ♂ ♀; ovary inferior, 1-celled; ovule solitary; no endosperm.

Notes on Affinity (Origin and further Development).	Sequence of Orders (Cohorts) and Families. A cross-line indicates the end of a group.	General Characters and Tendencies of Orders (Cohorts).

59. UMBELLIFLORAE

Probably partly derived from the *Celastrales, Rhamnales*, and *Hamamelidales* groups, but origin or origins doubtful. Herbaceous element probably from *Saxifragales*.

209. *Cornaceae*, p. 260.
210. *Alangiaceae*, p. 261.
211. *Nyssaceae*, p. 261.
212. *Araliaceae*, p. 262.
213. *Umbelliferae*, p. 264.

Woody to herbaceous; constant and complete epigyny; syncarpous; stamens definite; great specialisation of inflorescence with reduction of flowers; leaves simple or compound.

DIVISION II. METACHLAMYDEAE
60. ERICALES

Undoubtedly one of the most primitive groups of the *Metachlamydeae* and perhaps linked most closely with the *Archichlamydeae* through the *Theales*, especially by the family *Clethraceae*, which has free petals. Perhaps some affinity between *Epacridaceae* and *Bruniaceae*, No. 149.

214. *Clethraceae*, p. 265.
215. *Ericaceae*, p. 266.
216. *Vacciniaceae*, p. 267.
217. *Epacridaceae*, p. 268.
218. *Monotropaceae*, p. 269.
219. *Diapensiaceae*, p. 269.
220. *Lennoaceae*, p. 270.

Corolla actinomorphic to slightly zygomorphic; stamens often double the number of the corolla - lobes, hypogynous; anthers often opening by pores; ovary superior to inferior, with axile very rarely parietal placentation; seeds with fleshy endosperm and straight embryo. — Trees or shrubs, very rarely herbs and then parasitic; leaves mostly alternate, simple, without stipules.

61. EBENALES.

Perhaps some affinity here with some *Anonaceae* and the Order *Theales*, though rather remote. Except for the epipetalous stamens almost equally primitive with the *Ericales*.

221. *Ebenaceae*, p. 271.
222. *Sapotaceae*, p. 273.

Corolla actinomorphic, short, lobes in 1 or 2 series ; stamens hypogynous to epipetalous, often numerous and 2- or more - seriate, often alternating with staminodes and opposite the petals ; anthers opening lengthwise ; ovary superior with axile placentation; ovules 1-2 in each cell ; seeds with some endosperm.—Trees or shrubs with hard wood and often milky juice ; leaves alternate, simple; stipules absent.

Notes on Affinity (Origin and further Development).	Sequence of Orders (Cohorts) and Families. A cross-line indicates the end of a group.	General Characters and Tendencies of Orders (Cohorts).

62. MYRSINALES

A close general affinity with *Rhamnaceae* and *Heteropyxidaceae*, which may show the origin of this small order.

223. *Myrsinaceae*, p. 273.

More or less as in *Ebenales*, but stamens the same number and opposite the petals; free-basal placentation; petals sometimes free; leaves gland-dotted.

63. STYRACALES

A small group probably most closely allied and finding its origin in the *Olacales*, and some affinity also with the family *Alangiaceae*.

224. *Styracaceae*, p. 274.
225. *Symplocaceae*, p. 275.
226. *Diclidantheraceae*, p. 275.
227. *Lissocarpaceae*, p. 276.

Corolla actinomorphic, sometimes the petals free; stamens the same number and alternate with or more numerous than the corolla-lobes, inserted on the corolla or rarely free; anthers opening lengthwise; ovary superior to inferior, 2-5-celled, with axile few to many ovules; seeds with copious endosperm and straight or slightly curved embryo. — Trees or shrubs, often with stellate indumentum; leaves alternate; stipules absent.

64. LOGANIALES

A very mixed group either mimicking or having direct affinity with several other families such as *Rubiaceae* (*Gaertnera* [Log.] and *Psychotria* [Rub.]), *Melastomaceae*, (*Strychnos* [Log.] and *Memecylon* [Melast.]), *Apocynaceae* (*Gelsemium*), *Caprifoliaceae* (*Mostuea*), etc.

228. *Loganiaceae*, p. 277.
229. *Oleaceae*, p. 278.

Corolla actinomorphic; stamens epipetalous, alternate with the corolla-lobes; anthers opening lengthwise; ovary superior, 2-4-celled; ovules numerous, axile or ascending; seeds with endosperm and straight embryo. — Trees, shrubs, or herbs; leaves opposite, simple, with or without stipules.

Notes on Affinity (Origin and further Development).	Sequence of Orders (Cohorts) and Families. A cross-line indicates the end of a group.	General Characters and Tendencies of Orders (Cohorts).

65. APOCYNALES

		Corolla actinomorphic; stamens epipetalous, alternate with the corolla-lobes; anthers opening lengthwise; ovary superior; carpels 2, often free, or becoming free in fruit; styles united; ovules mostly numerous, parietal or on the septa; seeds usually with endosperm and straight embryo. — Leaves opposite, simple; stipules absent.
Advanced fixed types from the preceding group and perhaps from *Sapotaceae*. The tendency to free carpels in this group is probably not primitive, because of the common style or stigma.	230. *Apocynaceae*, p. 279. 231. *Asclepiadaceae*, p. 281.	

66. RUBIALES

		Corolla actinomorphic to rarely zygomorphic; stamens epipetalous, alternate with the corolla-lobes; anthers free, opening lengthwise; ovary inferior, syncarpous; axile placentation; style 1; ovules numerous to solitary; seeds mostly with endosperm.—Leaves opposite, simple, and entire or rarely compound; stipules inter- or intrapetiolar, very rarely absent.
A very natural group, but probably derived from more than one source, *i.e. Loganiales* and *Umbelliflorae*.	232. *Rubiaceae*, p. 282. 233. *Caprifoliaceae*, p. 283.	

Notes on Affinity (Origin) and further Development).	Sequence of Orders (Cohorts) and Families. A cross-line indicates the end of a group.	General Characters and Tendencies of Orders (Cohorts).

67. ASTERALES

A polyphyletic group, probably derived from several lower groups, including the *Umbelliflorae, Rubiales, Campanales.*

234. *Adoxaceae*, p. 284.
235. *Valerianaceae*, p. 284.
236. *Dipsacaceae*, p. 285.
237. *Calyceraceae*, p. 286.
238. *Compositae*, p. 286.

Corolla actinomorphic to zygomorphic; stamens epipetalous, with some reduction in number and great tendency to cohesion of the anthers; ovary inferior, mostly 1-celled with 1 ovule; seeds mostly without endosperm. — Leaves various, without stipules. Flowers usually crowded into heads surrounded by an involucre of bracts.

68. GENTIANALES

Very great affinity with the orders *Caryophyllales* and *Saxifragales,* of which they appear to be gamopetalous representatives; mostly herbaceous; seems the best position for *Plantaginaceae.*

239. *Gentianaceae*, p. 288.

Corolla actinomorphic; stamens epipetalous, alternate with the corolla-lobes; anthers free; disk often present; ovary superior, 1-celled with parietal placentation; ovules numerous; seeds with copious endosperm and small embryo.—Herbs.

69. PRIMULALES

240. *Primulaceae*, p. 290.
241. *Plumbaginaceae*, p. 290.

More or less as above, but stamens usually opposite the petals; ovary mostly 1-celled with free basal placentation; seeds mostly with copious endosperm. — Herbs often with radical leaves.

70. PLANTAGINALES
242. *Plantaginaceae*, p. 291.

Notes on Affinity (Origin and further Development).	Sequence of Orders (Cohorts) and Families. A cross-line indicates the end of a group.	General Characters and Tendencies of Orders (Cohorts).

71. CAMPANALES

Perhaps derived from early *Gentianales*, the genus *Cyananthus* (*Campanulaceae*) having a superior ovary; perhaps also recruited from the next order, *Polemoniales*.

243. *Campanulaceae*, p. 292.
244. *Lobeliaceae*, p. 293.
245. *Goodeniaceae*, p. 293.
246. *Stylidiaceae*, p. 294.

Corolla actinomorphic to zygomorphic; epigynous; stamens free or inserted low on the corolla; anthers free to connivent; ovary inferior; ovules numerous to few on axile placentas.—Herbaceous to somewhat woody.

72. POLEMONIALES

I take these to be most nearly related to the *Geraniaceae* in the *Archichlamydeae*, of which they appear to be advanced types.

247. *Polemoniaceae*, p. 295.
248. *Hydrophyllaceae*, p. 295.

Corolla actinomorphic; stamens epipetalous; anthers free; ovary superior, not lobed; placentas parietal or axile; ovules numerous to few.— Herbaceous to rarely climbers or subwoody.

73. BORAGINALES

249. *Boraginaceae*, p. 296.

More or less as in preceding group, but ovary deeply lobed with gynobasic style, composed of 2 carpels and with paired ovules.

74. SOLANALES

A large natural subphylum, showing progressive reduction in the number of stamens accompanied by increasing zygomorphy of the corolla with deep lobing of the ovary in the highest families. These groups show a longer and more gradual series of evolution than in the *Asterales*, and the *Lamiales* should probably be regarded as the highest of the *Metachlamydeae*.

250. *Solanaceae*, p. 297.
251. *Convolvulaceae*, p. 297.

Corolla actinomorphic to very slightly zygomorphic. Stamens the same number and alternate with corolla-lobes, epipetalous; ovary superior, 1-4-(mostly 2-) celled, with numerous to solitary ovules on axile placentas. — Herbaceous to rarely woody, often climbing.

Notes on Affinity (Origin and further Development).	Sequence of Orders (Cohorts) and Families. A cross-line indicates the end of a group.	General Characters and Tendencies of Orders (Cohorts).
	75. PERSONALES	
A large natural subphylum, showing progressive reduction in the number of stamens accompanied by increasing zygomorphy of the corolla with deep lobing of the ovary in the highest families. These groups show a longer and more gradual series of evolution than in the *Asterales*, and the *Lamiales* should probably be regarded as the highest of the *Metachlamydeae*.	252. *Scrophulariaceae*, p. 300. 253. *Orobanchaceae*, p. 301. 254. *Lentibulariaceae*, p. 301. 255. *Columelliaceae*, p. 302. 256. *Gesneriaceae*, p. 303. 257. *Bignoniaceae*, p. 303. 258. *Pedaliaceae*, p. 305. 259. *Acanthaceae*, p. 306.	More or less as in preceding, but corolla nearly always zygomorphic; stamens fewer than the corolla-lobes.—Mostly herbaceous; leaves alternate to opposite.
	76. LAMIALES	
	260. *Globulariaceae*, p. 307. 261. *Myoporaceae*, p. 308. 262. *Selaginaceae*, p. 308. 263. *Verbenaceae*, p. 309. 264. *Labiatae*, p. 309.	As in preceding groups, but leaves mostly opposite or whorled; ovary becoming deeply lobed with gynobasic style; ovules mostly paired. —Mostly herbaceous, with inflorescences tending to capitula or verticillasters.

KEY TO THE FAMILIES OF DICOTYLEDONES

Up to the middle of last century, and even later, the practice of determining plants by means of a *key* was very much discouraged, as tending to superficial observation. Thus no analytical keys are to be found in De Candolle's Prodromus, which through lack of them failed to fulfil the purpose for which it was intended. In those days once the name of a plant was ascertained nothing more was thought to be required. But we have come to realise that to identify a plant is but a means to an end, and not the end itself. Botanists now want to know something more than the mere name, something about its habitat, its distribution, its structure, and affinities from a phylogenetic point of view, and so on, and although the old method of wading through innumerable descriptions may have conduced to accurate and painstaking observation, many mistakes were no doubt made for want of a good analytical key.

As time went on the known species became more numerous and confusing, and a compromise appeared in the shape of the *conspectus*. In most floristic works the conspectus is all that is provided for the determination of the family. But if the family is not easily ascertainable, then it is not possible to determine the genus, and least of all the species. It seems highly desirable, therefore, that a floristic work should now be prefaced by a key based on macroscopic and easily observed characters.

The following is an attempt in this direction. Like most keys it will not prove infallible, but it will achieve its purpose if it brings to the student that preliminary knowledge of the families of flowering plants which is so necessary for work in the field, the garden, the herbarium or laboratory.

HINTS FOR USING THE KEY TO THE BEST ADVANTAGE

Do not start to use the key before you have examined your plant thoroughly. If you do you may easily go wrong. Make out (1) whether the carpels are *free* from each other or *united* ; (2) if united, then make quite sure whether the ovules are on the *walls* (parietal placentation) or at the *apex, base* or *centre* of the ovary (apical, basal and central placentation respectively). Then note the number of stamens, and if few, whether *opposite to* or *alternate with* the petals. Then see whether there are *stipules*. The stipules may have fallen off ; if so, you will be able to detect a *scar*, and then the leaves *are* stipulate. You must use a lens for these characters, and a razor or sharp pen-knife for the ovary.

Do not be afraid to cut a section of the ovary to see the arrangement of the ovules ; in any case, with this key, you need not trouble whether the ovule is *anatropous, orthotropous,* or *campylotropous,* or whether it has one or two coats, which is something to be thankful for.

After you have arrived at what you think may be the family, always compare your plant with the fuller description further on and see if it bears a general resemblance to the typical example figured.

Do not, in using this key, read only the paragraph which seems to fit the plant you wish to determine. You will be much more sure if you read also the contrasting paragraph further on.

Do not always blame the key if you cannot arrive at the family readily. You may have misread it, or your own observation may be at fault. If it *is* the fault of the key, write and tell the author, and you will help to make it more perfect for use in the final work.

KEY TO THE ARTIFICIAL GROUPS [1]

Gynaecium (pistil) composed of 2 or more *separate* or nearly
  quite separate carpels with *separate styles* and stigmas
  (rarely the free carpels immersed in the expanded torus
  (*Nymphaeaceae*))   .   .   .   .   .   .   " APOCARPAE "
Petals present, free from each other, sometimes considerably
  modified   .   .   .   .   Group 1 (p. 30)
Petals present, more or less united   .   .   .   .   Group 2 (p. 34)
Petals absent   .   .   .   .   Group 3 (p. 34)
Gynaecium (pistil) composed of 1 carpel or of 2 or more
  united carpels with free or united styles, or if carpels
  free below, then the styles or stigmas united   .   .   " SYNCARPAE "
Ovules attached to the wall or walls of the ovary   .   .   " PARIETALES "
Ovary superior :
  Petals present, free from each other   .   .   .   Group 4 (p. 35)
  Petals present, more or less united   .   .   .   Group 5 (p. 39)
  Petals absent .   .   .   .   Group 6 (p. 41)

---

[1] The names used for these groups are applied here for convenience. The " Parietales " in this sense are not the *Parietales* of either Bentham and Hooker or of Engler. The student should on no account mistake this artificial grouping for the new system of classification proposed in this work, the conspectus and sequence of which appears on pp. 9-28.

Ovary inferior :
  Petals present, free from each other . . . Group 7 (p. 42)
  Petals present, more or less united . . . Group 8 (p. 43)
  Petals absent . . . . Group 9 (p. 44)
Ovules attached to the central axis or to the base or apex
  of the ovary . . . . " AXILES "
Ovary superior :
  Petals present, free from each other . . . Group 10 (p. 44)
  Petals present, more or less united . . . Group 11 (p. 58)
  Petals absent . . . . Group 12 (p. 64)
Ovary inferior :
  Petals present, free from each other . . . Group 13 (p. 71)
  Petals present, more or less united . . . Group 14 (p. 75)
  Petals absent . . . . Group 15 (p. 77)

GROUP I

Two or more free carpels : petals present, free from each other

Leaves opposite or verticillate (never all radical) (to p. 31) :
  Stamens numerous (15 or more) :
  Stamens arranged all to one side of the flower ; seeds arillate ; trailing or
    climbing shrubs *Dilleniaceae.*
  Stamens arranged symmetrically around the carpels :
  Leaves stipulate ; fruits follicular or indehiscent, sometimes arranged on a
    large fleshy torus ; style often lateral or basal *Rosaceae.*
  Leaves without stipules :
    Herbs or succulents, sometimes slightly woody only at the base :
    Carpels more or less free from the beginning ; leaves often fleshy and
      connate at the base ; flowers usually 5-merous *Crassulaceae.*
    Carpels connivent at first, then free and torulose ; lower leaves alternate,
      not fleshy ; sepals 3 ; petals 6 *Papaveraceae.*
    Trees, shrubs or woody climbers :
    Receptacle more or less campanulate or deeply concave ; no tendrils :
    Anthers opening by valves or slits ; carpels at or towards the base of a
      hollow receptacle ; seeds with endosperm ; mainly tropical
        Monimiaceae.
    Anthers opening by slits ; sepals and petals in several series ; carpels
      numerous, lining the hollow receptacle ; seeds without endosperm ;
      temperate regions *Calycanthaceae.*
    Receptacle neither hollow nor concave ; petals numerous, linear ; anthers
      opening by longitudinal slits ; petiole ending in a tendril
        Ranunculaceae.
  Stamens up to 15 in number :
    Herbs, often succulent ; leaves mostly connate at the base, exstipulate ;
      flowers often cymose ; carpels the same number as the petals ; seeds
      minute, with fleshy endosperm *Crassulaceae.*
    Trees, shrubs or woody climbers :
    Carpels inserted at or near the base of a hollow receptacle (calyx-tube) ;
      anthers opening by valves or slits ; seeds with endosperm *Monimiaceae.*
    Carpels inserted on a more or less convex slightly concave torus :
    Carpels 3-7 ; flowers large ; petals yellow, not clawed, inserted at the base
      of a fleshy torus ; stipules paired, axillary ; anthers opening by short
      or long pores *Ochnaceae.*

Carpels 5-10 ; petals persistent and thickened after flowering ; shrubs
with angular branchlets ; stipules absent; flowers small, green ; anthers
large *Coriariaceae.*

Carpels 1-3 ; petals often clawed, thin, not thickened after flowering ;
stipules mostly intrapetiolar, often connate at the base ; sepals often
biglandular at the base *Malpighiaceae.*

Carpels 2; petals not clawed, scarious ; flowers in axillary heads ; calyx
not glandular ; stipules caducous *Cunoniaceae.*

Leaves alternate or all radical :

Leaves stipulate, sometimes the stipules minute or adnate to the petiole, or
enclosing the young buds :

Carpels numerous, spirally arranged on a somewhat elongated receptacle ;
sepals often 3 or indistinguishable from the 6 or more petals ; flowers
solitary, mostly large and conspicuous ; seeds with copious endosperm
and minute embryo ; trees or shrubs *Magnoliaceae.*

Carpels few or numerous on a globose small or hollow receptacle ; sepals or
calyx-lobes often 5, quite distinct from the petals :

Stamens free from one another or nearly so or shortly united into separate
bundles ; calyx imbricate or valvate :

Herbs, more or less scapigerous, with mostly radical leaves ; seeds not
arillate ; endosperm usually copious ; sepals mostly imbricate
Saxifragaceae.

Habit various ; seeds not arillate ; fruits follicular or indehiscent, often
achenes arranged on a large fleshy torus ; endosperm absent or very
scanty ; sepals mostly imbricate *Rosaceae.*

Trees, shrubs or climbers, rarely herbs, with often scabrid prominently
pinnately nerved leaves ; stipules adnate to the petiole ; seeds arillate,
aril often laciniate ; calyx imbricate, often hardened in fruit
Dilleniaceae.

Trees with large leaves and with stellate hairs ; seeds not arillate ; endosperm copious ; calyx valvate *Tiliaceae.*

Stamens more or less united into a column ; calyx valvate; hairs on the
leaves often stellate or lepidote *Sterculiaceae.*

Leaves without stipules :

Carpels completely sunk in the tissue of the large broad torus :

Aquatic plants with floating leaves; endosperm not ruminate *Nymphaeaceae.*

Not aquatic ; branched trees or shrubs ; endosperm ruminate
Eupomatiaceae.

Carpels not sunk in the tissue of the torus or only very slightly so :

Stamens the same number as and opposite to the petals; carpels usually 3
or rarely numerous :

Leaves compound ; petals smaller than the sepals, sometimes minute ;
fruit usually baccate ; endosperm never ruminate :

Carpels few (up to 9), in whorls *Lardizabalaceae.*

Carpels numerous, spirally arranged *Sargentadoxaceae.*

Leaves simple ; fruit drupaceous ; endosperm sometimes ruminate
Menispermaceae.

Stamens alternate with the petals or monadelphous or more numerous
(rarely fewer) than the petals :

Stamens numerous, more than 12, or more than double the number of
petals (to p. 33) :

Sepals and petals connate into a calyptrum :

Styles connate into a mass ; endosperm ruminate ; carpels sunk in the
torus *Eupomatiaceae.*

Styles free ; seeds not arillate ; endosperm smooth ; carpels sessile, not
sunk in the torus :
Indumentum not lepidote ; leaves gland-dotted ; carpels remaining
free in fruit   *Winteraceae.*
Indumentum lepidote ; carpels concrescent in fruit   *Himantandraceae.*
Styles free ; seeds covered with a multifid aril ; carpels on a short
common stipe ; leaves neither gland-dotted nor lepidote
                                                              Crossosomataceae.
Sepals and petals not connate into a calyptrum ; styles free or rarely
slightly connivent at the base :
Sepals and petals in 3 distinct series (3 + 3 + 3), rarely in 2 series :
Anthers usually with a broad truncate connective ; flowers usually
hermaphrodite ; seed with copious ruminate endosperm and minute
embryo ; trees, shrubs, or woody climbers   *Anonaceae.*
Anthers with a narrow connective ; flowers dioecious   *Menispermaceae.*
Sepals and petals in 2 series or rarely the sepals gradually passing into
the petals, usually in 4's or 5's, or rarely the petals numerous ; endosperm not ruminate :
Herbs, sometimes rather woody at the base :
Carpels in a single whorl and elevated on a stipe-like torus ; petals 3
or more times divided   *Resedaceae.*
Carpels not elevated on the torus usually spirally arranged ; petals
entire, bifid, or tubular :
Carpels free from the beginning ; sepals and petals usually 5 each
or the latter more numerous ; flowers actinomorphic or zygomorphic ; rarely aquatics ; fruit an achene, follicle or rarely a
berry   *Ranunculaceae.*
Carpels free from the beginning ; sepals and petals 3 each ; flowers
actinomorphic ; aquatic herbs with the floating peltate leaves
                                                              Cabombaceae.
Carpels at first connivent, at length free and torulose ; sepals 3 ;
petals 6 ; flowers actinomorphic ; not aquatics   *Papaveraceae.*
Trees, shrubs or woody climbers :
Petals and stamens hypogynous :
Flowers hermaphrodite or very rarely polygamous :
Calyx imbricate :
Leaves aromatic, pellucid-punctate ; sepals deciduous ; seeds
not arillate ; petals numerous   *Winteraceae.*
Leaves not aromatic ; lateral nerves prominent and parallel ; sepals
persistent and often accrescent ; seeds often arillate
                                                              Dilleniaceae.
Calyx valvate ; indumentum stellate or lepidote :
Connective of anthers not enlarged   *Tiliaceae.*
Connective of anthers enlarged, not petaloid   *Anonaceae.*
Connective of anthers petaloid   *Himantandraceae.*
Flowers unisexual :
Leaves simple ; seeds with copious endosperm and small embryo ;
filaments more or less united towards the base or in a mass
                                                              Schizandraceae.
Leaves pinnate or simple ; seeds with or without endosperm and
fairly large embryo   .   *Simarubaceae.*
Petals and stamens perigynous :
Disk absent :
Endosperm present, fleshy ; seeds arillate   *Crossosomataceae.*

Endosperm absent ; seeds not arillate   *Rosaceae.*
Disk present, adnate to the inside of the calyx-tube ; anthers often opening by valves ; leaves mostly pellucid-dotted ; calyx-lobes in 2 or more series ; carpels arranged on the inside of the hollow receptacle   *Monimiaceae.*
Stamens 12 or fewer, or double the number of petals when more than 6 :
Leaves gland-dotted :
Leaves simple : carpels in a spiral, mostly numerous ; stamens more or less united in a mass ; fruiting carpellary axis elongated ; flowers solitary   *Schizandraceae.*
Leaves often compound ; carpels whorled ; the axis in fruit not elongated ; stamens more or less free from one another   *Rutaceae.*
Leaves not gland-dotted :
Leaves compound :
Flowers unisexual or polygamous ; carpels usually 3, rarely 6 or 9 ; stamens often monadelphous   *Lardizabalaceae.*
Flowers hermaphrodite :
Herbs ; seeds with copious endosperm and small embryo   *Ranunculaceae.*
Herbs, shrubs or trees ; seeds without endosperm :
Wood with resin ducts ; seeds not arillate   *Anacardiaceae.*
Wood without resin ducts ; seeds often arillate   *Connaraceae.*
Wood without resin ducts ; seeds not arillate   *Rosaceae.*
Leaves simple (sometimes the submerged ones of aquatics dissected) :
Stamens free or slightly united at the base :
Flowers hermaphrodite :
Shrubs or trees ; seeds usually arillate :
Leaves reduced to scales ; aril laciniate   *Dilleniaceae.*
Leaves not reduced to scales ; seeds not arillate ; leaves pinnatisect ; carpels 5-10, with 2 ovules in the middle ; stamens 5 or 10   *Ranunculaceae.*
Leaves not reduced to scales ; aril entire, more or less cupular ; carpels with 2 basal collateral ovules   *Connaraceae.*
Leaves not reduced, not pinnatisect ; no aril   *Anacardiaceae.*
Herbs ; seeds not arillate :
Aquatics with peltate floating leaves   *Cabombaceae.*
Not aquatics :
Carpels at the top of a gynophore   *Resedaceae.*
Carpels not on a gynophore, but sometimes on an elongated axis :
Torus elongated or cone-like ; annual herbs with entire leaves ; carpels usually very numerous   *Ranunculaceae.*
Torus flat or concave ; carpels few :
Carpels the same number as the petals   *Crassulaceae.*
Carpels fewer than the petals   *Saxifragaceae.*
Flowers dioecious ; petals and stamens in 3's or multiples of 3   *Menispermaceae.*
Stamens united into a column ; flowers unisexual :
Carpels numerous   *Schizandraceae.*
Carpels definite, often 3, rarely 6 or 9   *Menispermaceae.*

D

GROUP 2

Two or more free carpels ; petals present, more or less united

Leaves simple ; flowers dioecious ; seeds sometimes with ruminate endosperm, not arillate ; fruit a drupe ; mostly climbers with soft wood and broad medullary rays *Menispermaceae.*

Leaves usually pinnate or unifoliolate ; flowers hermaphrodite ; seeds often arillate ; fruit a capsule ; trees, shrubs or climbers *Connaraceae.*

Leaves 1-7-foliolate ; flowers somewhat zygomorphic, hermaphrodite ; fruit a capsule ; seeds not arillate ; trees or shrubs ; leaves often punctate *Rutaceae.*

Leaves simple, opposite or scattered, often fleshy, not punctate; flowers actinomorphic, hermaphrodite ; fruits dehiscent ; herbs or shrubs *Crassulaceae.*

GROUP 3

Two or more free carpels ; petals absent

Trees, shrubs or hard-wooded climbers ; leaves simple or rarely compound ; sepals not or rarely slightly petaloid :
Leaves stipulate :
Stamens free or slightly connate at the base :
Calyx imbricate :
Stipules free from or adnate to the petiole ; fruits acheniolar drupaceous, often included by the tubular calyx ; disk usually present ; flowers hermaphrodite or polygamo-dioecious *Rosaceae.*
Stipules laterally adnate to the petiole; fruits follicular; disk absent; flowers unisexual, dioecious *Cercidiphyllaceae.*
Stipules intrapetiolar, amplexicaul ; fruits follicular ; disk absent ; flowers unisexual, polygamo-monoecious *Lactoridaceae.*
Calyx valvate :
Leaves alternate, simple, covered with stellate hairs ; disk absent from the flowers, the latter hermaphrodite *Sterculiaceae.*
Leaves opposite or verticillate, usually compound ; disk present in the flowers, the latter dioecious ; male flowers with a rudimentary ovary *Brunelliaceae.*
Leaves opposite or verticillate, simple ; male flowers without a rudimentary ovary *Cunoniaceae.*
Stamens united into a column ; anthers in a ring or unequally arranged *Sterculiaceae.*
Leaves exstipulate :
Leaves compound ; stamens often 6 and monadelphous *Lardizabalaceae.*
Leaves simple :
Seeds with ruminate endosperm ; stamens numerous, mostly with broad more or less truncate connective ; carpels usually numerous, free in fruit *Anonaceae.*
Seeds sometimes with ruminate endosperm ; stamens definite, often in 3's, with narrow connective ; carpels few, free ; mostly climbers *Menispermaceae.*
Seeds with uniform endosperm ; stamens usually with a narrow connective :
Stamens hypogynous :
Carpels in several series or in an irregular series, concrescent in fruit ; trees or shrubs with lepidote leaves *Himantandraceae.*

Carpels mostly 3, free ; woody climbers ; not lepidote   *Menispermaceae.*
Carpels in a single series, free or nearly so in fruit ; mostly herbs ; not lepidote   *Phytolaccaceae.*
Stamens more or less perigynous or on a widened or hollow receptacle :
  Receptacle obscure and solid, bearing the stamens on its outside ; carpels in a single whorl, connate towards the base ; anthers opening lengthwise by slits   *Trochodendraceae.*
  Receptacle more or less hollow, bearing the stamens on its inside ; anthers often opening by valves   *Monimiaceae.*
Herbs with radical or alternate leaves (or very soft wooded climbers with opposite leaves and rather broad medullary rays) :
Carpels usually numerous, achenial and 1-seeded in fruit or follicular with several seeds, often with long hairy tails ; flowers mostly hermaphrodite ; sepals usually petaloid, valvate or imbricate   *Ranunculaceae.*
Carpels mostly few ; sepals not petaloid, sometimes rather scarious :
  Flowers hermaphrodite ; stamens free amongst themselves ; leaves alternate :
    Carpels in a single whorl ; sepals more or less free ; style terminal or nearly so :
      Leaves·not modified into pitchers   *Phytolaccaceae.*
      Leaves modified into pitchers   *Cephalotaceae.*
    Carpels in more than 1 whorl ; sepals free ; style terminal or nearly so   *Ranunculaceae.*
    Carpels 1-4 ; sepals united into a tube ; style basal or lateral   *Rosaceae.*
    Carpels 1-4 ; sepals free ; stigma terminal ; small annual herb   *Circaesteraceae.*
  Flowers unisexual ; sepals usually biseriately imbricate ; stamens free or variously connate :
    Climbers ; carpels mostly 3 or 6   *Menispermaceae.*
    Low, often annual herbs ; fruiting carpels 5   *Molluginaceae.*

GROUP 4

One carpel or more than one united carpels with parietal placentation ; ovary superior ; petals present, free from each other

Leaves opposite (to p. 36) :
  Stamens more or less united into three or more separate bundles ; leaves often gland-dotted or with resin canals :
    Mostly herbaceous or suffruticose ; leaves often with pellucid dots ; styles free or nearly so   *Hypericaceae.*
    Trees or shrubs ; leaves with lines of resin canals and very numerous lateral nerves ; stigma sessile or subsessile   *Guttiferae.*
  Stamens free or more or less united at the base into not more than two separate bundles (diadelphous), sometimes adnate to a gynophore ; leaves not or rarely glandular :
    Connective of the anthers produced above the cells ; flowers often somewhat zygomorphic (irregular), the lower petal often gibbous or saccate at the base   *Violaceae.*
    Connective of the anthers not produced ; flowers usually actinomorphic (regular) :
      Stamens 6, tetradynamous ; sepals 4 ; petals 4, often clawed ; ovary of 2 carpels   *Cruciferae.*
      Stamens not tetradynamous, often many :
        Stamens more than double the number of the petals :

Ovary stipitate :
  Stamens hypogynous   *Capparidaceae.*
  Stamens perigynous, inserted on the calyx-tube   *Lythraceae.*
Ovary sessile :
  Petals and stamens hypogynous :
    Sepals imbricate :
      Style or sessile stigma 1 ; indumentum when present often stellate ;
          leaves not gland-dotted ; petals fugacious   *Cistaceae.*
      Styles or sessile stigmas 2 or more ; leaves often gland-dotted
                                          Hypericaceae.
    Sepals induplicate - valvate ; leaves mostly subconnate at the base,
      often small and ericoid   *Frankeniaceae.*
  Petals and stamens perigynous ; leaves not gland-dotted   *Samydaceae.*
Stamens the same or double the number of the petals :
  Stamens and petals hypogynous ; style 1, divided into as many stigmas
    as placentas ; no corona :
    Leaves small, often more or less connate at the base ; flowers usually
      sessile   *Frankeniaceae.*
    Leaves not small, not connate at the base; flowers stalked *Flacourtiaceae.*
  Stamens and petals perigynous ; no corona present :
    Stamens not diadelphous ; flowers actinomorphic :
      Styles free ; seeds with endosperm ; stamens erect in bud :
        Herbs with fleshy exstipulate leaves ; carpels as many as the petals
                                          Crassulaceae.
        Shrubs with deciduous bark and thin leaves ; carpels fewer than the
          petals ; no gynophore   *Hydrangeaceae.*
        Mostly climbers with tendrils; leaves usually stipulate; ovary on a
          gynophore   *Passifloraceae.*
      Styles united ; seeds without endosperm ; stamens often inflexed in
        bud   *Lythraceae.*
    Stamens diadelphous ; flowers zygomorphic   *Papilionaceae.*
  Stamens hypogynous to perigynous ; corona present ; stamens adnate
    to a gynophore   *Passifloraceae.*
Leaves alternate or all radical :
  Stamens numerous (more than 12) (to p. 38) :
    Filaments connate into a tube or column :
      Anthers free, small ; petals often valvate ; flowers mostly in heads or
        dense spikes   *Mimosaceae.*
      Anthers extrorse, adnate to the tube ; glabrous aromatic trees ; leaves
        pellucid-punctate ; flowers cymose   *Canellaceae.*
    Filaments connate into separate bundles :
      Bundles of filaments opposite the sepals   *Tiliaceae.*
      Bundles of filaments opposite the petals   *Samydaceae.*
    Filaments free or partially adnate to a gynophore, or shortly connate only
      at the base :
    Ovary supported on a gynophore   *Capparidaceae.*
    Ovary sessile or very nearly so :
      Anthers horseshoe-shaped (see Fig. 91) ; ovary placentas 2 ; ovules
        numerous ; stipules caducous, leaving a wide scar ; leaves large ;
        pedicels often with 5 large glands below the sepals   *Bixaceae.*
      Anthers straight or nearly so :
        Anthers opening by apical pores or short pore-like slits :
          Seeds hairy ; ovary entire : leaves digitately nerved or lobed
                                      Cochlospermaceae.

Seeds not hairy ; ovary often deeply lobed, especially in fruit ; leaves
    pinnately nerved   *Ochnaceae.*
Anthers opening by longitudinal slits :
Flowers actinomorphic (regular) :
Fleshy plants, often spiny and with reduced or fleshy leaves ; no
    stipules ; stigmas often many   *Cactaceae.*
Above characters not associated :
  Stipules present, sometimes early deciduous, free or adnate to the
    petiole :
  Sepals contorted ; petals very fugacious, often 4 ; placentas 3-5,
    parietal or adnate to the partially intrusive septa   *Cistaceae.*
  Sepals imbricate or valvate ; petals often 5 :
    Corona absent :
      Ovary of more than 1 carpel, *i.e.* with 2 or more placentas :
        Petals and stamens hypogynous :
          Leaves simple ; sepals at length reflexed or deciduous
                    Flacourtiaceae.
          Leaves mostly pinnate ; sepals not or rarely reflexed, not
            deciduous   *Anacardiaceae.*
        Petals and stamens perigynous :
          Sepals persistent, accrescent   *Samydaceae.*
          Sepals not accrescent or only very slightly so   *Rosaceae.*
      Ovary of 1 carpel and with 1 placenta ; stamens and petals
        hypogynous :
        Sepals persistent, very imbricate   *Dilleniaceae.*
    Corona present   *Passifloraceae.*
Stipules absent :
  Trees, shrubs or woody climbers :
    Leaves simple :
      Flowers mostly solitary ; endosperm of seeds ruminate ; stamens
        and petals hypogynous   *Anonaceae.*
      Flowers rarely solitary, sometimes spicate-racemose ; endosperm
        smooth :
        Ovary wholly superior :
          Leaves rather small or very small ; flowers often spicate or
            racemose   *Tamaricaceae.*
          Leaves rather large ; flowers rarely spicate   *Flacourtiaceae.*
        Ovary semi-inferior   *Samydaceae.*
    Leaves mostly bipinnate ; petals valvate ; calyx tubular, often
      valvate ; flowers often in heads or spikes   *Mimosaceae.*
  Herbs :
    Sepals more than 2 ; juice not milky :
      Leaves ternately compound ; sepals petaloid ; carpel 1, baccate
        in fruit   *Ranunculaceae.*
      Leaves pinnatisect ; sepals not petaloid 4 ; petals 4, clawed ;
        ovary of 2 carpels   *Cruciferae* (Megacarpaea).
    Sepals 2 ; juice milky ; petals often 4, fugacious, not clawed ;
      ovary of more than 1 carpel   *Papaveraceae.*
Flowers zygomorphic (irregular) :
Petals and stamens hypogynous ; petals often considerably modified ;
    ovary of 1 carpel   *Ranunculaceae.*
Petals and stamens hypogynous or slightly perigynous ; petals mostly
    laciniate ; ovary of more than 1 carpel
                    Resedaceae.

Petals and stamens perigynous or subperigynous ; petals not laciniate :
 Fleshy plants with thick or reduced leaves ; ovary of more than 1
  carpel   *Cactaceae.*
 Not fleshy ; leaves not reduced ; ovary of 1 carpel :
  Odd petal adaxial   *Papilionaceae.*
  Odd petal not adaxial   *Caesalpiniaceae.*
Stamens 12 or fewer :
 Stamens 6, four long and two short (tetradynamous); sepals 4 ; petals 4 ;
  ovary of 2 carpels, often divided by a false septum   *Cruciferae.*
 Stamens not as above, rarely 6 :
 Flowers markedly zygomorphic :
  Stamens 4 or 6, opposite the petals, more or less united into 2 bundles ;
   inflorescence often leaf-opposed   *Fumariaceae.*
  Stamens with at least one row alternate with the petals :
   Fertile stamens about 2 ; ovary often supported on a short or long
    gynophore :
    Ovary of more than 1 carpel   ˙ *Capparidaceae.*
    Ovary of 1 carpel (1 placenta) ; leaves usually pinnate *Caesalpiniaceae.*
   Fertile stamens more than 2 :
    Fleshy plants with numerous petals   *Cactaceae.*
    Not fleshy :
     Herbs or rarely shrubs or trees ; anthers often with produced connective,
      mostly connivent or connate around the style   *Violaceae.*
     Herbs, shrubs or trees ; anther connective not produced or only
      glandular :
      Placentas 3 ; 5 fertile stamens, with the same number of staminodes
                                                         Moringaceae.
      Placenta 1 :
       Odd petal adaxial ; corolla of standard, wings and keel (papilion-
        aceous)   *Papilionaceae.*
       Odd petal not adaxial ; corolla not as above ; anthers opening by
        slits   *Caesalpiniaceae.*
       Odd petal not adaxial ; anthers opening by pores *Polygalaceae.*
 Flowers actinomorphic (regular) or nearly so :
  Parasitic leafless plants destitute of chlorophyll ; anthers elongated,
   opening lengthwise by slits   *Monotropaceae.*
  Not parasitic ; leaves more or less green :
   Flowers with a distinct corona, this sometimes membranous or represented
    by a definite ring of hairs towards the base of the calyx-tube : ovary
    of more than 1 carpel :
    Styles connate or continuous at the base, or style 1 :
     Ovary 1-celled ; fruit opening loculicidally (if capsular) *Passifloraceae.*
     Ovary imperfectly celled ; capsule opening septicidally ; leaves
      sheathing at base   *Greyiaceae.*
    Styles widely separated at the base ; calyx-tube long *Malesherbiaceae.*
   Flowers without a corona :
    Stamens completely united into a column with the anthers extrorse
     on the outside ; leaves pellucid-punctate ; endosperm not ruminate
                                                         Canellaceae.
    Stamens united with the anthers in a ring around the apex of
     the column ; leaves not punctate ; endosperm often ruminate
                                                         Menispermaceae.
    Stamens free or united only at the base or rarely only the anthers
     connivent :

Leaves stipulate :
Anthers with the connective produced above the cells :
Anthers connivent around the style   *Violaceae.*
Anthers not connivent around the style   *Flacourtiaceae.*
Anthers without a produced connective :
Staminodes present, sometimes petaloid ; stipules sometimes
   pectinate   *Ochnaceae.*
Staminodes absent :
Leaves with numerous very sticky gland-tipped hairs, mostly
   circinate in bud ; seeds not carunculate   *Droseraceae.*
Leaves without sticky hairs, not circinate ; seeds often carunculate
   or arillate :
Styles free to the base   *Turneraceae.*
Styles simple, shortly divided :
Mostly climbers with tendrils   *Passifloraceae.*
Shrubs or trees without tendrils   *Flacourtiaceae.*
Leaves exstipulate :
Stamens the same number as and opposite the petals :
Sepals and petals usually in threes ; anthers mostly opening by
   valves   *Berberidaceae.*
Sepals and petals 2 and 4 respectively ; flowers solitary or terminal
   or leaf-opposed ; anthers opening by slits   *Fumariaceae.*
Stamens with one row alternate with the petals :
Herbs :
Calyx-tube long ; stamens usually perigynous   *Turneraceae.*
Calyx-tube short ; stamens hypogynous   *Tovariaceae.*
Trees, shrubs or climbers :
Leaves simple, but sometimes deeply divided :
Leaves very small and more or less ericoid   *Tamaricaceae.*
Leaves not small :
Leaves digitately lobed   *Caricaceae.*
Leaves pinnately lobed or subdigitately nerved ; calyx-tube very
   short ; stamens hypogynous :
No staminodes   *Pittosporaceae.*
Ring of staminodes outside the stamens   *Greyiaceae.*
Leaves pinnately nerved or lobed ; calyx-tube long ; stamens
   mostly perigynous   *Turneraceae.*
Leaves compound :
Flowers in heads or dense spikes ; petals valvate ; ovary of 1
   carpel ; ovules more than 1   *Mimosaceae.*
Flowers not in heads or dense spikes ; ovary usually of more than
   1 carpel ; ovule solitary   *Anacardiaceae.*
Flowers racemose ; ovary of 5 carpels with numerous ovules
    Caricaceae.

GROUP 5
*One carpel or two or more united carpels with parietal placentation ;
ovary superior ; petals present, more or less united*

Stamens free from the corolla-tube (to p. 40) :
Ovary composed of more than one carpel :
Stamens numerous, more than twice the number of the corolla-lobes :
Anthers opening by a longitudinal slit, with broadened truncate connective ;
   seeds with copious ruminate endosperm ; shrubs, trees or climbers
   with exstipulate simple leaves   *Anonaceae.*

Anthers without a broadened connective ; fleshy plants with reduced leaves and often very spiny   *Cactaceae.*

Anthers without a broadened connective ; not fleshy ; leaves coriaceous ; flowers spicate-racemose ; petals with induplicate margins   *Samydaceae.*

Stamens definite in relation to the corolla-lobes ; anthers opening by terminal pores or pore ; leaves mostly opposite with parallel main nerves
Melastomaceae.

Stamens 4, connate at the base or up to the middle ; anthers opening by a terminal pore ; leaves not parallel nerved, alternate   *Polygalaceae.*

Stamens 5-12 ; anthers neither appendaged nor opening by pores ; leaves alternate or fasciculate, exstipulate ; erect trees or shrubs ; never aquatic :

Branches with hooks ; climbers   *Ancistrocladaceae.*

Branches without hooks :

Leaves fairly large ; flowers more or less corymbose or paniculate :

Not spiny ; leaves not fasciculate   *Pittosporaceae.*

Spiny shrubs ; leaves often fasciculate   *Fouquieraceae.*

Leaves very small and scale-like ; flowers in slender spikes or racemes
Tamaricaceae.

Stamens 5 ; glabrous aquatic herbs with verticillate leaves ; flowers axillary, solitary   *Droseraceae.*

Ovary composed of a single carpel (usually a legume) ; stamens free or more usually diadelphous or monadelphous, often 10, rarely numerous :

Stamens connate into a sheath, or free ; flowers mostly hermaphrodite :

Flowers actinomorphic (regular) ; petals valvate ; calyx gamosepalous or valvate ; leaves usually bipinnate, rarely simply pinnate or reduced to phyllodes ; flowers often collected into heads   *Mimosaceae.*

Flowers zygomorphic (irregular) or rarely actinomorphic ; sepals imbricate or rarely valvate ; petals imbricate, the upper (adaxial) one inside the others ; leaves often pinnate or bipinnate   *Caesalpiniaceae.*

Flowers zygomorphic ; petals imbricate, the upper (adaxial) one (the standard) outside the others, the lateral two (the wings) outside the abaxial pair (the keel) which are more or less united along their lower edges ; leaves simple, digitate or simply pinnate   *Papilionaceae.*

Stamens connate into a column with the anthers in a ring at the top ; flowers dioecious ; fruit a drupe ; slender climbers   *Menispermaceae.*

Stamens inserted on the corolla-tube, sometimes near the base :

Stamens double the number of the corolla-lobes :

Flowers zygomorphic   *Polygalaceae.*

Flowers actinomorphic   *Caricaceae.*

Stamens the same number as the corolla-lobes ; corolla actinomorphic or nearly so :

Leaves opposite :

Carpels 2, more or less free ; pollen granular   *Apocynaceae.*

Carpels 2, free ; styles separate up to the common thickened apex ; pollen agglutinated into masses ; corolla with a corona   *Asclepiadaceae.*

Carpels 2, connate into a 1- or 2-celled ovary ; pollen not agglutinated :

Stamens 5 ; ovules numerous :

Corolla-lobes valvate   *Gentianaceae.*

Corolla-lobes imbricate or contorted   *Hydrophyllaceae.*

Stamens 4 ; ovules numerous   *Bignoniaceae.*

Stamens 4 ; ovules 1-2 in each cell   *Verbenaceae.*

Leaves alternate or radical :

Corolla-lobes without opposite glands ; flowers hermaphrodite :

Corolla-lobes imbricate or rarely contorted   *Hydrophyllaceae.*

Corolla-lobes induplicate-valvate ; leaves simple or trifoliolate
Gentianaceae.
Corolla-lobes with glands opposite to them ; flowers unisexual
Achariaceae.
Stamens fewer than the corolla-lobes, 4 or 2 ; corolla zygomorphic or rarely
subactinomorphic :
Leafless parasitic (on roots), never green herbs ; seeds minute, very numerous,
with endosperm *Orobanchaceae.*
Leafy and not or rarely parasitic :
Ovules numerous on each placenta :
Mostly trees ; seeds transverse, winged *Bignoniaceae.*
Mostly herbaceous ; seeds minute, not winged *Gesneriaceae.*
Herbs ; seeds not winged *Pedaliaceae.*
Ovules 1-2 on each placenta ; stem and branches often 4-sided
Verbenaceae.

GROUP 6

*One carpel or more than one united carpels with parietal placentation ;
ovary superior ; petals absent*

Leaves modified into pitchers ; flowers dioecious ; stamens united into a column ;
ovary 3-4-celled with numerous ovules in each cell ; seeds elongate-fusi-
form ; embryo straight *Nepenthaceae.*
Leaves not modified into pitchers :
Submerged aquatic moss- or alga-like herbs ; flowers dioecious ; ovules
numerous in each cell ; seeds microscopic, compressed
Hydrostachyaceae.
Not submerged, etc., as in preceding :
Stamens 6, four long and two short (tetradynamous) ; fruits often with a
thin membranous false septum between the placentas ; seeds without
endosperm, with accumbent or incumbent cotyledons ; sepals usually 4
Cruciferae.
Stamens rarely 6, and then not tetradynamous :
Stamens more than 1 (to p. 42) :
Ovary composed of 1 carpel ; fruit usually a legume :
Stamens more than 4 ; sepals not or rarely valvate :
Stamens 10 or fewer by abortion :
Leaves usually compound ; flowers zygomorphic *Caesalpiniaceae.*
Leaves mostly simple ; flowers actinomorphic *Ulmaceae.*
Leaves stipulate :
Anthers erect in bud *Ulmaceae.*
Anthers inflexed in bud *Moraceae.*
Leaves exstipulate ; flowers in catkins *Leitneriaceae.*
Stamens numerous :
Flowers zygomorphic ; fruit mostly a legume *Papilionaceae.*
Flowers actinomorphic ; fruit a berry *Flacourtiaceae.*
Stamens 4, opposite the valvate calyx-segments *Proteaceae.*
Ovary composed of more than 1 carpel ; at least with 2 or more placentas
or more than 1 ovule :
Ovary and fruit stipitate :
Flowers not in catkins :
Stamens more than 4 ; sepals rarely valvate *Capparidaceae.*
Stamens 4 ; sepals valvate, often coloured *Proteaceae.*
Flowers in catkins *Salicaceae.*

Ovary sessile :
Flowers without a corona but sometimes with a hypogynous disk :
  Stamens hypogynous or flowers unisexual :
    Filaments connate into a tube, anthers up to 20, adnate to the outside
      of the tube ; leaves pellucid-punctate   *Canellaceae.*
    Filaments free or slightly connate at the base :
      Seeds with endosperm :
        Leaves opposite ; mostly shrubs ; stipules mostly present   *Cistaceae.*
        Leaves alternate ; trees or shrubs ; stipules small, caducous or
          absent   *Flacourtiaceae.*
        Leaves alternate ; more or less herbaceous ; with large pinnately
          or digitately nerved leaves ; flowers paniculate ; no stipules
            Papaveraceae.
      Seeds without endosperm ; torus not dilated ; fruit a capsule ;
        branches leafy   *Salicaceae.*
      Seeds without endosperm ; torus dilated at the back ; stamens
        10-20 ; fruit a berry ; often spiny shrubs more or less aphyllous
          Resedaceae.
  Stamens distinctly perigynous :
    Anthers inflexed in bud ; staminodes rarely present ; filaments free
      Lythraceae.
    Anthers not inflexed in bud ; staminodes often alternating with the
      fertile stamens ; filaments free or connate ; indumentum some-
      times stellate   *Samydaceae.*
    Anthers not inflexed in bud ; no staminodes ; stamens 4, opposite
      the valvate sepals   *Proteaceae.*
  Flowers with a distinct corona, more or less perigynous   *Passifloraceae.*
Stamen 1 :
  Stems not articulated ; leaves well developed ; flowers hermaphrodite,
    spicate ; anther erect in bud   *Lacistemaceae.*
  Stems articulated ; leaves reduced to scales ; flowers unisexual, male
    spicate ; anther inflexed in bud   *Casuarinaceae.*

GROUP 7

*One carpel or two or more united carpels with parietal placentation ;
ovary inferior ; petals present, free from each other*

Aquatic herbs with usually floating leaves ; petals numerous in several series ;
  fruit a several-celled berry   *Nymphaeaceae.*
Not aquatic, rarely marsh plants :
Flowers hermaphrodite :
  Anthers opening by pores ; leaves mostly opposite with parallel main nerves ;
    stamens definite, often double the number of the petals   *Melastomaceae.*
  Anthers not opening by pores :
    Ovary-cells not superposed :
      Stamens numerous, more than twice as many as the petals :
        Shrubs or trees with gland-dotted mostly opposite leaves   *Myrtaceae.*
        Leaves not gland-dotted, sometimes reduced or fleshy :
          Fleshy herbs or shrubs with reduced leaves   *Cactaceae.*
          Herbs with rough hairs ; stamens often in bundles opposite the petals
            Loasaceae.

      Trees or shrubs :
        Sepals gradually passing into the petals ; endosperm ruminate
          Eupomatiaceae.

Sepals distinct from the petals   *Samydaceae.*
Stamens 4-12 ; shrubs or trees ; calyx imbricate or valvate :
Leaves alternate :
Leaves often gland-dotted, not stipulate   *Escalloniaceae.*
Leaves not glandular, mostly stipulate   *Grossulariaceae.*
Leaves opposite, not stipulate   *Hydrangeaceae.*
Stamens definite ; usually herbs or weak climbers :
Sepals and petals imbricate   *Saxifragaceae.*
Sepals valvate ; petals contorted ; ovary usually 4-celled   *Onagraceae.*
Sepals imbricate or valvate ; petals imbricate or induplicate-valvate ;
    herbs or climbers with often rough stinging hairs   *Loasaceae.*
Ovary-cells superposed in two series ; leaves opposite or subopposite
    Punicaceae.

Flowers unisexual :
Leaves gland-dotted ; style simple   *Myrtaceae.*
Leaves not gland-dotted ; styles or stigmas usually 3 :
Stamens numerous ; leaves stipulate ; no tendrils ; ovary closed, often
    winged   *Begoniaceae.*
Stamens 3 or 5 ; no stipules ; often with tendrils ; ovary closed   *Cucurbitaceae.*
Stamens 4 to many ; stipules absent ; no tendrils ; ovary often gaping
    Datiscaceae.

GROUP 8

One carpel or two or more united carpels with parietal placentas ;
ovary inferior ; petals present more or less united

Stamens numerous ; leaves often gland-dotted, mostly opposite   *Myrtaceae.*
Stamens usually definite, rarely numerous, rarely more than twice the number
of the corolla-lobes :
Fleshy plants (often) usually with minute leaves ; calyx-lobes, petals and
stamens numerous ; style radiate at the apex   *Cactaceae.*
Above characters never combined ; stamens mostly the same number, double
or fewer than the petals :
Flowers unisexual ; leaves alternate ; tendrils often present ; stamens mostly
3 ; anthers often twisted   *Cucurbitaceae.*
Flowers hermaphrodite ; leaves opposite or verticillate, without stipules ;
anthers mostly opening by terminal pores   *Melastomaceae.*
Flowers hermaphrodite very rarely unisexual ; leaves opposite or alternate,
often stipulate ; anther not opening by pores, sometimes connivent at
the apex :
Leaves with interpetiolar or intrapetiolar stipules ; flowers actinomorphic ;
stamens usually the same number as the corolla-lobes :
Ovules numerous on the walls of the ovary ; branches not hooked   *Rubiaceae.*
Ovule solitary ; branches hooked   *Ancistrocladaceae.*
Leaves exstipulate (sometimes the leaves anisophyllous, the smaller appear-
ing like a stipule) :
Evergreen trees or shrubs ; corolla subactinomorphic ; stamens 2, with
very broad connective and sinuous anther-cells   *Columelliaceae.*
Shrubs ; corolla actinomorphic ; stamens numerous, with narrow con-
nective ; anther-cells straight   *Samydaceae.*
Usually herbaceous, rarely subwoody plants ; corolla more or less zygo-
morphic :
Stamens 4 or 2, often didynamous   *Gesneriaceae.*
Stamens numerous ; plants often roughly hairy   *Loasaceae.*

GROUP 9

One carpel or two or more united carpels with parietal placentas ;
ovary inferior ; petals absent

Leaves gland-dotted, opposite or alternate ; stipules absent ; stamens numerous ;
    shrubs or trees rarely herbaceous   *Myrtaceae.*
Leaves not gland-dotted or the leaves reduced to scales ; mostly herbs :
  Root parasites with scale-like leaves ; stamens monadelphous :
    Flowers unisexual   *Cytinaceae.*
    Flowers hermaphrodite   *Hydnoraceae.*
  Not as above :
    Leaves alternate :
      Leaves stipulate, stipules sometimes adnate to the petiole :
        Flowers hermaphrodite :
          Inflorescence not leaf-opposed ; calyx present   *Saxifragaceae.*
          Inflorescence leaf-opposed ; calyx absent   *Saururaceae.*
        Flowers unisexual ; stamens usually numerous ; ovary often winged
                 Begoniaceae.
      Leaves exstipulate ; ovary often gaping at the top ; stamens 4 to many ;
        calyx not unilateral   *Datiscaceae.*
      Leaves exstipulate ; ovary closed at the top ; stamens 6 to many ; calyx
        unilateral, coloured ; climbers   *Aristolochiaceae.*
    Leaves opposite, ericoid ; flowers glomerate   *Grubbiaceae.*

GROUP 10

One carpel or two or more united carpels with axile, basal or apical placentation ;
ovary superior ; petals present, free from each other

Perfect stamens the same number as the petals and opposite to them ; leaves
    alternate or rarely opposite or all radical (to p. 45) :
Leaves not gland-dotted ; petals and stamens more or less hypogynous or
    subperigynous ; disk usually conspicuous :
Calyx-lobes or sepals imbricate :
  Petals imbricate or biseriately imbricate :
    Ovary 1-celled ; ovules basal :
      Petals often biglandular towards the base ; ovules few ; leaves simple
        or compound ; anthers opening by valves   *Berberidaceae.*
      Petals not glandular at the base ; anthers opening by longitudinal slits :
        Ovules more than 1 in each ovary   *Primulaceae.*
        Ovule 1 in each ovary   *Portulacaceae.*
    Ovary 2-3-celled ; ovules 2 in each cell, horizontal or pendulous ; stamens
      4-5, sometimes about 2 only bearing anthers ; no petaloid staminodes
                 Sabiaceae.
    Ovary 1-2-celled ; ovule solitary, pendulous from near the top :
    Sepals free or only shortly united :
      Stamens alternating with petaloid staminodes   *Corynocarpaceae.*
      No staminodes ; shrubs or small trees   *Samydaceae.*
    Sepals united high up ; leaves often crowded ; mostly undershrubs
                 Thymelaeaceae.
  Petals valvate, mostly climbers with swollen nodes and leaf-opposed in-
    florescences   *Ampelidaceae.*

Calyx-lobes valvate :
 Disk absent from the flowers :
 Trees and shrubs or rarely herbs ; flowers not scapose :
 Leaves stipulate ; stamens hypogynous   *Sterculiaceae.*
 Leaves exstipulate ; stamens perigynous   *Lythraceae.*
 Herbs, mostly with rosettes of leaves ; flowers on scapose inflorescences
     Plumbaginaceae.
 Disk present, perigynous ; leaves mostly stipulate ; ovary 2-4-celled ;
 ovules erect ; seeds mostly with copious endosperm and large straight
 embryo   *Rhamnaceae.*
 Disk present ; leaves exstipulate :
 Ovules erect   *Olacaceae.*
 Ovules pendulous   *Opiliaceae.*
Leaves pellucid-punctate :
 Leaves simple, without stipules ; ovules numerous ; trees or shrubs ; no
 tendrils :
 Petals and stamens hypogynous ; ovary 1-celled ; ovules numerous on a
 free-central placenta   *Myrsinaceae.*
 Petals and stamens perigynous ; ovary 2-3-celled ; ovules numerous on an
 axile placenta   *Heteropyxidaceae.*
 Leaves mostly compound, usually stipulate ; inflorescence leaf-opposed ;
 ovules 1-2 in each cell ; mostly climbers with tendrils   *Ampelidaceae.*
Perfect stamens the same number as the petals and alternate with them or more
 numerous, very rarely fewer :
 Stamens 6, tetradynamous (4 long and 2 short) ; flowers usually actinomorphic
 (regular) ; petals 4, often clawed ; placentas 2   *Cruciferae.*
 Stamens not as above, rarely 6 :
 Style basal ; stipules mostly persistent :
 Leaves simple ; stamens numerous ; stomata of the leaves usually with
 special subsidiary cells   *Rosaceae.*
 Leaves pinnate ; stamens 10 ; disk large   *Simarubaceae.*
 Style or styles terminal or subterminal, sometimes gynobasic :
 Flowers markedly zygomorphic (irregular) (to p. 46) :
 Stamens definite in number, 12 or fewer :
 Lower sepal not spurred ; sepals 5, the inner 2 larger and often petaloid
 wing-like ; anthers often opening by an apical pore ; seeds mostly
 with endosperm   *Polygalaceae.*
 Lower sepal not spurred ; sepals 4-5 or rarely up to 12, subequal ; anthers
 opening by longitudinal slits ; seeds mostly with copious endosperm
     Saxifragaceae.
 Lower sepal subsaccate ; trees or shrubs with pinnate stipulate leaves ;
 stamens 4-5, free, inserted within the disk   *Melianthaceae.*
 Lower sepal more or less elongated into a spur :
 Sepals usually 3 ; anthers connivent around the ovary, opening length-
 wise ; seeds without endosperm   *Balsaminaceae.*
 Sepals 5, anthers free, opening lengthwise ; seeds usually without
 endosperm :
 Stamens about 8 ; leaves alternate   *Tropaeolaceae.*
 Stamens 3-12, unilateral ; leaves sometimes opposite   *Trigoniaceae.*
 Stamens 1-2 (rarely a few staminodes) ; leaves opposite
     Vochysiaceae.

 Stamens more than 12 :
 Stamens and petals hypogynous   *Tamaricaceae.*
 Stamens and petals perigynous or epigynous   *Rosaceae.*

Flowers actinomorphic or very slightly zygomorphic :
Stamens united into more than one separate bundle (phalanges) often
    opposite the petals :
    Leaves opposite, often gland-dotted or with resinous lines, exstipulate ;
        calyx imbricate :
        Herbs or shrubs ; styles free from the base or nearly so ; flowers herma-
            phrodite   *Hypericaceae.*
        Trees or shrubs ; styles mostly more or less united or stigma one and
            sessile or subsessile ; flowers mostly unisexual   *Guttiferae.*
    Leaves alternate (or if opposite then stipulate) or all radical :
        Sepals imbricate :
        Trees or shrubs :
            Flowers hypogynous :
                Leaves neither very small nor fleshy   *Theaceae.*
                Leaves often small and crowded or fleshy   *Tamaricaceae.*
            Flowers perigynous :   *Samydaceae.*
        Herbs or very small undershrubs :
            Ovary with a long beak ; carpels 5 completely united   *Geraniaceae.*
            Ovary with the carpels only partially united ; carpels 3
                                                Dilleniaceae.
        Sepals valvate ; hairs on the leaves, etc., often stellate :
        Stamens free or monadelphous, or if united into bundles then some
            sterile   *Sterculiaceae.*
        Stamens in separate bundles, all fertile   *Tiliaceae.*
Stamens free or at least not united into several bundles, sometimes more
    or less united at the base or into one bundle (monadelphous) :
    Leaves opposite or verticillate or rarely fasciculate, never all radical nor
        completely reduced (to p. 50) :
    Leaves compound, rarely unifoliolate and then with a distinctly tumid
        petiole, sometimes sessile (to p. 47) :
        Stamens numerous, more than twice the number of the petals :
            Leaves digitate :
                Leaves large ; flowers in terminal racemes   *Caryocaraceae.*
                Leaves very small, sessile ; flowers axillary, solitary   *Saxifragaceae.*
                Leaves pinnate ; petals and stamens subhypogynous   *Eucryphiaceae.*
        Stamens definite, not more than twice as many as the petals ; disk
            usually present :
            Leaves gland-dotted ; disk usually present between the stamens and
                ovary ; ovary often deeply lobed ; cells 2-ovuled ; ovules
                pendulous ; stipules rarely present   *Rutaceae.*
            Leaves not gland-dotted, sometimes fleshy :
                Leaves stipulate (to p. 47) :
                  Ovules pendulous from the central axis, 2 or more in each cell ;
                    disk often fleshy, rarely absent :
                    Stipules persistent and often paired ; shrubs or herbs ; leaves
                        mostly 2-foliolate or pinnate ; filaments often with a scale
                        or gland attached to the base   *Zygophyllaceae.*
                  Stipules often deciduous ; leaves 3-8-foliolate ; disk perigynous
                                              Cunoniaceae.
                Ovule pendulous, solitary in each cell ; disk usually within the
                  stamens ; trees or shrubs ; leaves mostly pinnate ; filaments
                  nude, pilose or with a scale at the base   *Simarubaceae.*
              Ovules ascending ; stamens inserted outside the disk
                                             Staphylleaceae.

Leaves exstipulate :
Stamens with free filaments, mostly twice as many as the petals :
  Leaves digitately 3-foliolate, sessile   *Saxifragaceae.*
  Leaves pinnate, stalked :
    Ovules mostly 2 in each cell   *Burseraceae.*
    Ovule 1 in each cell   *Simarubaceae.*
Stamens with more or less connate filaments, often double the
    number of the petals   *Meliaceae.*
Stamens free, fewer than the petals ; ovules 2 or rarely up to 8
                                                             Oleaceae.
Stamens as many as the petals, free ; ovules numerous in each cell,
    at least more than 2   *Staphylleaceae.*
Stamens as many as or more than the petals ; ovules 2 in each cell,
    collateral; ovary compressed contrary to the septum   *Aceraceae.*
Leaves simple, but sometimes deeply and variously divided :
Ovary stipitate on a gynophore ; stamens usually numerous, mostly
    more than twice as many as the petals, or if fewer then leaves
    gland-dotted ; seeds without endosperm or very little ; petals often
    clawed :
Leaves not gland-dotted :
  Ovules on the walls or on the intrusive septa   *Capparidaceae.*
  Ovules on the central axis or from the base of the ovary
                                                             Caryophyllaceae.
Leaves gland-dotted   *Rutaceae.*
Ovary sessile or rarely very slightly stipitate :
Stamens more than twice as many as the petals (to p. 48) :
Calyx imbricate or calyptrate (to p. 48) :
  Sepals mostly 2, caducous ; petals 4, often crumpled in bud ;
    filaments free   *Papaveraceae.*
  Sepals more than 2, mostly persistent ; petals usually 5 :
  Stipules absent :
    Stamens united into 5 bundles which are connate nearly to the
        top ; style single   *Hypericaceae.*
    Stamens free or united into a mass ; flowers usually dioecious or
        polygamous :
      Leaves opposite, not fasciculate ; not spiny   *Guttiferae.*
      Leaves fasciculate ; spiny fleshy shrubs   *Didiereaceae.*
  Stipules present :
    Leaves pinnately nerved :
      Stamens free or very shortly connate only at the base ; styles
          2-3, free ; leaves with numerous very fine transverse veins ;
          stipules mostly paired, lateral, rigid ; flowers paniculate
          or fascicled   *Quiinaceae.*
      Stamens free, very numerous :
        Styles 5-12 ; leaves with small caducous intrapetiolar stipules ;
            flowers solitary, showy   *Eucryphiaceae.*
        Styles 20-25 ; ovary with as many cells ; flowers paniculate
                                                             Medusagynaceae.
        Style 1 ; stigma 3-lobed   *Theaceae.*
      Stamens 10-15, free ; style with 2-6 stigmas ; leaves rather
          fleshy, with small persistent stipules ; flowers in cymes
                                                             Zygophyllaceae.
    Leaves with 3 or more longitudinally parallel nerves
                                                             Melastomaceae.

Calyx valvate :
  Stamens free or very shortly connate at the base :
    Stamens not inflexed in bud :
      Stipules paired, not interpetiolar   *Tiliaceae.*
      Stipules single, interpetiolar   *Rhizophoraceae.*
    Stamens inflexed in bud :
      Leaves stipulate ; indumentum often stellate   *Euphorbiaceae.*
      Leaves exstipulate ; indumentum rarely stellate :
        Flowers sometimes large and showy, clawed ; ovary few-celled
                                        Lythraceae.
        Flowers with small sessile petals ; ovary many-celled
                                 Sonneratiaceae.
  Stamens monadelphous or in fascicles opposite the petals, the latter
    contorted or imbricate ; leaves usually stipulate ; hairs often
    stellate   *Sterculiaceae.*
Stamens not more than twice as many as the petals :
  Trees, shrubs or woody climbers (to p. 50) :
  Leaves stipulate, sometimes stipules rudimentary or of hairs (to p. 49):
    Stipules intrapetiolar, often connivent into one or adnate to the
      petiole :
      Sepals not glandular outside and not accrescent in fruit ; hairs
        not medifixed   *Erythroxylaceae.*
      Sepals usually glandular outside or accrescent in fruit ; hairs
        medifixed ; leaves often biglandular at the base
                              Malpighiaceae.
    Stipules not intrapetiolar, sometimes rudimentary :
      Disk absent or inconspicuous or of separate glands ; calyx often
        glandular :
        Stamens free or shortly united only at the base :
          Calyx mostly with a pair of glands outside ; trees, shrubs or
            climbers ; filaments of stamens without a scale
                              Malpighiaceae.
          Calyx not glandular ; anther-cells collateral :
            Mostly herbaceous ; filaments of stamens often with a scale
              attached   *Zygophyllaceae.*
            Trees or shrubs ; filaments without a scale   *Cunoniaceae.*
          Calyx not glandular ; anther-cells back to back ; trees or
            shrubs ; filaments without a scale ; petals 4 ; stamens 4
                               Salvadoraceae.
        Stamens united into a long tube ; sepals not glandular ; ovary
          5-celled with 2 ovules in each ; calyx valvate
                               Rhizophoraceae.
      Disk present, conspicuous ; calyx not glandular :
        Flowers hermaphrodite :
          Stamens inserted on or below the margin of the disk ; filaments
            subulate :
            Stamens 3-5   *Celastraceae.*
            Stamens 8-10   *Rhizophoraceae.*
         Stamens usually 3, inserted on the disk ; filaments flattened
           or connivent, often adnate to the ovary   *Hippocrateaceae.*
      Flowers unisexual ; ovules pendulous from the apex of the cell :
        Seeds often carunculate; flowers rarely in heads   *Euphorbiaceae.*
        Seeds not carunculate ; flowers arranged in dense heads ; hairs
          stellate   *Hamamelidaceae.*

Leaves exstipulate or stipules gland-like :
  Stamens united into a tube :
    Stamens more than 4 ; flowers hermaphrodite   *Meliaceae.*
    Stamens 4 ; flowers unisexual   *Guttiferae.*
  Stamens free or very shortly united only at the base :
    Anthers opening at the apex by a pore ; stamens as many as or twice
      as many as the petals :
      Leaves often with 3-9 longitudinally parallel nerves ; anthers
        often appendaged at the base   *Melastomaceae.*
      Leaves without parallel nerves ; anthers not appendaged at the
        base   *Tremandraceae.*
    Anthers opening by slits lengthwise :
      Ovules numerous in each cell :
        Petals and stamens hypogynous ; flowers hermaphrodite
          Pittosporaceae.
        Petals and stamens hypogynous ; flowers unisexual   *Guttiferae.*
        Petals and stamens perigynous ; flowers hermaphrodite
          Lythraceae.
      Ovules few in each cell :
        Sepals 2-glandular outside ; hairs (when present) on the leaves
          medifixed ; shrubs or climbers :
          Fruits usually winged ; styles often 3   *Malpighiaceae.*
          Fruits drupaceous ; style one   *Simarubaceae.*
        Sepals not glandular ; hairs not medifixed :
          Ovules pendulous from the apex of the cells :
            Sepals imbricate or open :
            Sepals free or calyx-tube very short :
              Stamens hypogynous :
              Petals imbricate   *Linaceae.*
              Petals valvate   *Icacinaceae.*
              Stamens perigynous :
                Ovary 5-celled ; ovules 2 in each   *Escalloniaceae.*
                Ovary 4-celled ; ovule solitary   *Cunoniaceae.*
             Sepals connate into a long or rather long tube
              Thymelaeaceae.
            Sepals valvate :
              Stamens hypogynous   *Tremandraceae.*
              Stamens perigynous   *Combretaceae.*
          Ovules erect or ascending from the base of the cells :
            Calyx imbricate :
              Filaments subulate or filiform :
              Leaves mostly palmately lobed, or if not so then disk
                absent ; ovary and fruit flattened contrary to the
                septum   *Aceraceae.*
              Leaves pinnately lobed ; disk present :
                Flowers hermaphrodite   *Celastraceae.*
                Flowers dioecious or polygamous   *Guttiferae.*
              Filaments flattened   *Hippocrateaceae.*
            Calyx valvate ; stamens 3-5 ; style short :
              Leaves not gland-dotted :
                Sepals free or nearly so   *Anacardiaceae.*
                Sepals united into a long tube ; the 2 posticous petals often
                  larger than the others   *Lythraceae.*
              Leaves gland-dotted   *Rutaceae.*

E

Herbs, sometimes slightly woody at the base :
Ovary incompletely septate with free-central or basal placentation ;
  leaves mostly stipulate :
Sepals the same number as the petals, 3-5, free or connate ; petals
  3-5, often clawed   *Caryophyllaceae.*
Sepals the same number as the petals but often with as many
  accessory lobes, connate into a tube ; stamens inflexed in bud
                                        Lythraceae.
Sepals fewer than the petals, usually 2 ; petals 4-5 or more
                                     Portulacaceae.

Ovary completely septate :
Leaves stipulate :
Stipules paired :
Branches not articulate ; ovules numerous, attached to the
  central axis   *Elatinaceae.*
Branches usually not articulated ; ovules few, pendulous ; sepals
  often unequal   *Geraniaceae.*
Branches articulated ; ovules few, pendulous or ascending ;
  sepals equal   *Zygophyllaceae.*
Stipules solitary, sometimes minute :
Stamens distinctly perigynous; capsule circumscissile *Ficoidaceae.*
Stamens hypogynous, or slightly perigynous :
Ovules pendulous ; fruit a capsule or drupe, not circumscissile
        Linaceae.
Ovules basal or axile and spreading ; fruit a valvular capsule,
  not circumscissile   *Molluginaceae.*
Leaves exstipulate :
Leaves with 3 or more longitudinally parallel nerves ; anthers
  usually appendaged and opening by a terminal pore
        Melastomaceae.
Leaves not as above ; anthers opening by longitudinal slits :
Stamens hypogynous or nearly so   *Molluginaceae.*
Stamens perigynous :
Anthers erect in bud   *Ficoidaceae.*
Anthers inflexed in bud   *Lythraceae.*
Leaves alternate or all radical :
Stamens more than twice the number of the sepals or petals (to p. 53) :
Sepals valvate or open in bud (to p. 51) :
Anthers 2-celled (to p. 51) :
Anthers narrowly horseshoe-shaped, the cells bent on themselves
  (see Fig. 129)   *Gonystylaceae.*
Anthers straight :
Stamens free or slightly united only at the base :
Petals and stamens hypogynous or flowers unisexual :
Stipules present :
Flowers hermaphrodite ; indumentum often stellate *Tiliaceae.*
Flowers unisexual ; indumentum rarely stellate *Euphorbiaceae.*
Stipules absent ; calyx cupular ; stamens in several series ; anthers
  opening by a pore or short slit   *Scytopetalaceae.*
Petals and stamens perigynous or epigynous :
Leaves stipulate ; stipules mostly paired ; ovary 2-celled ; styles
  subulate, free   *Hamamelidaceae.*
Leaves exstipulate :
Anthers inflexed in bud ; calyx tubular   *Lythraceae.*

Anthers erect in bud :
Leaves simple ; wood not resinous :
Ovary incompletely septate, wholly superior   *Olacaceae.*
Ovary completely septate, partly inferior   *Styracaceae.*
Leaves compound or unifoliolate ; wood resinous   *Anacardiaceae.*
Stamens more or less united into a tube or into bundles, hypogynous ;
indumentum usually stellate :
Anthers opening longitudinally   *Sterculiaceae.*
Anthers opening by pore-like short slits   *Scytopetalaceae.*
Anthers 1-celled ; stamens monadelphous ; calyx with or without an
epicalyx :
Trees or rarely shrubs ; leaves digitately compound or simple ;
carpels not or very rarely splitting away from the central axis
in fruit   *Bombacaceae.*
Mostly herbs ; leaves simple ; carpels often splitting away from the
central axis or becoming free in fruit   *Malvaceae.*
Sepals imbricate or rarely completely connate or calyptrate or cupulate :
Anthers narrowly horseshoe-shaped, the cells bent on themselves
(see Fig. 129)   *Gonystylaceae.*
Anthers straight :
Petals and stamens perigynous :
Leaves stipulate :
Seeds with endosperm and a curved embryo ; mostly herbs
        Portulacaceae.
Seeds without endosperm or with very little :
Ovary with usually more than 2 carpels or sometimes only one ;
flowers not or very rarely capitate   *Rosaceae.*
Ovary of 2 carpels ; flowers often capitate   *Hamamelidaceae.*
Leaves exstipulate :
Stamens free from the petals :
Flowers not capitate :
Petals not crumpled in bud ; ovules pendulous from the apex
of the cells :
Leaves stipulate   *Rhizophoraceae.*
Leaves without stipules   *Samydaceae.*
Petals often crumpled in bud ; ovules basal or from the inner
angle of the cell ; sepals valvate   *Lythraceae.*
Flowers capitate, asymmetric ; involucre coloured
        Hamamelidaceae.
Stamens inserted on the base of the petals   *Styracaceae.*
Petals and stamens more or less hypogynous or flowers unisexual ;
disk often present :
Trees, shrubs or woody climbers (to p. 53) :
Leaves compound or rarely unifoliolate and then with a tumid
petiole (to p. 52) :
Leaves pinnate ; petals not calyptrate :
Ovule ascending :
Leaves gland-dotted ; style or styles central   *Rutaceae.*
Leaves rarely gland-dotted ; styles or stigmas often separated :
Wood resinous   *Anacardiaceae.*
Wood not resinous, not bitter   *Sapindaceae.*
Wood not resinous, very bitter   *Simarubaceae.*
Ovule or ovules pendulous :
Stamens free ; wood with resin ducts   *Anacardiaceae.*

Stamens more or less free from one another; wood without resin
    ducts   *Simarubaceae.*
Stamens united into a tube   *Meliaceae.*
Leaves digitate 3-5-foliolate; petals calyptrately connate; styles
    short, 8-20; embryo spiral   *Caryocaraceae.*
Leaves simple:
Leaves stipulate:
Flowers unisexual:
  Disk present   *Euphorbiaceae.*
  No disk   *Flacourtiaceae.*
Flowers hermaphrodite:
  Torus enlarged after flowering; ovary mostly deeply lobed,
    the carpels becoming separated in fruit; anthers often
    opening by pores   *Ochnaceae.*
  Torus not enlarged:
  Ovary stipitate; sepals more or less connate into a tube
    Capparidaceae.
  Ovary sessile; sepals usually free:
  Sepals 3; stipules caducous; flowers cymose or paniculate;
    petals contorted; stamens 10 or more, inside a ring of
    staminodes; ovary 3-celled; Mascarene Islands
    Chlaenaceae.
  Sepals 5; no staminodes:
  Calyx enlarged and wing-like in fruit:
    Flowers mostly rather small and not showy; petals much
    contorted   *Dipterocarpaceae.*
    Flowers showy; ovary 1-celled with a basal placenta
    Ochnaceae.
  Calyx not enlarged; leaves digitately lobed; flowers hand-
    some; anthers opening by short pore-like confluent
    slits at the apex; petals imbricate or slightly contorted
    Cochlospermaceae.
Leaves not stipulate:
Ovary and fruit stipitate   *Capparidaceae.*
Ovary and fruit not stipitate:
Seeds arillate; ovary composed of 1 carpel; leaves mostly
  with very prominent pinnately parallel lateral nerves;
  stamens usually persistent   *Dilleniaceae.*
Seeds not arillate; ovary usually composed of 2 or more
  carpels:
Sterile flowers with modified pitcher-like saccate or spurred
  bracts   *Marcgraviaceae.*
Sterile flowers not present; no modified bracts:
Ovary 1-celled, composed of 1 carpel:
  Stamens more than 10, free:
  Leaves pellucid-punctate, rather large and coriaceous
    Winteraceae.
  Leaves usually very small and crowded   *Tamaricaceae.*
Ovary 2- or more-celled:
  Anthers basifixed; seeds usually few   *Theaceae.*
  Anthers versatile; seeds numerous, small:
  Climbers; flowers often unisexual; sepals scarcely im-
    bricate; styles numerous, free   *Actinidiaceae.*
  Erect trees or shrubs; flowers mostly hermaphrodite;

sepals very much imbricate ; styles 3-5, free or connate
at the base ; anthers opening by pores *Saurauiaceae.*
Trees or shrubs ; flowers hermaphrodite ; style simple,
slender, entire or minutely dentate *Humiriaceae.*
Anthers versatile ; seed solitary ; leaves fasciculate ; spiny
plants *Didiereaceae.*
Herbs, rarely somewhat woody at the base :
Carpels not sunk in the torus :
Leaves neither sticky glandular, setose-ciliate, nor modified into
pitchers :
Anthers opening by longitudinal slits :
Stamens quite free from one another :
Sepals more than 2 *Ranunculaceae.*
Sepals 2 *Portulacaceae.*
Stamens connate at the base ; leaves pinnate *Oxalidaceae.*
Anthers opening by a short pore-like terminal slit
Cochlospermaceae.
Leaves very sticky glandular or ciliate with setose teeth, not
modified into pitchers. *Droseraceae.*
Leaves modified into tubes or pitchers ; stamens numerous, free ;
ovary 3-5-celled ; ovules numerous *Sarraceniaceae.*
Carpels sunk in the torus ; aquatic plants with peltate leaves
Nymphaeaceae.
Stamens definite in number in relation to the sepals or petals, often the
same number or twice as many or fewer :
Leaves compound, rarely unifoliolate and then with a distinctly tumid
petiole (to p. 54) :
Stamens united into a tube ; leaves pinnate or rarely unifoliolate :
Leaves exstipulate *Meliaceae.*
Leaves with intrapetiolar stipules *Melianthaceae.*
Stamens free or united only at the base :
Leaves stipulate :
Herbaceous or slightly woody; leaves digitately or pinnately
compound :
Stamens without a scale at the base of the filaments ; flowers
actinomorphic *Oxalidaceae.*
Stamens with a scale at the base of the filaments ; flowers actino-
morphic *Zygophyllaceae.*
Stamens without a scale at the base ; flowers more or less zygo-
morphic *Melianthaceae.*
Trees, shrubs or climbers :
Ovules pendulous ; stipules convolute, axillary, often very long ;
leaves mostly simple *Simarubaceae.*
Ovules ascending ; leaves compound ; habit often climbing :
Stipules lateral *Sapindaceae.*
Stipules intrapetiolar *Melianthaceae.*
Leaves exstipulate :
Leaves gland-dotted *Rutaceae.*
Leaves not gland-dotted :
Ovules pendulous from towards the apex of the cells :
Ovules solitary or collateral :
Ovary of more than 1 carpel; wood mostly resinous *Burseraceae.*
Ovary of more than 1 carpel ; wood with bitter bark but not
resinous *Simarubaceae.*

Ovary of 1 carpel ; wood resinous   *Anacardiaceae.*
Ovules paired, superposed   *Akaniaceae.*
Ovules ascending or horizontal :
Ovules numerous on axile placentas, horizontally spreading ; sepals, petals and stamens 8, rarely 5 ; leaves trifoliolate ; stigmas sessile, 8-rayed   *Tovariaceae.*
Ovules mostly few or one ; above characters not associated :
Herbs with sensitive leaves   *Oxalidaceae.*
Trees or shrubs :
Ovules mostly 2 in each cell, superposed ; styles various
    Rutaceae.
Ovules about 8 in each cell ; style 1   *Meliaceae.*
Ovules 2 in each cell, collateral ; style simple   *Connaraceae.*
Ovules 1 or more in each cell, erect or ascending ; style simple or divided   *Sapindaceae.*
Ovule 1 in each cell ; style lobed or styles separate ; wood with resin ducts   *Anacardiaceae.*
Leaves simple, rarely completely reduced :
Anthers opening by valves :
Leafless parasitic herbs on roots of trees   *Monotropaceae.*
Leafy trees or shrubs ; but sometimes leafless at time of flowering :
Ovary composed of 2 carpels ; stipules often present, mostly paired ; flowers often capitate   *Hamamelidaceae.*
Ovary composed of 1 carpel ; stipules absent   *Lauraceae.*
Anthers opening by apical pores :
Leaves with 3 or more longitudinally parallel main nerves ; connective of the anthers often produced at the base
    Melastomaceae.
Leaves pinnately nerved or nerveless :
Petals induplicate-valvate ; ovary 2-celled ; anthers 2- or 4-celled
    Tremandraceae.
Petals imbricate or contorted :
Ovary deeply lobed ; torus enlarging in fruit and the carpels often becoming separate ; ovules 1-2 in each cell   *Ochnaceae.*
Ovary not deeply lobed ; torus not enlarged :
Ovules numerous in each cell ; leaves fairly large and broad
    Clethraceae.
Ovules 1-3 ; fruits winged   *Cyrillaceae.*
Ovules several in each cell or in the ovary ; leaves narrow
    Pittosporaceae.
Ovule usually solitary ; leaves very narrow ; not glandular
    Polygalaceae.
Ovules 1-2 ; leaves very glandular-pilose, circinate in bud
    Byblidaceae.
Anthers opening by slits lengthwise :
Shrubs or trees (to p. 57) :
Leaves stipulate (to p. 55) :
Calyx persistent and wing-like in fruit ; leaves often with prominent parallel lateral nerves ; petals contorted   *Dipterocarpaceae.*
Calyx not wing-like in fruit ; petals rarely contorted :
Flowers unisexual :
Disk absent ; petals not bilobed :
Male petals imbricate   *Flacourtiaceae.*
Male petals valvate   *Pandaceae.*

Disk present ; petals bilobed   *Chailletiaceae.*
Disk present :
  Stipules conspicuous, persistent   *Euphorbiaceae.*
  Stipules very inconspicuous, caducous   *Celastraceae.*
Flowers hermaphrodite :
  Stamens perigynous, inserted on the calyx-tube :
    Ovary 1-celled, composed of one carpel   *Rosaceae.*
    Ovary 2-celled, composed of 2 or more carpels *Hamamelidaceae.*
  Stamens hypogynous or inserted on or at the base of a disk :
    Stipules axillary, convolute in bud, often very long :
      Petals not appendaged inside   *Simarubaceae.*
      Petals appendaged inside   *Erythroxylaceae.*
    Stipules not axillary :
      Disk absent, or torus sometimes enlarging in fruit but not glandular :
        Sepals 3, much imbricate ; petals imbricate - contorted ; stamens inserted inside a cup of staminodes ; Mascarene Islands   *Chlaenaceae.*
        Sepals 5 ; no cup of staminodes present :
          Stamens 10, in 2 series ; hairs of the leaves when present not medifixed ; petiole not glandular   *Erythroxylaceae.*
          Stamens 8 ; hairs not medifixed ; petiole not glandular ; ovary 4-celled ; racemes catkin-like   *Stachyuraceae.*
          Stamens 10, in 1 series ; hairs of leaves often medifixed ; petiole often glandular like the sepals   *Malpighiaceae.*
          Stamens usually numerous ; hairs of leaves when present not medifixed ; petiole not glandular   *Ochnaceae.*
      Disk present, annular or of separate glands :
        Petals entire or emarginate ; ovules erect   *Celastraceae.*
        Petals often deeply lobed ; ovules pendulous   *Chailletiaceae.*
Leaves exstipulate :
  Stamens united into a tube   *Meliaceae.*
  Stamens free or connate only at the base :
    Stamens hypogynous or very slightly perigynous (to p. 57) :
      Sterile flowers with modified pitcher-like bracts ; mostly epiphytes
                    Marcgraviaceae.
      Sterile flowers without modified bracts, or sterile flowers not present :
        Stamens double the number of the petals or fewer only by the abortion of some anthers (to p. 56) :
          Sepals usually with two large glands outside ; hairs of leaves medifixed ; ovary 3-celled, with 1 ovule in each cell ; seeds without endosperm ; fruit often winged   *Malpighiaceae.*
          Sepals not glandular ; hairs rarely medifixed :
            Ovary 1-celled :
              Ovary of 1 carpel :
                Torus forming a stipe   *Anacardiaceae.*
                Torus not stipitate   *Phytolaccaceae.*
              Ovary of more than 1 carpel ; leaves very small ; flowers spicate-racemose   *Tamaricaceae.*
            Ovary completely 2- or more-celled (or nearly completely 5-celled) :
              No disk ; leaves reduced or scale-like ; placenta basal
                    Molluginaceae.

Disk present; leaves not gland-dotted; petals mostly
valvate :
Flowers hermaphrodite   *Olacaceae.*
Flowers polygamo-dioecious   *Sapindaceae.*
Disk present, often intrastaminal ; leaves gland-dotted
                                                        Rutaceae.
Disk extrastaminal, cupular, crowned with 10 gland-like
    staminodes ; ovary imperfectly 5-celled ; soft-wooded
    trees with geranium-like leaves   *Greyiaceae.*
Disk intrastaminal, closely girding the ovary, not lobed ;
    leaves not gland-dotted :
Ovary 5-7-celled   *Humiriaceae.*
Ovary 2-5-celled   *Cyrillaceae.*
Disk absent ; flowers unisexual ; ovary 3-4-celled ; male
    petals valvate   *Pandaceae.*
Stamens the same number as the petals or fewer :
Disk absent ; flowers polygamous, axillary, solitary or fascicu-
    late :
Carpels not on a gynophore :
Ovules numerous ; anthers opening lengthwise or by apical
    pores ; style simple ; embryo minute in copious endo-
    sperm   *Pittosporaceae.*
Ovules 1-2, pendulous :
Petals imbricate or contorted, clawed ; anthers opening by
    slits   *Linaceae.*
Petals imbricate, not clawed ; anthers opening by an apical
    pore   *Theaceae.*
Petals imbricate, sessile ; anthers opening by slits length-
    wise   *Aquifoliaceae.*
Carpels on a gynophore :   *Cneoraceae.*
Disk present :
Petals valvate ; ovules pendulous :
Stamens opposite the petals   *Olacaceae.*
Stamens the same number as and alternate with the petals
                                              Icacinaceae.
Petals imbricate or contorted :
Petals more or less spreading :
Leaves not gland-dotted :
Stamens usually 5 :
Ovules 1-3 in each cell :
Ovule solitary ; wood resinous   *Anacardiaceae.*
Ovules mostly 2 in each cell ; wood not resinous
                                          Celastraceae.
Ovules 1-3 ; wood not resinous ; flowers in slender
    racemes   *Cyrillaceae.*
Ovules several to many   *Pittosporaceae.*
Stamens 3, with flattened filaments ; wood not resin-
    ous ; flowers cymose   *Hippocrateaceae.*
Leaves gland-dotted   *Rutaceae.*
Petals erect, more or less connivent :
Petals connivent in the upper part ; small herbs with a
    woody branched rhizome   *Stackhousiaceae.*
Petals free in the upper part ; shrubs or small trees
                                            Epacridaceae.

Stamens very distinctly perigynous (from p. 55) :
Leaves with 3 or more longitudinally parallel main nerves
                                        Melastomaceae.
Leaves with more or less pinnate nervation :
  Carpels free at the apex ; leaves stipulate   *Hamamelidaceae.*
  Carpels completely united ; stipules absent :
    Anthers inflexed in bud   *Lythraceae.*
    Anthers erect in bud :
      Petals scale-like, opposite the sepals ; ovary wholly superior
                                        Thymelaeaceae.
      Petals not scale-like, alternate with the sepals :
        Ovary wholly superior ; petals more or less clawed ; stamens
          only slightly perigynous ; woody only at the base
                                        Molluginaceae.
        Ovary semi-inferior ; stamens very clearly perigynous ;
          flowers often in heads ; low shrubs with small leaves
                                        Bruniaceae.
        Ovary quite superior ; trees or shrubs with fairly large
          leaves   *Escalloniaceae.*
Herbs, rarely slightly woody at the base :
  Parasites destitute of chlorophyll ; leaves reduced to scales
                                        Monotropaceae.
  Not parasitic ; leaves green :
    Leaves covered with dense sticky gland-tipped hairs or processes
      or setose-ciliate and bilobed, stipulate, often circinate in bud
                                        Droseraceae.
    Leaves not glandular :
    Leaves stipulate :
      Stamens and petals hypogynous or flowers unisexual :
        Flowers hermaphrodite :
          Sepals more than 2 :
            Sepals valvate   *Tiliaceae.*
            Sepals imbricate :
              Ovary more or less deeply lobed   *Geraniaceae.*
              Ovary entire :
                Stipules not scarious ; petals contorted   *Linaceae.*
                Stipules scarious ; petals imbricate or small *Molluginaceae.*
          Sepals 2, very much imbricate   *Portulacaceae.*
        Flowers unisexual   *Euphorbiaceae.*
      Stamens and petals perigynous ; anthers inflexed in bud
                                        Lythraceae.
    Leaves exstipulate :
      Sepals 2, much imbricate   *Portulacaceae.*
      Sepals more than 2 :
        Petals connivent in the upper part ; small herbs from a woody
          branched rhizome   *Stackhousiaceae.*
        Petals not connivent :
          Petals and stamens hypogynous or very slightly perigynous :
            Petals contorted, fugacious, mostly large and conspicuous ;
              embryo straight :
                Ovules pendulous ; leaves entire or nearly so   *Linaceae.*
                Ovules ascending ; leaves dissected   *Limnanthaceae.*
            Petals imbricate or very small and inconspicuous embryo
              curved   *Molluginaceae.*

Petals and stamens perigynous :
  Seeds with endosperm   *Saxifragaceae.*
  Seeds without endosperm ; carpels with a gland or scale at
    the base ; anthers erect in bud   *Crassulaceae.*
  Seeds without endosperm ; carpels without a gland or scale ;
    anthers inflexed in bud   *Lythraceae.*

GROUP 11

*One carpel or two or more united carpels with axile, basal or apical placentation ;
ovary superior ; petals present, more or less united*

Stamens the same number as and opposite to the corolla-lobes :
  Ovules solitary in the whole ovary or in each cell of the ovary ; style often
    lobed :
    Trees or shrubs, often with hard wood :
      Flowers dioecious ; petals imbricate or valvate ; stamens mostly free from
        the corolla   *Ebenaceae.*
      Flowers hermaphrodite ; stamens epipetalous :
        Petals imbricate ; hairs often stellate or medifixed   *Sapotaceae.*
        Petals valvate ; hairs usually simple :
          Inflorescence not leaf-opposed ; leaves simple   *Olacaceae.*
          Inflorescence leaf-opposed ; leaves often compound   *Ampelidaceae.*
    Herbs or climbers :
      Corolla-lobes valvate ; tendrils often present ; inflorescence usually cymose-
        paniculate, leaf-opposed ; leaves usually with the stipules adnate to
        the petiole   *Ampelidaceae.*
      Corolla-lobes imbricate :
        Stamens connate into a column, free from the petals ; stipules absent
                                                             Menispermaceae.
        Stamens free from each other and from the petals ; stipules scarious, rarely
          absent   *Portulacaceae.*
        Stamens more or less adnate to or inserted on the corolla *Plumbaginaceae.*
  Ovules 2 or more in each cell ; style undivided ; placentas often basal :
    Trees or shrubs with often gland-dotted leaves ; ovules 2 or more in the
      ovary   *Myrsinaceae.*
    Herbs or climbers with usually compound leaves and leaf-opposed inflorescence
                                                              Ampelidaceae.
    Herbs often with rosettes of leaves ; leaves not gland-dotted   *Primulaceae.*
Stamens the same number as the corolla-lobes and alternate with them or more
  numerous or fewer :
  Stamens more than twice as many as the corolla-lobes :
    Anthers opening by apical pores or short pore-like slits :
      Corolla-tube very short ; stamens numerous, adnate to the base of the
        corolla ; anthers not tailed   *Saurauiaceae.*
      Corolla-tube usually fairly long ; stamens rarely many more than double
        the number of the corolla-lobes, not adnate to the corolla-tube ; anthers
        often with tails   *Ericaceae.*
    Anthers opening by longitudinal slits :
      Flowers hermaphrodite :
        Leaves simple, sometimes deeply divided :
          Bracts more or less pouch-like and adnate to the pedicels ; stems climbing
            or epiphytic   *Marcgraviaceae.*
          Bracts and habit not as above :

Stamens hypogynous :
  Sepals imbricate :
    Trees or shrubs   *Theaceae.*
    Herbs or slightly woody at the base   *Molluginaceae.*
  Sepals valvate :
    Stamens free or nearly so   *Tiliaceae.*
    Stamens monadelphous   *Malvaceae.*
  Stamens perigynous or epigynous ; sepals usually imbricate :
    Leaves often gland-dotted and opposite   *Myrtaceae.*
    Leaves not gland-dotted, alternate   *Lecythidaceae.*
  Leaves digitately compound, opposite or alternate   *Caryocaraceae.*
  Flowers unisexual :
    Disk absent ; leaves without stipules   *Ebenaceae.*
    Disk present ; leaves usually with stipules   *Euphorbiaceae.*
Stamens as many as or up to twice as many as the corolla-lobes or fewer :
Stamens as many as or more than the corolla-lobes (to p. 63) :
  Flowers zygomorphic (irregular) :
    Ovary deeply 4-lobed ; style gynobasic   *Labiatae.*
    Ovary not 4-lobed ; style not gynobasic :
    Lower sepal elongated into a tubular spur ; ovary 5-celled
                                Balsaminaceae.

    Lower sepal not spurred ; ovary usually 2-celled :
      Ovules numerous :
        Corolla-lobes induplicate or contorted   *Solanaceae.*
        Corolla-lobes imbricate or folded   *Scrophulariaceae.*
      Ovules few :
        Anthers 2-celled, opening by a longitudinal slit   *Verbenaceae.*
        Anthers 1-celled, opening by a longitudinal slit   *Selaginaceae.*
        Anthers 1-2-celled, opening by a terminal pore *Polygalaceae.*
  Flowers actinomorphic (regular) :
    Leaves opposite or verticillate, mostly exstipulate :
    Anthers opening by apical pores or pore-like slits :
      Filaments of the stamens often geniculate and inflexed ; anthers mostly
        opening by a single (rarely 2) pore ; leaves mostly with the main
        nerves longitudinally parallel   *Melastomaceae.*
      Filaments of the stamens neither geniculate nor inflexed ; anthers
        opening by 2 pores ; leaves without longitudinally parallel nerves :
        Woody plants with usually evergreen leaves ; stamens hypogynous
                                Ericaceae.
        Herbaceous ; stamens epipetalous   *Gentianaceae.*
    Anthers opening by longitudinal slits :
      Leaves gland-dotted or pustulate ; petals usually shortly tubular :
        Styles terminal ; stamens epipetalous   *Loganiaceae.*
        Style not inserted at the inner base of the carpels ; stamens not epi-
         petalous   *Rutaceae.*
        Style inserted at the very inner base of the carpels ; stamens epipetalous
                              Boraginaceae.
      Leaves not gland-dotted ; petals usually joined high up :
        Style single with often a large more or less capitate stigma :
         Pollen granular ; leaves stipulate or sheathing at the base :
          Corolla scarious ; mostly herbs with radical leaves and dense spikes
           of flowers   *Plantaginaceae.*
         Corolla not scarious ; flowers not in dense spikes :
          Trees or shrubs ; leaves often stipulate   *Loganiaceae.*

Mostly herbs or scramblers ; leaves not stipulate   *Solanaceae.*
Pollen agglutinated in wax-like masses ; corolla with a corona ; leaves
    exstipulate   *Asclepiadaceae.*
Pollen granular ; corolla without a corona ; leaves exstipulate :
    Corolla-lobes contorted or rarely valvate   *Apocynaceae.*
    Corolla-lobes imbricate :
      Leaves not verticillate   *Scrophulariaceae.*
      Leaves verticillate   *Verbenaceae.*
Styles with more than 1 separate stigmas :
Stamens double the number of the corolla-lobes ; petals united only
    at the base :
    Mostly herbaceous ; flowers hermaphrodite :
      Petals not numerous   *Lythraceae.*
      Petals numerous   *Molluginaceae.*
    Trees or shrubs ; flowers dioecious   *Ebenaceae.*
Stamens the same number as the corolla-lobes :
    Rudimentary stipules often present ; stamens and corolla-lobes 4 :
        Salvadoraceae.
Stipules absent :
Style gynobasic   *Boraginaceae.*
Style terminal :
    Trees or shrubs :
      Ovules numerous in each cell, or if solitary then corolla-lobes
        valvate   *Loganiaceae.*
      Ovules 1-2 in each cell ; corolla-lobes imbricate   *Verbenaceae.*
    Herbs or herbaceous climbers :
      Ovary imperfectly celled by the intrusive parietal placentas
        Gentianaceae.
      Ovary perfectly celled with axile placentas :
        Ovary 3-5-celled ; style 3-5-lobed   *Polemoniaceae.*
        Ovary 2-celled ; style simple   *Solanaceae.*
Leaves alternate or all radical or reduced to scales :
Leafless parasites destitute of chlorophyll ; flowers hermaphrodite :
    Ovary 1-4-6-lobed and celled ; ovules very numerous in each cell
        Monotropaceae.
    Ovary 10-14-lobed, 20-28-celled ; ovules solitary in each cell
        Lennoaceae.
Ovary more or less 2-celled ; ovules 4 in each ovary   *Convolvulaceae.*
Not parasitic or rarely so ; leaves more or less green and normally
    developed :
Leaves stipulate, stipules sometimes soon falling off :
    Leaves densely covered with viscid gland-tipped hairs, mostly all
      radical ; often stemless herbs ; flowers mostly in simple circinate
      cymes ; placentas subbasal ; styles 3-5, mostly free   *Droseraceae.*
    Leaves not as above :
      Flowers unisexual ; petals not bifid ; ovary usually 3-lobed and
      3-celled ; calyx not wing-like in fruit   *Euphorbiaceae.*
      Flowers hermaphrodite or unisexual ; petals bifid or bilobed ; calyx
      not wing-like in fruit   *Chailletiaceae.*
      Flowers hermaphrodite ; petals not bilobed ; ovary 1-celled, 1-ovulate ;
      stamens 5 or 10 ; calyx wing-like in fruit   *Ancistrocladaceae.*
Leaves exstipulate :
Stamens hypogynous or perigynous, free from the corolla or slightly
    adnate to its base :

Anthers opening by terminal pores, often with appendages ; calyx
  persistent, sometimes petaloid; corolla-lobes contorted or imbricate;
  woody plants   *Ericaceae.*
Anthers opening by pores ; without appendages ; glandular-pilose
  herbs   *Byblidaceae.*
Anthers opening by longitudinal slits :
  Stamens 4-6 :
    Leaves gland-dotted ; ovary mostly deeply lobed ; petals connivent
      by their claws ; disk usually conspicuous between the stamens
      and ovary   *Rutaceae.*
    Leaves not gland-dotted ; ovary mostly entire :
    Petals only slightly united at the base :
      Disk present in the flowers, usually conspicuous :
        Corolla-segments valvate ; ovules 2-5 in each cell :
          Stamens opposite the petals or more numerous than them
                                     Olacaceae.
          Stamens the same number as and alternate with the petals
                              Icacinaceae.
        Corolla - segments imbricate ; ovules numerous ; sepals im-
          bricate :
          Leaves not small and ericoid   *Pittosporaceae.*
          Leaves small and ericoid   *Tamaricaceae.*
      Disk absent, or if present, adherent to the ovary :
        Ovules numerous ; sepals imbricate ; not epiphytic
                                   Pittosporaceae.
        Ovules numerous ; sepals very imbricate ; epiphytic or scandent ;
          bracts 3-lobed   *Marcgraviaceae.*
        Ovules 1-2 in each cell ; indumentum not stellate or lepidote ;
          calyx-lobes imbricate ; leaves simple   *Aquifoliaceae.*
        Ovules 2 in each cell, collateral, ascending ; leaves pinnate
                                   Connaraceae.
        Ovules few in each cell ; indumentum often stellate or lepidote ;
          calyx-lobes valvate or open   *Styracaceae.*
    Petals united high up ; sometimes free at the base :
      Calyx-lobes valvate, herbaceous ; anthers connivent around the
      style :
        Herbs ; not aquatic   *Campanulaceae.*
        Trees or shrubs   *Burseraceae.*
      Calyx - lobes imbricate, rather leathery ; shrubs or shrublets ;
      anthers free   *Epacridaceae.*
      Calyx-lobes imbricate ; herbs from a woody rhizome
                                 Stackhousiaceae.
      Calyx-lobes very imbricate ; aquatic herbs   *Plantaginaceae.*
  Stamens more than 6 :
    Stamens connate into a tube   *Meliaceae.*
    Stamens free or slightly connate only at the base :
      Disk absent ; corolla long and tubular ;
        Calyx very much imbricate ; flowers hermaphrodite
                                   Fouquieraceae.
        Calyx not or very slightly imbricate ; flowers unisexual
                                   Ebenaceae.
      Disk present, or if inconspicuous or absent then the corolla-tube
      very short :
        Leaves gland-dotted, often compound or unifoliolate   *Rutaceae.*

Leaves not gland-dotted, simple or very rarely compound :
Disk present in the flowers :
Leaves well developed, not small and ericoid :
Leaves simple ; bark not bitter :
Petals contorted *Cyrillaceae.*
Petals valvate *Olacaceae.*
Leaves compound or unifoliolate ; bark usually bitter
Simarubaceae.
Leaves small and ericoid ; flowers in spikes or racemes
Tamaricaceae.
Disk absent :
Trees or shrubs :
Ovules 1-2 in each cell ; indumentum not stellate ; calyx-lobes
imbricate :
Calyx-tube very short *Aquifoliaceae.*
Calyx-tube long and slender *Thymelaeaceae.*
Ovules few in each cell ; indumentum often stellate or lepidote ;
calyx-lobes valvate or open *Styracaceae.*
Herbs ; sepals often scarious *Molluginaceae.*
Stamens inserted on the corolla-tube or in a column adnate to the
stigma :
Style gynobasic :
Style 1 ; fruit composed of pyrenes or nutlets *Boraginaceae.*
Style 2 ; fruit mostly capsular *Convolvulaceae.*
Style not gynobasic, terminal :
Corolla valvate or plaited in bud (in the latter case the limb may be
somewhat twisted but not truly imbricate) :
Ovules 1-4 in each ovary cell :
Ovules basal, erect *Convolvulaceae.*
Ovules pendulous from the top of the ovary *Icacinaceae.*
Ovules numerous in each ovary cell *Gentianaceae.*
Flowers with a corona ; pollen agglutinated in wax-like masses
Asclepiadaceae.
Flowers without a corona ; pollen not agglutinated in wax-like
masses *Solanaceae.*
Corolla imbricate or contorted in bud :
Corolla contorted ; ovary mostly 3-celled with axile placentas
Polemoniaceae.
Corolla contorted ; ovary 1-2-celled :
Carpels completely united *Hydrophyllaceae.*
Carpels more or less free :
Pollen agglutinated in wax-like masses *Asclepiadaceae.*
Pollen not agglutinated in wax-like masses *Apocynaceae.*
Corolla imbricate ; ovary 1-2- (rarely up to 5-) celled :
Flowers arranged in a dense leafy head ; shrubs with sessile im-
bricate leaves ; ovary 2-celled *Bruniaceae.*
Flowers in dense spikes ; herbs with radical leaves and broad
sheathing petioles *Plantaginaceae.*
Flowers neither in heads nor in spikes, sometimes corymbose or
cymose :
Ovary 3-celled ; leaves evergreen :
Stamens 5 *Diapensiaceae.*
Stamens 10 *Diclidantheraceae.*
Ovary 1-2- or spuriously 4-celled :

Herbs :
  Style undivided or very shortly lobed ; lower leaves opposite
Gentianaceae.
  Style deeply 2-lobed or styles 2 ; all the leaves alternate or radical , *Hydrophyllaceae.*
  Style undivided ; stigmas terminal, small or more or less dilated ; all the leaves alternate *Solanaceae.*
  Trees or shrubs ; fruits a pyrene or nut *Boraginaceae.*
Stamens fewer than the corolla-lobes ; leaves mostly opposite :
Flowers actinomorphic :
Stamens more than 1 :
  Ovules numerous ; corolla not dry and scarious :
  Ovary constantly and completely 2-celled :
    Corolla-lobes induplicate or contorted-plicate *Solanaceae.*
    Corolla-lobes imbricate *Scrophulariaceae.*
  Ovary 1-celled or imperfectly 2-celled by the intrusive placentas
Gesneriaceae.
  Ovules 1-8 in each cell of the ovary ; capsule circumscissile ; corolla scarious with 4 lobes ; mostly herbs with radical leaves and spicate inflorescences *Plantaginaceae.*
  Ovules 1-2 in each cell of the ovary ; corolla not scarious :
  Corolla-lobes not more than the calyx-lobes :
    Corolla-lobes quite equal ; ovules mostly pendulous *Oleaceae.*
    Corolla-lobes slightly unequal or limb oblique ; ovules erect
Verbenaceae.
  Corolla-lobes about 3 times as many as the calyx-lobes *Sapotaceae.*
Stamen 1 ; corolla articulating above the base ; flowers in corymbose panicles *Loganiaceae.*
Flowers zygomorphic :
Placenta free-basal, more or less globose ; ovules numerous ; ovary 1-celled ; stamens 2, anthers 1-celled ; stigma sessile or style very short ; aquatic or swamp plants *Lentibulariaceae.*
Placentas axile, or if subbasal then ovules very few :
  Ovules numerous in the whole ovary or in each cell of the ovary, or if 2 then superposed :
  Anthers mostly free from each other ; ovary completely 2-celled, with the placentas on the septum ; cells ad- and abaxial *Scrophulariaceae.*
  Anthers often coherent ; ovary imperfectly 2-celled by the variously intrusive parietal placentas, the latter placed right and left of the floral axis *Gesneriaceae.*
  Anthers free but connivent ; ovary mostly 2-celled and then the cells ad- and abaxial (antero-posterior) ; leaves often compound ; woody plants, very rarely herbaceous ; seeds often winged, transverse
Bignoniaceae.
  Anthers often connivent in pairs ; ovary 1-4-celled ; fruit usually with a hard endocarp ; seeds not winged :
  Herbs with vesicular glands ; leaves opposite or alternate ; fruit sometimes prickly ; disk mostly inconspicuous *Pedaliaceae.*
  Herbs or rarely shrubs with tumid nodes and opposite or verticillate leaves ; seeds inserted on hardened outgrowths from the central placentas ; leaves often prominently marked with cystoliths ; valves of the capsule opening elastically from the apex ; disk cupular or annular *Acanthaceae.*
Shrubs ; nodes not tumid ; leaves alternate ; 2 inner lobes of the corolla

broadly emarginate or bifid ; fruit a drupe ; disk subannular or
lobed   *Chailletiaceae.*
Ovule solitary in each cell of the ovary, or if 2 then collateral :
Leaves opposite or verticillate :
Ovary entire ; style terminal :
Filaments free from each other   *Verbenaceae.*
Filaments forming a sheath split on its upper edge   *Polygalaceae.*
Ovary 4-lobed ; style gynobasic   *Labiatae.*
Leaves alternate :
Filaments free from each other :
Anthers 2-celled ; leaves usually studded with resinous glands
                                                    Myoporaceae.
Anthers 1-celled opening by a slit ; leaves not studded with glands :
Ovary 2-celled   *Selaginaceae.*
Ovary 1-celled   *Globulariaceae.*
Filaments more or less monadelphous and split along the top ; anthers
1- or rarely 2-celled, opening by a pore at the top   *Polygalaceae.*

GROUP 12

*One carpel or two or more united carpels with axile, basal or apical placentation ;
ovary superior ; petals absent*

Hermaphrodite or male (and often the female) flowers without a calyx (perianth) :
Fleshy herbs parasitic on roots, without green colouring matter ; ovule solitary
in a 1-celled ovary   *Balanophoraceae.*
Moss-like or hepatic-like aquatic herbs with minute flowers ; ovules 2 or more
in a 1-celled ovary   *Podostemonaceae.*
Neither parasites nor aquatic plants with above habit :
Leaves radical, palminerved ; flowers in a slender spike ; carpel 1 ; ovule 1,
erect from the base of the cell ; herb with creeping rhizome
                                                 Berberidaceae.
Leaves not all radical ; above characters not associated :
Trees or shrubs with whorled scale-like leaves   *Casuarinaceae.*
Trees, shrubs or herbs with normally developed leaves :
Leaves stipulate ; stipules sometimes adnate to the petiole :
Ovary 1-celled :
Herbs or shrubs ; leaves usually alternate ; flowers in dense spikes ;
petiole not dilated and not enclosing the young bud   *Piperaceae.*
Trees or shrubs with alternate leaves ; flowers minute on a common
open receptacle, the fruit becoming immersed in it   *Moraceae.*
Herbs, shrubs or trees with opposite leaves   *Chloranthaceae.*
Large trees ; leaves alternate, palmately nerved and lobed, the dilated
petiole enclosing the young bud   *Platanaceae.*
Ovary 2- or more-celled ; leaves alternate :
Ovules 1-2 in each cell of the ovary ; stipules rarely spinulose, often
caducous :
Flowers various, sometimes in an involucre margined with fleshy glands ;
seeds usually with copious endosperm ; ovary usually 2-3- or
more-celled   *Euphorbiaceae.*
Male flowers in catkins or slender spikes ; endosperm absent from the
seeds ; ovary 2-6-celled :
Fruit with a cupular involucre or enclosed by the latter   *Fagaceae.*
Fruit cone-like, with imbricate scales   *Betulaceae.*

Ovules numerous ; stipules not spinulose ; large trees ; leaves not plicately nerved *Hamamelidaceae.*

Ovules numerous ; stipules spinulose when old ; leaves opposite, plicately nerved ; low shrubs *Myrothamnaceae.*

Leaves without stipules :

Trees or shrubs with hard wood :

Flowers in a cyathium *Euphorbiaceae.*

Flowers not in a cyathium :

Leaves not aromatic ; flowers dioecious :

Males in catkins on the young branchlets or below the leaves *Balanopsidaceae.*

Male and female flowers solitary, precocious *Eucommiaceae.*

Leaves aromatic, often glandular ; flowers in dense spikes ; mostly swamp plants ; leaves simple *Myricaceae.*

Leaves not aromatic, pinnate ; not swamp plants *Oleaceae.*

Leaves not aromatic, fleshy ; flowers dioecious ; ovary 4-celled ; stamens 4 ; leaves simple ; maritime plants *Batidaceae.*

Herbs, sometimes slightly woody at the base :

Ovary 1-celled :

No stinging hairs ; stems not fibrous ; epidermal cells without cystoliths *Chenopodiaceae.*

No stinging hairs ; stems not fibrous ; flowers minute, usually densely spicate ; epidermal cells often with cystoliths *Piperaceae.*

Stinging hairs often present ; stems often fibrous ; epidermal cells mostly with prominent cystoliths *Urticaceae.*

Ovary 2-3-celled ; flowers much reduced, often arranged in a cyathium with glands on the margin *Euphorbiaceae.*

Ovary 4-celled ; annual herbs with minute unisexual flowers ; styles 2 ; stamen 1 *Callitrichaceae.*

All the flowers (or at any rate the male) with a calyx, sometimes minute or petaloid and long tubular :

Moss-like or hepatic-like herbs with minute flowers (submerged in fresh water) *Podostemonaceae.*

Not as above :

Leaves opposite or verticillate, never all radical (to p. 68) :

Leaves stipulate (to p. 67) :

Stamens more than twice the number of the sepals :

Flowers unisexual :

Style terminal *Euphorbiaceae.*

Style basal *Cynocrambaceae.*

Flowers hermaphrodite :

Sepals free or nearly so ; stamens hypogynous :

Filaments trifid at the apex, the two lateral lobes overlapping the anther ; ovary 10-celled ; stamens 10 *Zygophyllaceae.*

Filaments entire ; ovary 5-celled ; stigma ligulate, thick *Geraniaceae.*

Filaments entire ; ovary 1-5-celled ; stigmas not ligulate :

Herbs or slightly woody at the base *Molluginaceae.*

Trees ; stipules large and membranous *Cunoniaceae.*

Sepals united into a tube ; stamens inserted on the calyx-tube, more or less perigynous :

Fruit capsular *Ficoidaceae.*

Fruit an achene *Rosaceae.*

Stamens definite, up to twice as many as the sepals :

Stamens the same number as and alternate with the sepals, 4 or 5 :

Trees or shrubs, not fleshy ; leaves often toothed :
  Ovules 1-2   *Rhamnaceae.*
  Ovules numerous   *Crypteroniaceae.*
  Herbs or undershrubs with fleshy entire leaves   *Ficoidaceae.*
Stamens the same number as and opposite the sepals or more numerous
  or fewer :
  Ovary with free-central placentation ; ovules usually several to numerous
        Caryophyllaceae.
  Ovary with axile, basal or apical placentation :
    Flowers arranged in an involucre (cyathium) margined with fleshy
      often more or less semilunar glands ; male flower with only one
      stamen, jointed about the middle ; ovary often stipitate, mostly
      3-celled   *Euphorbiaceae.*
    Flowers not as above ; stamens usually more than 1 ; ovary mostly
      sessile :
      Flowers unisexual :
        Ovary 2- or more-celled   *Euphorbiaceae.*
        Ovary 1-celled :
          Ovule erect :
            Filaments inflexed in bud ; mostly herbaceous plants with
              fibrous stems and sometimes stinging hairs ; juice not milky
                    Urticaceae.
            Filaments not inflexed in bud ; mostly trees and shrubs, very
              rarely herbs ; juice mostly milky ; flowers often minute and
              arranged on or inside an enlarged " receptacle "   *Moraceae.*
          Ovule pendulous :
            Filaments not inflexed in bud :
              Fruit a drupe ; flowers monoecious or subdioecious   *Ulmaceae.*
              Fruit a small dry achene ; flowers dioecious   *Cannabinaceae.*
            Filaments erect or inflexed in bud   *Moraceae.*
      Flowers hermaphrodite :
        Sepals free or nearly so ; stamens more or less hypogynous ; ovary
          3-10-celled :
          Ovules numerous in each cell ; ovary 3-5-celled ; stamens often
            5, rarely up to 10 :
            Stipules often lobed or lacerate, persistent ; mostly herbs
                  Molluginaceae.
            Stipules membranous, deciduous ; trees   *Cunoniaceae.*
          Ovules 2 or more in each cell ; ovary 5-10-celled ; stamens 5 or 10 :
            Filaments 3-fid at the apex ; ovary 10-celled ; ovules 2-3 in each
              cell, ascending ; leaves opposite, connate, subterete
                    Zygophyllaceae.
            Filaments entire ; ovary 5-celled ; ovules pendulous from the
              inner angle of the cells ; ovary beaked ; leaves opposite,
              entire or 3-lobed   *Geraniaceae.*
        Sepals free or nearly so ; stamens hypogynous or perigynous ;
          ovary 1-celled :
          Stipules forming a tube (ochrea) around the stem ; fruit a nut
                Polygonaceae.
          Stipules not forming a tube round the stem, often scarious and
            bilobed or more divided ; leaves opposite   *Illecebraceae.*
          Stipules minute ; leaves verticillate   *Molluginaceae.*
        Sepals connate into a tube ; stamens perigynous ; ovary 1-5-celled :
          Flowers hermaphrodite ; leaves simple   *Ficoidaceae.*

Flowers dioecious ; leaves 1-3-foliolate · *Rosaceae.*
Leaves without stipules :
Ovary 1-celled, with free - central placentation, not septate or only imperfectly septate at the base ; ovules usually numerous
Caryophyllaceae.
Ovary with axile, basal or apical placentation :
Ovary and fruit compressed contrary to the septum, 2-celled ; trees or shrubs with perulate buds ; leaves simple or palmately lobed or pinnately foliolate ; flowers andromonoecious or dioecious *Aceraceae.*
Ovary if compressed then not contrary to the septum or septa :
Ovules 2 or more in each cell of the ovary or in a 1-celled ovary :
Flowers hermaphrodite :
Shrubs or trees with woody branches :
Calyx more or less spreading, or not tubular :
Large disk often present *Celastraceae.*
No disk *Geissolomataceae.*
Calyx tubular, lobes valvate ; disk absent or inconspicuous :
Ovary 2-4-celled ; calyx not or rarely petaloid, often with accessory lobes *Lythraceae.*
Ovary many-celled *Sonneratiaceae.*
Ovary 4-celled ; calyx petaloid, lobes valvate ; stamens opposite the lobes ; flowers often in heads *Proteaceae.*
Ovary 4-celled ; calyx more or less petaloid ; stamens alternate with the lobes *Penaeaceae.*
Herbs :
Sepals united into a tube ; stamens perigynous :
Sepals imbricate, without accessory lobes *Ficoidaceae.*
Sepals valvate, often with accessory lobes *Lythraceae.*
Sepals free or nearly so ; stamens usually hypogynous :
Style-branches or styles 2-3 ; leaves connate at the base ; ovules 1-2
Illecebraceae.
Styles more or less free ; leaves not connate at the base
Amarantaceae.
Flowers unisexual :
Leaves digitately compound *Euphorbiaceae.*
Leaves simple *Buxaceae.*
Ovule solitary in each cell of the ovary or in a 1-celled ovary :
Stamens circinately involute in bud ; calyx usually long-tubular, often coloured ; bracts sometimes petaloid *Nyctaginaceae.*
Stamens sometimes inflexed but not circinate in bud ; calyx often scarious but rarely petaloid ; bracts often scarious :
Submerged aquatics with verticillate divided leaves ; flowers monoecious *Ceratophyllaceae.*
Not submerged aquatics ; leaves very rarely verticillate :
Flowers not arranged in a cyathium ; mostly hermaphrodite :
Trees, shrubs or undershrubs with woody stems ; embryo straight, usually very small :
Stamens numerous *Monimiaceae.*
Stamens 6-9 ; flowers dioecious ; calyx not petaloid, deeply lobed ; flowers cymose *Barbeyaceae.*
Stamens definite (sometimes reduced to one) ; calyx often petaloid, usually long-tubular ; flowers often in heads *Thymelaeaceae.*
Stamens 4 ; calyx membranous, campanulate, 2-lipped ; flowers densely spicate *Batidaceae.*

Herbs sometimes a little woody at the base ; embryo more or less curved :

Sepals united into a tube ; stamens perigynous   *Ficoidaceae.*

Sepals free or nearly so ; stamens mostly hypogynous :

Calyx scarious only on the margin ; stamens hypogynous ; styles free or nearly so   *Molluginaceae.*

Calyx often hyaline all over ; stamens often slightly perigynous and connate at the base   *Amarantaceae.*

Calyx herbaceous ; stamens hypogynous or slightly perigynous, mostly free   *Chenopodiaceae.*

Flowers ♂ ♀, arranged in a cyathium margined with glands   *Euphorbiaceae.*

Leaves alternate or radical or reduced to scales ; sometimes tubiform or pitcher-like :

Parasitic plants with the leaves reduced to scales :

Anthers opening by slits :

Flowers spicate ; sepals imbricate   *Monotropaceae.*

Flowers densely crowded ; sepals valvate   *Balanophoraceae.*

Anthers opening by valves   *Lauraceae.*

Not parasitic ; leaves normally developed :

Leaves stipulate :

Stamens monadelphous, usually numerous ; calyx mostly valvate :

Anthers 2-celled ; flowers unisexual   *Sterculiaceae.*

Anthers 1-celled ; flowers hermaphrodite   *Malvaceae.*

Anthers 2-celled ; flowers unisexual   *Euphorbiaceae.*

Stamens free or shortly connate at the base :

Stamens the same number as the sepals and alternate with them :

Herbs   *Molluginaceae.*

Trees, shrubs or climbers   *Rhamnaceae.*

Stamens the same number as the sepals and opposite to them or more numerous or fewer :

Leaves compound :

Flowers unisexual :

Ovary 1-celled, of 1 carpel   *Moraceae.*

Ovary 2- or more-celled   *Euphorbiaceae.*

Flowers hermaphrodite :

Flowers actinomorphic :

Seeds without endosperm ; style basal or ventral on the 1-carpelled ovary   *Rosaceae.*

Seeds usually with endosperm ; style or styles more or less terminal ; ovary of more than 1 carpel   *Saxifragaceae.*

Flowers slightly zygomorphic ; leaves pinnate   *Melianthaceae.*

Leaves simple :

Ovary 2- or more-celled :

Flowers unisexual :

Ovary quite superior ; anthers opening by slits :

Male flowers not in catkins   *Euphorbiaceae.*

Male flowers in catkins   *Betulaceae.*

Ovary semisuperior ; anthers often opening by valves   *Hamamelidaceae.*

Flowers hermaphrodite :

Trees or shrubs ; ovary 2-celled ; carpels often free at the top ; anther-cells often opening by valves ; stipules often paired   *Hamamelidaceae.*

Herbs :
   Stamens perigynous ; ovary 1-3-celled   *Saxifragaceae.*
   Stamens hypogynous ; ovary 3-5-celled, very rarely 2-celled
                                               Molluginaceae.
Ovary 1-celled, mostly of 1 carpel :
   Stipules ochreate, *i.e.* sheathing and more or less membranous around
     the stem   *Polygonaceae.*
   Stipules not ochreate :
     Ovary of 1 carpel ; stamens inflexed in bud ; flowers mostly uni-
       sexual   *Urticaceae.*
     Ovary of 1 carpel ; stamens erect in bud ; flowers hermaphrodite
                                       Rosaceae.
     Ovary usually of more than 1 carpel ; stamens erect in bud ; flowers
       always unisexual   *Euphorbiaceae.*
     Ovary usually of more than 1 carpel ; stamens erect in bud ; flowers
       hermaphrodite   *Phytolaccaceae.*
Leaves exstipulate :
   Stamens the same number as and alternating with the calyx-lobes :
   Leaves compound, mostly pinnate :
     Flowers mostly hermaphrodite, not involucrate   *Burseraceae.*
     Flowers dioecious, the females solitary, enclosed in and adnate to an
       involucre   *Julianiaceae.*
   Leaves simple, minute ; small shrubs   *Ficoidaceae.*
   Leaves simple, dentate ; annual herb ; stamens 1-2   *Circaeasteraceae.*
   Stamens the same number as the calyx-lobes and opposite to them or
     more numerous or fewer :
   Leaves compound :
     Herbs ; ovary composed of 1 carpel ; leaves ternately compound ;
       flowers paniculate or racemose, usually very small   *Ranunculaceae.*
     Shrubs or trees :
       Stamens the same number as and opposite to the calyx-(perianth)
         segments ; leaves often many times divided ; flowers often in
         heads or dense spikes or racemes; calyx mostly petaloid *Proteaceae.*
       Stamens usually more numerous than the calyx-lobes ; calyx rarely
         petaloid :
         Flowers unisexual ; leaves digitate   *Euphorbiaceae.*
         Flowers mostly polygamous ; leaves pinnate ; bark bitter, not
           resinous   *Simarubaceae.*
         Flowers mostly polygamous dioecious ; leaves pinnate ; bark not
           bitter ; wood not resinous   *Sapindaceae.*
         Flowers various ; leaves pinnate or trifoliolate ; wood resinous
                                 Anacardiaceae.

   Leaves simple :
   Leaves modified into pitchers or tubes :
     Flowers dioecious ; stamens united into a column ·   *Nepenthaceae.*
     Flowers hermaphrodite ; stamens free   *Sarraceniaceae.*
   Leaves not modified as above :
     Stamens circinately involute in bud ; calyx-tube often rather long ;
       ovary 1-celled ; ovule 1, basal   *Nyctaginaceae.*
     Stamens sometimes inflexed but not circinate in bud :
       Stamens more or less connate into a central column :
         Herbs or weak climbers ; calyx (perianth) often long-tubular and
           oblique ; ovules numerous ; seeds with smooth endosperm ;
           flowers hermaphrodite   *Aristolochiaceae.*

Habit various ; flowers unisexual ; calyx not oblique ; disk or disk-glands often present ; ovules pendulous ; endosperm smooth *Euphorbiaceae.*

Trees or shrubs ; calyx mostly small, not oblique ; ovule erect ; seeds with ruminate endosperm *Myristicaceae.*

Stamens free or the filaments shortly connate only at the base :

Stamens distinctly perigynous or flowers unisexual ; sepals connate into a tube below :

Herbs or twiners ; anthers opening by longitudinal slits :

Twiners ; flowers in axillary spikes, racemes or panicles ; ovule solitary, basal *Basellaceae.*

Not twiners ; herbs :

Calyx long and tubular, many - ribbed ; stamens about 11, unequal ; ovules 2 or more *Lythraceae.*

Calyx-tube short or almost absent :

Ovary quite superior ; leaves often thick and fleshy *Crassulaceae.*

Ovary semisuperior ; leaves not fleshy *Ficoidaceae.*

Trees or shrubs ; anthers opening by valves or longitudinal slits :

Small shrubs ; stamens numerous, in bundles alternate with the calyx-lobes *Ficoidaceae.*

Mostly undershrubs with often rather long and usually petaloid calyx (perianth) ; leaves frequently small and evergreen, sometimes much divided ; stamens definite :

Calyx-lobes imbricate *Thymelaeaceae.*

Calyx-lobes valvate :

Stamens the same number as and opposite the calyx-lobes *Proteaceae.*

Stamens more than the primary lobes of the calyx *Lythraceae.*

Trees or shrubs ; leaves usually large ; stamens mostly numerous *Monimiaceae.*

Trees or shrubs ; leaves large, very rarely reduced ; stamens usually double the number of the calyx-lobes, in 2 or 4 rows *Lauraceae.*

Stamens hypogynous or slightly perigynous if accompanied by a disk, or flowers unisexual :

Flowers in a cyathium margined by bracts *Euphorbiaceae.*

Flowers not in a cyathium :

Trees or shrubs :

Leaves glandular ; flowers in catkin-like spikes or racemes ; berry often warted *Myricaceae.*

Leaves not glandular ; flowers not in catkin-like inflorescences :

Leaves very small and ericoid ; fruit drupaceous, succulent ; ovary 2-9-celled with 1 axile ovule in each cell ; stamens 2-3 *Empetraceae.*

Leaves not as above and other characters not associated :

Flowers unisexual ; ovule solitary, pendulous ; seeds with straight embryo *Euphorbiaceae.*

Flowers hermaphrodite ; ovule solitary, pendulous ; embryo straight *Olacaceae.*

Flowers unisexual or polygamous ; ovules 2 in each cell, collateral or the lower ascending ; seeds without endosperm and spirally twisted embryo *Sapindaceae.*

Flowers hermaphrodite or unisexual ; ovule solitary, basal ;
seeds with the embryo curved around the endosperm
Phytolaccaceae.

Herbs :
Ovule 1 or more in each carpel   *Molluginaceae.*
Ovule 1 in each carpel or ovary ; ovary of several subdistinct
carpels   *Phytolaccaceae.*
Ovule 1 : ovary 1-celled :
Perianth herbaceous   *Chenopodiaceae.*
Perianth more or less scarious   *Amarantaceae.*
Imperfectly known family of this group
Scyphostegiaceae (see Fig. 168).

GROUP 13

*One carpel or more than one carpel with axile, basal or apical placentas ;
ovary inferior ; petals present*

Leaves opposite or verticillate, never all radical, rarely reduced to scales (to p. 72) :
Leaves compound, much divided or unifoliolate ; flowers mostly umbellate or
capitate, rarely racemose ; calyx small, entire or toothed ; petals usually
5, valvate or slightly imbricate ; disk on top of the ovary, often confluent
with the style or styles ; ovule solitary in each cell, pendulous ; seeds
with copious endosperm and small embryo :
Trees or shrubs ; petals usually valvate ; ovary 1-many-celled ; fruit usually
a berry or drupe   *Araliaceae.*
Herbs ; petals imbricate, rarely valvate ; ovary 2-celled ; styles 2 ; fruit of
dry indehiscent mericarps   *Umbelliferae.*
Leaves simple :
Leaves stipulate :
Stamens the same number as and opposite the petals   *Rhamnaceae.*
Stamens alternate with the petals or more numerous :
Ovary composed of 2 carpels, more or less free at the apex ; flowers mostly
capitate ; ovules pendulous ; trees or shrubs ; anthers often opening
by valves   *Hamamelidaceae.*
Ovary mostly 2-celled ; flowers rarely capitate ; anthers opening by slits
Cunoniaceae.
Ovary composed of 2-6 carpels, 2-6-celled or 1-celled by suppression of the
septa ; flowers rarely congested ; ovules pendulous ; mostly maritime
trees or shrubs   *Rhizophoraceae.*
Ovary various ; flowers rarely in heads ; ovules ascending or attached
to the central axis ; trees, shrubs or herbs   *Rosaceae.*
Leaves exstipulate :
Trees, shrubs or climbers :
Stamens numerous :
Ovary cells not superposed :
Leaves gland-dotted ; style simple with a small capitate stigma or very
rarely 3-4-lobed   *Myrtaceae.*
Leaves with pellucid lines or with stellate hairs ; style 5-10-lobed or
styles 3-5 and more or less free ; ovary 2-10-celled   *Hydrangeaceae.*
Leaves not gland-dotted, with longitudinally parallel nerves ; stamens
jointed, the connective often produced at the base ; anthers opening
by a terminal pore   *Melastomaceae.*
Ovary cells superposed ; leaves not gland-dotted ; style simple
Punicaceae.

Stamens as many to twice as many as the petals :
Stamens the same number as and opposite to the petals ; mostly parasitic
   shrubs or trees ; calyx usually much reduced   *Loranthaceae.*
Stamens the same number as and alternate with the petals or more
   numerous :
   Anthers opening by a terminal pore ; filaments often jointed ; leaves
      often with 3-9 longitudinally parallel nerves   *Melastomaceae.*
   Anthers opening by longitudinal slits ; calyx mostly valvate :
      Ovule solitary ; fruits mostly drupaceous ; endosperm copious ; petals
         without alternate scales   *Cornaceae.*
      Ovules up to 3 in each cell ; fruit a drupe, not winged ; flowers small,
         in cymes ; petals with alternating scales   *Oliniaceae.*
      Ovules numerous ; fruit a capsule or berry ; flowers conspicuous ; no
         scales   *Hydrangeaceae.*
      Ovules 2 or more ; fruits mostly winged ; endosperm absent ; flowers
         in heads, spikes, racemes or panicles   *Combretaceae.*
      Ovules numerous ; stamens double the number of the petals
                                                      Onagraceae.
Herbs ; sometimes slightly woody, but then often with fleshy leaves :
   Anthers opening by a terminal pore ; leaves mostly with longitudinally
      parallel nerves ; connective of anthers usually produced at the base
      and jointed to the filament   *Melastomaceae.*
   Anthers opening by longitudinal slits :
      Flowers in umbels or heads ; ovary 2-celled ; carpels separating in fruit
         and suspended by the divided thread-like central axis (carpophore)
                                                      Umbelliferae.
      Flowers in heads surrounded by bracts ; ovary 2-3-celled ; carpels not as
         above   *Cornaceae.*
      Flowers not in umbels or heads ; carpels not separating in fruit :
         Placenta pendulous from the apex of the 1-celled ovary ; ovules numerous
                                                      Saxifragaceae.
         Ovules 1-4, pendulous from the top of the ovary-cells   *Haloragaceae.*
         Placentas axile with numerous ovules, or ovules very few and pendulous
            from the apex of the usually 4-celled ovary   *Onagraceae.*
         Placentas at the bottom of the ovary-cells; petals numerous   *Ficoidaceae.*
Leaves alternate or all radical :
Flowers unisexual :
   Flowers not in heads or umbels, sometimes paniculate or racemose :
      Leaves stipulate ; stipules paired ; no tendrils ; stamens mostly numerous,
         straight ; flowers often somewhat zygomorphic   *Begoniaceae.*
      Leaves without stipules ; tendrils often present ; stamens definite or rarely
         many, anthers often conduplicate or twisted, mostly 3 ; flowers actino-
         morphic, conspicuous   *Cucurbitaceae.*
      Leaves without stipules or if present then adnate to the petiole, sometimes
         anisophyllous and then the smaller leaf appearing like a stipule ; no
         tendrils ; anthers straight :
         Styles 4 ; petals 4, involute in bud ; leaves with 3-5 main nerves ; ovary
            4-celled ; flowers not minute ; trees or shrubs   *Rhizophoraceae.*
         Styles 1-4, separate ; petals 2 or 4, valvate in bud ; ovary 1-4-celled ;
            flowers mostly minute ; mostly herbs, sometimes with large radical
            leaves or often aquatic   *Haloragaceae.*
   Flowers arranged in heads, umbels or corymbs :
      Fruit of dry indehiscent mericarps ; ovary 2-celled ; styles 2 ; herbs with
         usually much dissected leaves   *Umbelliferae.*

Characters not as above :

Anthers opening by a single lateral valve ; petals linear-spathulate ; ovary 2-celled ; ovules solitary ; leaves stipulate

Hamamelidaceae.

Anthers opening by slits ; petals usually not linear-spathulate :

Leaves usually stipulate ; flowers usually umbellate   *Araliaceae.*

Leaves without stipules ; flowers capitate or corymbose :

Petals imbricate   *Nyssaceae.*

Petals valvate   *Cornaceae.*

Leaves without stipules ; male flowers corymbose, female solitary

Onagraceae.

Flowers hermaphrodite :

Stamens numerous :

Aquatic herbs with floating leaves ; flowers usually large and showy ; ovules numerous   *Nymphaeaceae.*

Not aquatic :

Herbs :

Leaves exstipulate ; sepals more than 2 :

Styles more or less free ; low herbs often with rosettes of leaves

Saxifragaceae.

Styles more or less united ; erect or climbing, mostly roughly hispid-pilose herbs   *Loasaceae.*

Leaves stipulate, stipules often laciniated and thread-like ; seeds with more or less copious endosperm ; sepals 2   *Portulacaceae.*

Leaves stipulate, not laciniate ; seeds without endosperm ; sepals more than 2   *Rosaceae.*

Trees or shrubs :

Leaves gland-dotted ; stamens mostly very numerous :

Fruits not winged   *Myrtaceae.*

Fruits broadly winged   *Lecythidaceae.*

Leaves not gland-dotted :

Style more or less divided or styles separate ; rarely maritime ; leaves often compound ; leaves stipulate :

Stipules not intrapetiolar   *Rosaceae.*

Stipules intrapetiolar and connate ; leaves digitate   *Araliaceae.*

Style simple ; usually maritime ; leaves simple   *Rhizophoraceae.*

Stamens definite in relation to the sepals and petals, the same number as or about twice as many, rarely fewer :

Stamens the same number as and opposite the petals :

Leaves stipulate or not ; not parasites ; flowers often crowded into heads ; ovary 3-celled   *Rhamnaceae.*

Leaves exstipulate ; often parasitic ; ovary 1-celled   *Loranthaceae.*

Stamens the same number as and alternate with the petals or more numerous or fewer :

Anthers opening by apical pores ; leaves often with very prominent longitudinally parallel nerves ; anthers often unequal, with the connective produced at the base   *Melastomaceae.*

Anthers not opening by pores ; leaves usually not as above :

Leaves stipulate :

Herbs :

Leaves simple ; sepals 2 ; fruit a capsule   *Portulacaceae.*

Leaves usually compound or much dissected, sometimes peltate ; sepals obsolete or more than 2 ; fruit of 2 indehiscent mericarps

Umbelliferae.

Trees or shrubs :
Flowers actinomorphic ; corolla not gibbous at the base ; stamens not unilateral :
Leaves simple ; stipules paired ; flowers often capitate ; fruit woody ; stamens up to twice as many as the petals   *Hamamelidaceae.*
Leaves compound, rarely simple ; stamens as many as the petals ; fruit a berry or drupaceous ; flowers often umbellate   *Araliaceae.*
Leaves compound or simple ; stamens more than the petals ; fruit not woody   *Rosaceae.*
Flowers zygomorphic ; corolla often gibbous at the base ; stamens unilateral   *Trigoniaceae.*
Leaves exstipulate :
Flowers arranged in heads surrounded by a brightly coloured involucre and simulating a single flower ; petals very unequal, fewer than the stamens ; styles subulate, elongate   *Hamamelidaceae.*
Flowers not as above and other characters not associated :
Herbs :
Flowers umbellate ; ovules solitary, pendulous :
Ovary 2-celled ; carpels separating in fruit into 2 indehiscent mericarps   *Umbelliferae.*
Ovary 3-4-celled ; carpels not separating in fruit   *Araliaceae.*
Flower not umbellate :
Ovules more than 1 in each cell or in a 1-celled ovary :
Mostly scapigerous herbs ; ovary 1-3-celled   *Saxifragaceae.*
Leafy stemmed herbs ; ovary mostly 4-celled   *Onagraceae.*
Ovules solitary in each cell of the ovary :
Style 1, with a capitate or shortly lobed stigma ; flowers mostly fairly large and conspicuous :
Neither rough-setose nor scabrid ; ovules 1 or more   *Onagraceae.*
Usually rough-setose or scabrid ; ovules solitary from the apex of a one-celled ovary   *Loasaceae.*
Styles more than 1 :
Styles 5-10 ; carpels 5-10, radiating ; stigmas capitate   *Rosaceae.*
Styles up to 4 ; ovary up to 4-celled ; carpels not radiating ; stigmas not capitate   *Haloragaceae.*
Shrubs or trees :
Flowers umbellate ; fruit a berry or drupe   *Araliaceae.*
Flowers not umbellate :
Leaves 3-foliolate ; petals 5 ; stamens 5, alternating with glands ; anthers opening by valves   *Hernandiaceae.*
Leaves simple ; anthers opening by slits :
Petals contorted ; stamens mostly 4 or 8   *Onagraceae.*
Petals valvate or imbricate :
Petals loriform, valvate   *Alangiaceae.*
Petals not loriform :
Petals imbricate ; stamens various   *Combretaceae.*
Petals valvate, or if slightly imbricate then stamens usually 5 :
Fruit a capsule or berry   *Escalloniaceae.*
Fruit a drupe   *Cornaceae.*
Petals convolute or inflexed ; leaves anisophyllous   *Rhizophoraceae.*

GROUP 14

*One carpel or two or more united carpels with axile, basal, or apical placentation ;
ovary inferior ; petals present, more or less united*

Leaves opposite :
  Leaves stipulate, stipules mostly inter- or intra-petiolar; anthers free from
    each other :
    Leaves simple, entire ; corolla actinomorphic   *Rubiaceae.*
    Leaves pinnate ; flowers actinomorphic or zygomorphic   *Caprifoliaceae.*
  Leaves exstipulate :
    Leaves usually with longitudinally parallel main nerves ; stamens often
      double the number of the corolla-lobes, mostly jointed, the connective
      produced at the base into an appendage   *Melastomaceae.*
    Leaves and stamens not as above :
      Anthers free from each other ; ovules mostly pendulous :
      Leaves not gland-dotted ; mostly herbaceous plants, rarely shrubs; stamens
        definite :
      Stigma not indusiate :
        Herbaceous or woody at the base :
        Flowers zygomorphic :
          Ovary with 1 perfect 1-ovulate cell and often 2 empty cells
                                    Valerianaceae.
          Ovary 1-celled, without additional empty cells ; flowers often capitate
                                    Dipsaceae.
        Flowers actinomorphic :
          Anthers 2-celled ; stamens usually 5   *Campanulaceae.*
          Anthers 1-celled ; stamens appearing to be double the number of the
            corolla-lobes by division of the filaments   *Adoxaceae.*
        Trees, shrubs, or woody climbers or parasites ; corolla often saccate or
          spurred at the base :
          Stamens double the number of the corolla-lobes ; ovary 6-celled ; a
            large tree   *Lythraceae.*
          Stamens the same number as the corolla-lobes :
            Stamens alternate with the usually imbricate corolla-lobes ; not
              parasitic   *Caprifoliaceae.*
           Stamens opposite the valvate corolla-lobes ; often parasitic
                               Loranthaceae.
      Stigma indusiate ; ovary 1-2-celled : flowers not capitate   *Goodeniaceae.*
      Leaves gland-dotted; stamens mostly numerous; trees or shrubs   *Myrtaceae.*
    Anthers mostly connivent or in pairs around the style :
      Ovule solitary ; flowers mostly in heads :
      Ovule erect ; calyx usually modified into a pappus of barbellate or plumose
        bristles   *Compositae.*
      Ovule pendulous ; calyx not modified into a pappus   *Calyceraceae.*
      Ovules numerous ; flowers usually not in heads :
      Flowers actinomorphic ; stamens the same number as the corolla-lobes
                                      Campanulaceae.
      Flowers zygomorphic ; stamens usually fewer (4 or 2) than the corolla-
        lobes   *Gesneriaceae.*
Leaves alternate or radical :
  Stamens 1-2 :
    Flowers hermaphrodite :

Anthers with a narrow connective or the cells divergent ; filaments free
from each other   *Gesneriaceae.*
Anthers with very broad connective (Fig. 255) ; filaments free from each
other   *Columelliaceae.*
Anthers with narrow connective ; filaments connate   *Stylidiaceae.*
Flowers unisexual ; tendrils often present   *Cucurbitaceae.*
Stamens 3 or more :
 Anthers free from one another or very slightly connate only at the base :
  Stamens the same number as and opposite the corolla-lobes :
   Herbaceous, leaves not gland-dotted   *Primulaceae.*
   Trees and shrubs :
    Not parasitic ; leaves gland-dotted   *Myrsinaceae.*
    Often parasitic ; leaves not gland-dotted   *Loranthaceae.*
  Stamens alternate with the corolla-lobes or more numerous or fewer :
   Corolla actinomorphic :
    Herbaceous plants with often milky juice :
     Flowers unisexual ; stems usually climbing by the tendrils ; anthers
      often sinuous or twisted   *Cucurbitaceae.*
     Flowers hermaphrodite ; no tendrils ; anthers usually straight :
      Leaves stipulate ; sepals 2   *Portulacaceae.*
      Leaves exstipulate ; sepals more than 2 :
       Filaments free or nearly so ; ovary usually 2- or more-celled
                   Campanulaceae.
       Filaments monadelphous ; ovary 1-celled   *Calyceraceae.*
    Woody, rarely subherbaceous ; juice not milky :
     Leaves gland-dotted ; stamens mostly numerous   *Myrtaceae.*
     Leaves not gland-dotted :
      Stamens free from the corolla :
       Petals valvate ; stipules present, often adnate to the petiole
                   Araliaceae.
       Petals valvate ; stipules absent   *Lecythidaceae.*
       Petals imbricate, rarely valvate :
        Stipules absent ; leaves simple   *Vacciniaceae.*
        Stipules present, adnate to the petiole ; leaves compound *Araliaceae.*
       Petals contorted ; small stipules present ; branches hooked
                   Ancistrocladaceae.
      Stamens epipetalous :
       Ovary 1-2- (rarely 3-) celled ; ovules 2, pendulous ; flowers in a leafy
        capitulum   *Bruniaceae.*
       Ovary 3-5-celled ; ovules 1, or when more axile ; flowers not in a
        capitulum :
        Stamens numerous ; filaments free or partially connate *Symplocaceae.*
        Stamens mostly 5 or 10 ; filaments not united at the base *Styracaceae.*
        Stamens 8, connate   *Lissocarpaceae.*
       Ovary 1-2-celled ; ovule solitary, pendulous ; flowers in cymes
                   Alangiaceae.
   Corolla zygomorphic :
    Ovule solitary, pendulous   *Valerianaceae.*
    Ovules numerous   *Lobeliaceae.*
 Anthers more or less united into a ring around the style :
  Anthers straight, not flexuous :
   Flowers not in heads surrounded by a common involucre :
    Flowers hermaphrodite, zygomorphic ; no tendrils   *Lobeliaceae.*
    Flowers unisexual, actinomorphic ; tendrils usually present *Cucurbitaceae.*

Flowers in heads surrounded by a common involucre :
  Ovule erect from the base of the ovary-cell ; filaments usually free from
    each other ; calyx modified into a pappus   *Compositae.*
  Ovule pendulous from the top of the ovary-cell ; filaments more or less
    connate ; calyx not modified into a pappus   *Calyceraceae.*
  Anthers flexuous or conduplicate ; plants often with tendrils
         Cucurbitaceae.

GROUP 15

One carpel or two or more united carpels with axile, basal or apical
placentation ; ovary inferior ; petals absent

Parasitic herbs destitute of chlorophyll, the leaves reduced to scales ; ovules
  nude or with a single integument :
  Ovules 3 from the apex of a central placenta ; flowers dioecious
         Myzodendraceae.
  Ovules solitary, pendulous ; flowers densely crowded into inflorescences ;
    fruits nut-like, 1-seeded ; anthers opening by slits   *Balanophoraceae.*
  Ovules solitary, pendulous ; flowers spicate, racemose or capitate ; anthers
    opening by valves   *Lauraceae.*
  Ovules very numerous ; flowers large, solitary or rarely spicate ; fruit with
    very numerous minute seeds :
    Flowers unisexual   *Cytinaceae.*
    Flowers hermaphrodite   *Hydnoraceae.*
Not parasitic, or if so then more or less woody and often with normally developed
  leaves (at least with chlorophyll) :
  Leaves stipulate :
    Flowers unisexual ; stipules often paired :
      Stamens and ovules numerous ; fruit often winged ; outer pair of calyx-lobes
        valvate ; herbs, often with obliquely shaped leaves   *Begoniaceae.*
      Stamens and ovules few, the latter solitary or paired :
        Trees or shrubs ; stipules not adnate :
          Male flowers with a calyx :
            Ovule 1 in each ovary   *Moraceae.*
            Ovules 2 in each cell   *Fagaceae.*
          Male flowers without a calyx   *Corylaceae.*
        Herbs ; stipules adnate to the petiole   *Haloragaceae.*
    Flowers hermaphrodite, often solitary or racemose :
      Stamens the same number as and alternate with the sepals   *Rhamnaceae.*
      Stamens the same number as and opposite or more numerous than the sepals :
        Leaves alternate ; ovules 2, pendulous ; flowers racemose   *Rosaceae.*
        Leaves alternate or opposite ; ovules 2 to many ; flowers solitary or in
          short racemes   *Rhizophoraceae.*
    Flowers rarely unisexual, spicate or capitate, often precocious ; leaves
      alternate ; ovule 1, pendulous :
      Trees or shrubs ; calyx sometimes absent   *Hamamelidaceae.*
      Herbs, sometimes with large leaves   *Haloragaceae.*
  Leaves exstipulate ; but sometimes when opposite connate and sheathing at
    the base :
    Flowers usually in catkins or slender spikes, or rarely the males in panicles,
      unisexual :
      Leaves pinnate ; ovule 1, erect   *Juglandaceae.*
      Leaves simple, alternate ; ovules 1-2, descending   *Cupuliferae.*
      Leaves simple, opposite ; ovules 2, collateral, pendulous   *Garryaceae.*

Leaves simple, opposite ; ovule 1 in each cell, pendulous   *Chloranthaceae.*
Flowers not in catkins, mostly hermaphrodite :
Calyx calyptrate ; leaves opposite, gland-dotted   *Myrtaceae.*
Calyx not calyptrate ; leaves not gland-dotted :
Flowers in simple or compound umbels ; herbs ; leaves sheathing at the
base ; ovary 2-celled, separating in fruit into 2 mericarps with resinous
lines   *Umbelliferae.*
Flowers not or rarely in umbels ; fruit not separating into mericarps :
Ovules numerous on axile placentas :
Calyx actinomorphic :
Ovary many-celled   *Sonneratiaceae.*
Ovary 1-4-celled   *Onagraceae.*
Calyx zygomorphic   *Aristolochiaceae.*
Ovules solitary or few, inserted at the top or base of the ovary :
Ovules pendulous from the apex of the ovary or at the apex of a basal
placenta, usually more than 1 :
Mostly trees, shrubs or woody climbers ; sepals mostly valvate :
Anthers opening by valves :
Ovary 1-celled :
Leaves simple ; calyx-lobes imbricate   *Lauraceae.*
Leaves simple or compound ; calyx-lobes valvate   *Hernandiaceae.*
Ovary 2-3-celled :   *Gomortegaceae.*
Anthers opening by longitudinal slits :
Stamens erect in bud, often double the number of the sepals
      Nyssaceae.
Stamens inflexed in bud, often double the number of the sepals :
Ovules at the apex of the ovary   *Combretaceae.*
Ovules on a free-basal placenta   *Grubbiaceae.*
Stamens erect in bud, the same number as and opposite the sepals :
Placenta not reaching the top of the ovary ; hairs not stellate (tufted
in *Exocarpus*)   *Santalaceae.*
Placenta reaching to the top of the ovary and adnate to it ; hairs
stellate   *Octoknemataceae.*
Herbaceous ; sepals mostly imbricate   *Ficoidaceae.*
Ovule 1, erect :
Mostly maritime trees and shrubs with often lepidote leaves ; flowers
not capitate   *Elaeagnaceae.*
Not maritime ; leaves not lepidote ; flowers capitate or densely crowded ;
ovule well developed at flowering time   *Rhamnaceae.*
Mostly parasitic ; flowers not capitate ; ovule scarcely developed at
time of flowering   *Loranthaceae.*

LIST OF FAMILIES WITH CERTAIN MORE OR LESS CONSTANT CHARACTERS

SOMETIMES a botanist is faced with the determination of imperfect material consisting perhaps of leaves only. As a help in the identification of such specimens, which can often be best brought about by a process of exclusion, I give below some lists of families in which certain macroscopic characters are constant or predominant.

LEAVES.

Opposite (or verticillate) leaves constant.

Families with *constantly opposite* (or verticillate) leaves :

Aceraceae. Batidaceae. Calycanthaceae. Caprifoliaceae. Caryophyllaceae. Casuarinaceae. Ceratophyllaceae. Chloranthaceae. Columelliaceae. Coriariaceae. Cunoniaceae. Dipsacaceae. Elatinaceae. Eucryphiaceae. Frankeniaceae. Gomortegaceae.[1] Grubbiaceae. Guttiferae. Hydrangeaceae. Labiatae. Loganiaceae. Melastomaceae. Penaeaceae. Rubiaceae. Salvadoraceae. Staphyleaceae. Valerianaceae.

Opposite (or verticillate) leaves predominant.

Families in which *opposite* (or verticillate) leaves are *predominant* :

Acanthaceae. Apocynaceae. Asclepiadaceae. Bignoniaceae. Cistaceae. Ficoidaceae. Gentianaceae. Illecebraceae. Loranthaceae. Lythraceae. Malpighiaceae. Molluginaceae. Monimiaceae. Myrtaceae. Nyctaginaceae. Oleaceae. Pedaliaceae. Rhizophoraceae. Rutaceae. Santalaceae. Scrophulariaceae.

Compound leaves constant.

Families with *constantly compound* (sometimes 1-foliolate) *leaves* :

Caryocaraceae. Connaraceae. Juglandaceae. Lardizabalaceae. Melianthaceae. Moringaceae. Oxalidaceae. Sapindaceae. Tovariaceae.

Compound leaves predominant.

Families in which *compound leaves* are *predominant* :

Ampelidaceae. Araliaceae. Bignoniaceae. Burseraceae. Caesalpiniaceae. Meliaceae. Mimosaceae. Papilionaceae. Rosaceae. Rutaceae. Simarubaceae. Umbelliferae. Valerianaceae. Zygophyllaceae.

Leaves sometimes compound.

Families in which compound leaves sometimes occur (those marked with an * rather frequently) :

Aceraceae. Berberidaceae. Bombacaceae.* Capparidaceae. Caprifoliaceae. Convolvulaceae. Crassulaceae. Cucurbitaceae. Dipsacaceae.* Euphorbiaceae. Gentianaceae. Geraniaceae. Hydrophyllaceae. Menispermaceae. Ochnaceae. Oleaceae. Passifloraceae. Polemoniaceae. Proteaceae.* Ranunculaceae.

---

[1] Except Buddleia alternifolia.

Sabiaceae.   Saxifragaceae.*   Staphyleaceae.*   Sterculiaceae.
Verbenaceae.

STIPULES.

Stipules are *constant* in the following families :

Leaves always stipulate.

Begoniaceae. Caesalpiniaceae. Chailletiaceae. Chloranthaceae. Cunoniaceae. Dipterocarpaceae. Droseraceae. Elatinaceae. Eucryphiaceae. Magnoliaceae. Malvaceae. Mimosaceae. Ochnaceae. Papilionaceae. Polygonaceae. Resedaceae. Rhamnaceae. Rubiaceae. Zygophyllaceae.

Families in which the leaves are *mostly stipulate* :

Leaves mostly stipulate.

Ampelidaceae. Araliaceae. Chlaenaceae. Hamamelidaceae. Linaceae. Molluginaceae. Moringaceae. Portulacaceae. Quiinaceae. Rhizophoraceae. Rosaceae. Sterculiaceae.

Families in which glandular or pellucid dots occur or sometimes occur in the leaves : [1]

Glandular leaves.

Acanthaceae. Alangiaceae. Ampelidaceae. Anacardiaceae. Anonaceae. Balsaminaceae. Bixaceae. Burseraceae. Cochlospermaceae. Calycanthaceae. Canellaceae. Capparidaceae. Chloranthaceae. Combretaceae. Compositae. Cornaceae. Crassulaceae. Dilleniaceae. Euphorbiaceae. Fagaceae. Flacourtiaceae. Geraniaceae. Guttiferae. Hypericaceae. Lacistemaceae. Lauraceae. Leguminosae. Lythraceae. Magnoliaceae. Meliaceae. Monimiaceae. Myoporaceae. Myricaceae. Myristicaceae. Myrsinaceae. Myrtaceae. Nymphaeaceae. Nyssaceae. Olacaceae. Phytolaccaceae. Piperaceae. Polygalaceae. Polygonaceae. Portulacaceae. Primulaceae. Rhamnaceae. Rubiaceae. Rutaceae. Sabiaceae. Samydaceae. Santalaceae. Sapindaceae. Saxifragaceae. Simarubaceae. Theaceae. Thymelaeaceae. Tropaeolaceae. Urticaceae. Verbenaceae. Violaceae.

Families in which the stamens are the same number as and *opposite* the petals :

Stamens opposite the petals.

Ampelidaceae. Berberidaceae. Corynocarpaceae. Ebenaceae. Heteropyxidaceae. Menispermaceae (some). Myrsinaceae. Olacaceae (some). Plumbaginaceae. Portulacaceae (some). Primulaceae. Rhamnaceae. Sabiaceae.[2] Sapotaceae. Sterculiaceae (some).

Families in which the ovary is *inferior* :

Inferior ovary.

Alangiaceae. Araliaceae. Balanophoraceae. Begoniaceae. Bruniaceae (most). Cactaceae. Calyceraceae. Caprifoliaceae. Chloranthaceae. Columelliaceae. Combretaceae. Compositae. Cornaceae. Cucurbitaceae. Cytinaceae. Datiscaceae. Dipsacaceae. Elaeagnaceae. Ficoidaceae (some). Gesneriaceae (some). Goodeniaceae. Grossulariaceae. Grubbiaceae. Haloragaceae. Hamamelidaceae. Juglandaceae. Loasaceae. Lobeliaceae. Loranthaceae. Melastomaceae (most). Myrsinaceae (few). Myrtaceae (most). Nymphaeaceae (some). Nyssaceae. Oliniaceae. Onagraceae. Portulacaceae (few). Punicaceae. Rhizophoraceae (many). Rosaceae (some). Rubiaceae. Santalaceae. Saxifragaceae (some). Stylidiaceae. Styracaceae. Umbelliferae. Vacciniaceae. Valerianaceae.

---

[1] This list is taken from Blenk, in *Flora*, 1884 : 385.
[2] In this family sometimes some anthers are aborted.

Division I. ARCHICHLAMYDEAE

Order 1. MAGNOLIALES

Entirely woody group; flowers hypogynous, ☿, rarely ♂ ♀ accompanied by reduction, acyclic to cyclic; petals usually present; stamens numerous, free or rarely connate in a mass; endosperm copious, not ruminate; embryo minute. Leaves alternate, very rarely opposite, simple, stipulate or not.—Mainly in North Temperate Regions.

1. MAGNOLIACEAE

Trees or shrubs; leaves alternate, simple; *stipules large, deciduous*, enclosing the young buds; flowers large, solitary, terminal or axillary, ☿; sepals and petals often similar, *in several series*, imbricate; stamens numerous, hypogynous, free; anthers long, 2-celled, opening lengthwise; pollination by

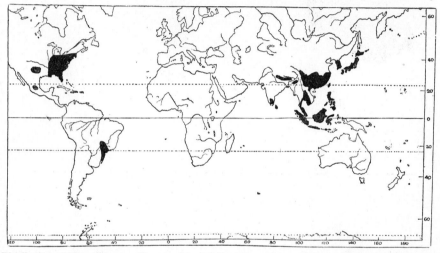

Distribution of Magnoliaceae. The complete isolation of members of this family, considered in conjunction with the anatomical and floral structure, indicates that it is of very great antiquity. The family is probably the most ancient of living Dicotyledons.

insects; carpels numerous, 1-celled, spirally arranged on an often *elongated axis*, rarely consolidated in fruit; ovules 2 or more; fruit dry or succulent, opening by the abaxial suture; seeds large; endosperm abundant, oily; embryo very small. B.H.[1] 1 : 16, partly. E.P.[1] 3, 2 : 12, partly. N. Temperate America, W. Indies, Brazil, E. Asia.—Magnolia, Liriodendron, Manglietia, Michelia, Talauma, Aromadendron.

Useful Products : *Tulip-tree* wood (Liriodendron tulipifera *L.*). Many handsome garden trees and shrubs.

2. WINTERACEAE

Trees or shrubs with aromatic alternate pellucid-dotted leaves; *stipules absent*; flowers small, mostly *cymose* or *fasciculate*, ☿ or rarely polygamous;

[1] B.H. = Bentham and Hooker, *Genera Plantarum.* E.P. = Engler and Prantl, *Pflanzenfamilien.*

G

sepals 2-6, free and imbricate or united (*Drimys*); petals 2- or more-seriate, mostly conspicuous in bud, imbricate; stamens several, hypogynous; anthers

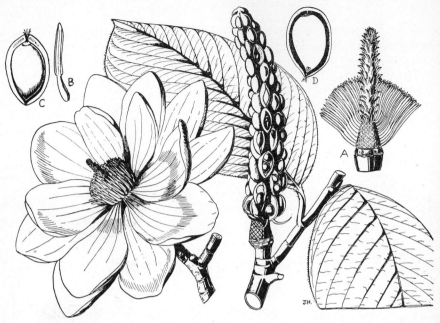

FIG. 1.—Magnolia Campbellii *Hk. f. & Thoms.* (Magnoliaceae). A, section showing arrangement of stamens and carpels. B, stamen. C, seed. D, section of seed.—After Hook. f.

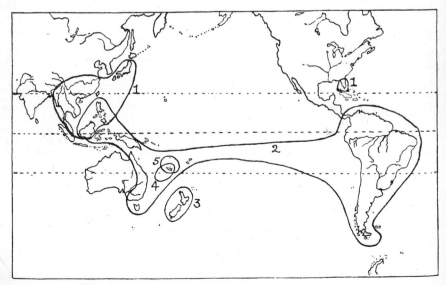

Distribution of Winteraceae. 1, Illicium; 2, Drimys; 3, Wintera; 4, Bubbia; 5, Exospermum; Belliolum, Zygogonum. This family is a little more advanced and more southerly and tropical in its distribution as compared with Magnoliaceae.

introrse, 2-celled, short, opening lengthwise ; carpels several to one, more or less in a *single whorl*, free or partially united, 1- to many-ovuled ; stigma sessile or styles distinct ; fruit a capsule or berry ; seeds with copious endosperm and minute embryo. B.H. 1 : 17. E.P. 3, 2 : 12 (under *Magnoliaceae*). Tropics and Subtropics, absent from Africa.—DRIMYS, ILLICIUM, etc.

USEFUL PRODUCTS : *Winter's Bark* (Drimys Winteri *Forst.*), S. America ; *Star Anise* (Illicium verum *Hk.f.*), S. China ; Japanese *Star Anise* (I. anisatum *L.*), Japan.

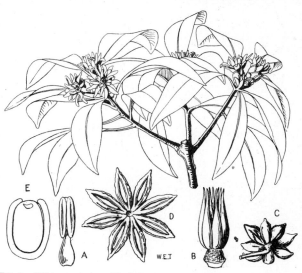

FIG. 2.—Illicium anisatum *Hk. f.* (Winteraceae). A, stamen. B, carpels. C, fruit. D, the same from above. E, section of seed.—After Bentl. & Trim.

A small family, more tropical than *Magnoliaceae*, but evidently derived from it ; no stipules, and the carpels reduced to a single whorl.

3. SCHIZANDRACEAE

Climbing or trailing shrubs ; leaves simple, alternate, often *pellucid-dotted* ; stipules absent ; flowers ♂ ♀, small, axillary, solitary ; sepals and petals

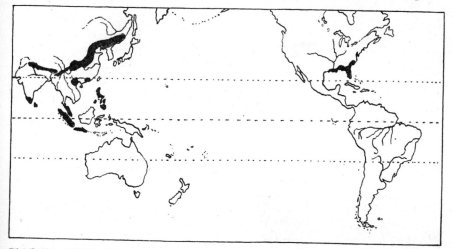

Distribution of Schizandraceae, a small family probably derived from the Magnoliaceae and with a very similar distribution (compare maps), but evidently a reduced type.

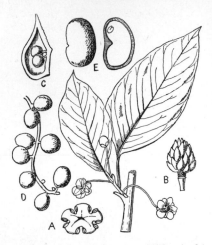

9-15, scarcely distinguishable from one another, the inner gradually petaloid, imbricate ; stamens numerous, short, *partially or wholly united into a fleshy globose mass* ; anthers small, 2-celled ; carpels numerous, with 2-3 ovules, in fruit either *spread on the much elongated axis* or crowded into a fleshy mass ; fruit baccate ; seeds immersed in the fleshy pulp ; endosperm oily, copious ; embryo small. B.H. 1 : 17. E.P. 3, 2 : 12 (under *Magnoliaceae*). N. Tropical and Subtropical Zone ; absent from Africa. SCHIZANDRA, KADSURA.

FIG. 3.—Schizandra coccinea *Michx.* (male) (Schizandraceae). A, stamens. B, carpels. C, section of carpel. D, fruiting axis. E, seed.—After Le Maout & Decne.

A very small and ancient family (see map) which, together with the separation of the sexes, has adopted a climbing habit. The distribution is almost identical with that of *Magnoliaceae*, from which it has apparently been derived.

4. HIMANTANDRACEAE

Aromatic trees covered with *peltate scaly indumentum* ; leaves alternate, entire, penninerved ; *stipules absent* ; flowers hermaphrodite, solitary or paired

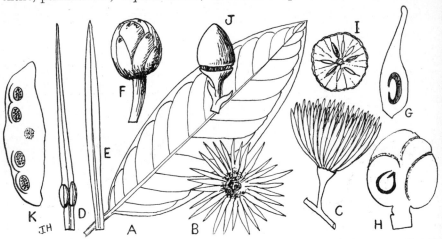

FIG. 4.—Himantandra Belgraveana *Diels* (Himantandraceae). A, leaf. B, scale from same. C, male flower. D, stamen. E, staminode. F, fruit. G, section of one carpel. H, section of fruit. I, section of fruit. J, opening bud.—Partly after Diels.

on short axillary branches, at first involucrate by two *calyptriform leathery deciduous sepals* ; inner sepals the one within the other ; petals about 7, lanceolate, very similar in size and shape to the numerous (about 40) stamens which have the anther-cells separated on each side towards the base, opening lengthwise ; *staminodes several*, subulate ; carpels 7-9, contiguous, free except at the base ; ovule solitary in each, pendulous from the apex, anatropous ; fruit globose, gall-like, fleshy, 7-10-celled by the *coalescence of the carpels* ; seed pendulous, with oily endosperm and small embryo. E. Australia, New Guinea, Moluccas.—HIMANTANDRA (Fig. 4).

A small and curious *relic*, with petaloid stamens ; remarkable in the order in having peltate scaly indumentum.

5. LACTORIDACEAE

Shrubs with alternate, small, obovate, emarginate, entire leaves and numerous minute *pellucid dots* ; stipules large, *interpetiolar,* membranous ; flowers poly-gamo-monoecious, small, soli-tary or up to 3, axillary ; sepals 3; *petals absent*; stamens 6, in 2 whorls ; anthers short, extrorse, 2-celled ; carpels 3, *free*, stigma beak-like ; ovules 6 in each carpel, in 2 vertical series on the intruded placentas; fruit follicular, beaked ; seeds 4-6 ; endosperm copious, oily ; embryo minute. B.H. 3 : 127 (under *Piperaceae*). E.P. 3, 2 :19. Juan Fernandez Island.—LAC-TORIS (Fig. 5).

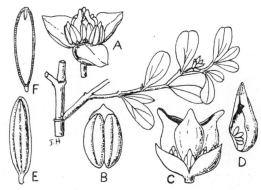

FIG. 5.—Lactoris fernandeziana *Philippi* (Lactoridaceae). A, flower. B, anther. C, fruit. D, one carpel. E, seed. F, section of seed.—After Hk. Ic. Pl.

A monotypic family closely related to the *Winteraceae*, of which it is probably a reduced derivative.

6. TROCHODENDRACEAE

Trees with *whorled* long-petiolate serrate leaves ; *buds perulate* ; stipules absent ; flowers ♀ or polygamous, racemose or subfasciculate, rather small ; *sepals absent* or very minute ; *petals absent* ; stamens numerous, hypogynous or subperigynous on the *expanded torus* ; anthers short or linear, extrorse, on slender filaments ; carpels 6-10, more or less in a *single whorl,* rather loosely united (*Trochodendron*) or quite free and stipitate (*Euptelea*) ; stigmas free ; ovules 1 to several in each carpel, pendulous ; fruit dehiscent or samaroid ; seeds with endo-

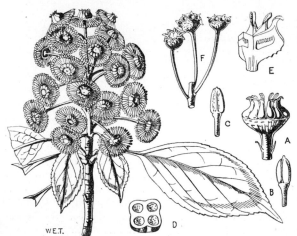

FIG. 6.—Trochodendron aralioides *Sieb. & Zucc.* (Trochodendraceae). A, flower with stamens removed. B and C, anthers. D, section of anther. E, section of carpels. F, fruits.—After Bot. Mag.

sperm and minute embryo.   B.H. 1 : 954 (under *Magnoliaceae*).   E.P. 3, 2 : 21.
Assam to Formosa and Japan.—TROCHODENDRON (Fig. 6), EUPTELEA.

A small family with a restricted distribution, related to but more advanced and
reduced than the *Winteraceae*, especially *Illicium* which occurs in the same area.   This
family may show the path of development to part of the *Hamamelidales*.

7. CERCIDIPHYLLACEAE

Trees ;   leaves deciduous, *opposite or alternate*, stipulate ;   *stipules adnate to
the petiole*, caducous ;   flowers *dioecious*, males subsessile, axillary, solitary or
fascicled, female pedicellate ;   sepals 4, small ;   *petals absent* ;   stamens 15-20 ;
filaments long and slender, on a conical torus ;   anthers oblong-linear, basifixed,

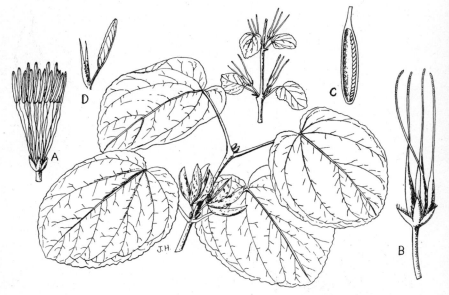

FIG. 7.—Cercidiphyllum japonicum *Sieb. & Zucc.* (Cercidiphyllaceae).   A, male flower.   B, female flower.
C, section of carpel.   D, young leaf and stipules.

opening lengthwise ;   carpels 4-6, *slightly stipitate*, gradually narrowed into
elongated slender styles stigmatic on their inner face ;   ovules in two rows,
descending, anatropous ;   fruit a cluster of 2-6 follicles splitting down the ventral
suture, which by twisting becomes external; endocarp woody and shining within;
seeds compressed, nearly square, winged at one end ;   embryo medium-sized
in copious endosperm ;   cotyledons flat.   China and Japan.—CERCIDIPHYLLUM
(Fig. 7).

USEFUL PRODUCTS : C. japonicum (see figure), the only species, is a magni-
ficent tree up to 55 ft. in girth in its native habitat ;   valuable timber.

A monotypic family of the *Magnoliales* and approaching the *Hamamelidales*, to
which it bears considerable external resemblance.

Order 2. ANONALES

Entirely woody group ; flowers hypogynous to perigynous, ☿ ; apo-carpous to rarely syncarpous with parietal placentation ; petaliferous with occasional gamopetaly ; stamens ∞, free ; endosperm constantly and markedly ruminate ; embryo minute. Leaves alternate, simple, ex-stipulate.—Tropics and Subtropics.

8. ANONACEAE

Trees, shrubs or climbers with aromatic wood and leaves ; leaves alternate, entire ; *stipules 0* ; flowers mostly ☿, rarely ♂♀, variously arranged ; sepals usually 3, separate or partly united, slightly imbricate or valvate ; petals hypogynous, often 6 in 2 series, rarely 4 or 3, imbricate or valvate in each series ; stamens hypogynous, numerous, spirally arranged ; filaments very short ; anthers 2-celled, opening lengthwise, often *overtopped by the truncate*

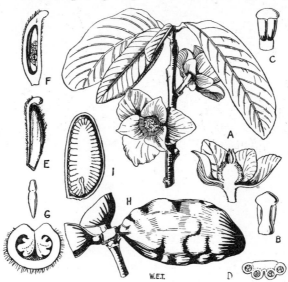

FIG. 8.—Asimina triloba *Dun.* (Anonaceae). A, section of flower. B and C, anthers. D, section of anther. E, carpel. F, longitudinal section of carpel. G, cross section of carpel. H, fruit. I, longitudinal section of seed.—After Le Maout & Decne.

enlarged connective ; carpels numerous or few, free or rarely united into a 1-celled ovary ; styles separate ; ovules 1 to many, basal or parietal ; carpels usually *stipitate in fruit*, free, rarely united into a 1- or many-celled mass, dry or fleshy, rarely dehiscent ; seeds often arillate, with copious and markedly *ruminate endosperm* and minute embryo. B.H. 1 : 20. E.P. 3, 2 : 23. Tropics and Subtropics.—UVARIA, GUATTERIA, ARTABOTRYS, ASIMINA, MONODORA, ROLLINIA, ANONA, XYLOPIA, etc.

USEFUL PRODUCTS : Various *Lancewoods* (Duguetia quitarensis *Bth.*), S. America ; (Bocagea laurifolia *B. & H.* and B. virgata *B. & H.*), West Indies. Fruits : *Cherimoyer* (Anona Cherimolia *Mill.*), W.S. America ; *Sour*

Sop (Anona muricata *L.*), Tropical America ; *Sweet Sop* (Anona squamosa *L.*), Malaya ; *Custard Apple* (Anona reticulata *L.*), Tropical America.

A large tropical family, related to but a more advanced and fixed type than the *Magnoliaceae.*

9. EUPOMATIACEAE

Shrubs ; leaves alternate, simple ; stipules 0 ; *flowers perigynous*, solitary, ♀, fairly large ; sepals and petals not differentiated from one another, forming a deciduous calyptra on the rim of the expanded concave torus ; stamens numerous, perigynous, the *inner ones sterile and petaloid*, the outer with two linear extrorse anther-cells and acuminate connective ; carpels numerous, *immersed in the turbinate receptacle* ; styles connate into a mass ; ovules several

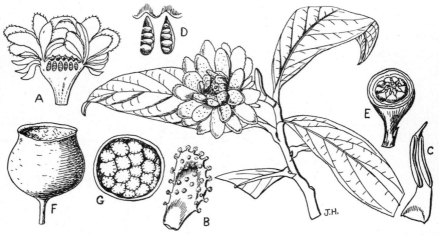

FIG. 9.—Eupomatia laurina *R. Br.* (Eupomatiaceae). A, section of flower showing carpels immersed in the receptacle. B, petal. C, stamen. D, section of two carpels. E, receptacle with petals, etc., removed. F, fruit. G, section of fruit.—Partly after Bot. Mag.

on the ventral side ; fruit a berry, truncate at the apex, girt with the remains of the perianth, several-celled ; seeds 1-2 in each cell, angular, with copious ruminate endosperm and very small embryo. B.H. 1 : 29 (under *Anonaceae*). E.P. 3, 2 : 39. Australia.—EUPOMATIA.

USEFUL PRODUCTS : Timber prettily marked (E. laurina *R. Br.*).

A remarkable type formerly included in the *Anonaceae*, but better treated as a separate family. The immersion of the otherwise free carpels in the expanded receptacle is probably a parallel to the similar condition found in *Nymphaeaceae*, in the herbaceous Ranalean phylum.

Order 3. LAURALES

Entirely woody group ; flowers hypogynous to perigynous, ♀ or ♂♀ ; cyclic ; apocarpous to one carpel ; apetalous ; stamens definite, free ; endosperm uniform to rarely ruminate or absent ; embryo often minute. Leaves alternate or opposite, simple, exstipulate.—Mainly Tropics.

10. MONIMIACEAE

Trees or shrubs, rarely climbers, usually fragrant, with opposite, or rarely alternate, entire or serrate, coriaceous leaves with pellucid dots ; *stipules absent* ; flowers actinomorphic, rarely oblique, hermaphrodite ; polygamous or unisexual,

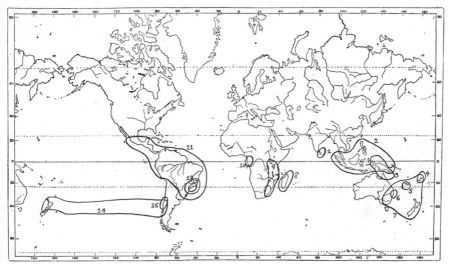

Distribution of some genera of Monimiaceae. 1, Hortonia ; 2, Matthaea ; 3, Levieria ; 4, Trimenia ; 5, Amborella, Carnegiea, Nemualon ; 6, Piptocalyx ; 7, Hedycarya ; 8, Ephippiandra ; 9, Xymalos ; 10, Glossocalyx ; 11, Mollinedia ; 12, Macropeplus ; 13, Macrotorus ; 14, Laurelia ; 15, Peumus.

cymose or racemose, rarely solitary, small or medium-sized ; inflorescence axillary or rarely terminal ; calyx inferior, with 4-many often connivent teeth or lobes in 2-many series, and imbricate, equal, or the outer sepaloid and the

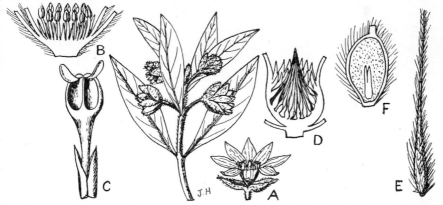

FIG. 10.—Atherosperma moschatum *Labill.* (Monimiaceae). A, flower. B section of flower. C, stamen. D, fruit. E, single carpel. F, section of seed.

inner petaloid, rarely obsolete ; disk adnate to the perianth-tube ; stamens numerous or few in 1-2 series ; filaments very short, often flattened, *with or without glands* at the base ; anthers erect, 2-celled, opening by a longitudinal slit or by *valves* from the base upwards. Female fl. : staminodes present or none ; carpels several or rarely solitary, 1-celled ; style short or elongated, stigma terminal ; ovule solitary, erect or pendulous ; carpels *separate in fruit*, enclosed by the perianth, or the latter deciduous, indehiscent, often drupaceous ; seed erect or pendulous ; testa membranous ; endosperm fleshy ; embryo small to half as large as the endosperm ; cotyledons erect or spreading. B.H. 3 : 137. E.P. 3, 2 : 94. Tropics and Subtropics.—MONIMIA, TAMBOURISSA, MOLLINEDIA, KIBARA, HEDYCARYA, SIPARUNA, LAURELIA, etc.

ECONOMIC PRODUCTS : *Boldo* (Peumus Boldus *Mol.*), Chile ; *Australian Sassafras* (Doryphora Sassafras *Endl.*), New South Wales.

A very interesting, mostly tropical family, showing strong tendency to perigyny ; probably an apetalous parallel to the *Rosaceae*. It is interesting that the valvular dehiscent anthers also occur in the *Hamamelidales*, themselves a further development of the *Rosales*.

11. LAURACEAE

Trees or shrubs, very rarely twining parasitic herbs, all parts with *aromatic oil-glands* ; leaves alternate, rarely opposite or subopposite, coriaceous and evergreen, variously nerved ; *stipules absent* ; flowers small, greenish or yellowish, usually cymose or racemose, hermaphrodite, polygamous or dioecious, actino-

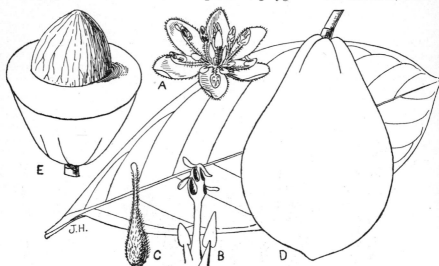

FIG. 11.—Persea gratissima *Gaertn.* (Lauraceae). A, flower. B, stamen. C, ovary. D, fruit. E, section of fruit.

morphic ; calyx usually inferior ; tube sometimes enlarging in fruit ; lobes usually 6, imbricate ; stamens typically in 4 whorls, often the fourth row suppressed or reduced to staminodes ; filaments sometimes glandular at the base, very rarely the glands fused into a disk ; anthers continuous with the filament, 2- or 4-valved, valves superimposed or more or less collateral, opening from the base upwards by flaps, introrse or sometimes the third whorl extrorse ; ovary superior, rarely inferior, 1-celled ; style terminal, simple ; stigma small ; ovule solitary, pendulous ; fruit baccate or drupaceous ; seed pendulous ;

without endosperm ; testa membranous ; embryo straight ; cotyledons thick, fleshy ; radicle superior. B.H. 3 : 146. E.P. 3, 2 : 106. Mainly Tropics, and Subtropics. CRYPTOCARYA, BEILSCHMIEDIA, AYDENDRON, CINNAMOMUM, MACHILUS, PERSEA, OCOTEA, NECTANDRA, SASSAFRAS, ACTINODAPHNE, LITSEA, UMBELLULARIA, LINDERA, LAURUS, CASSYTHA, etc.

USEFUL PRODUCTS : Many beautiful evergreen trees. *Sweet Bay Laurel* (Laurus nobilis *L.*) ; *Cinnamon* (Cinnamomum zeylanicum *Breyn*), Ceylon ; *Camphor* (Cinnamomum Camphora *Nees*), Japan and China ; *Sassafras* (Sassafras officinale *Nees*), N. America ; *Avocado Pear* (Persea gratissima *Gaertn.*), Tropical America. Timbers : *Nan-Mu Wood* (Persea Nanmu *Oliv.*), China ; *Greenheart Wood* (Nectandra Rodioei *Schk.*), British Guiana.

A large tropical family apparently showing the extreme limit of reduction in the Magnolian alliance. The tendency to valvular dehiscence of the anthers shown in the *Berberidaceae* is here almost a constant character and is probably due to parallel development and not a sign of true affinity.

12. GOMORTEGACEAE

Trees ; *leaves opposite*, evergreen, aromatic, simple ; *stipules absent* ; flowers ☿, racemose, axillary and terminal ; sepals 7-10, *spirally arranged* ; petals absent ; fertile stamens 2-3, anthers 2-locellate, introrse, opening by *valves* ;

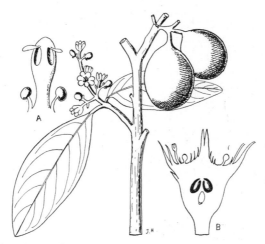

FIG. 12.—Gomortega nitida *Ruiz & Pavon* (Gomortegaceae). A, stamen and glands. B, vertical section of flower.—After R. & P.

ovary *inferior*, 2-3-celled, with 1 pendulous ovule in each ; style short, 2-3-partite ; fruit 1-3-celled ; drupe with bony putamen ; seeds with copious oily endosperm and large embryo. B.H. 3 : 149 (under *Lauraceae*). E.P.N. 172, 347. Chile.—GOMORTEGA.

A little-known monotypic family about which more knowledge is desired.—No material at Kew.

13. HERNANDIACEAE

Trees or shrubs, sometimes scandent, with alternate, simple or *digitately compound* leaves; stipules absent; flowers hermaphrodite, or monoecious or polygamous by abortion, actinomorphic, arranged in axillary corymbose or

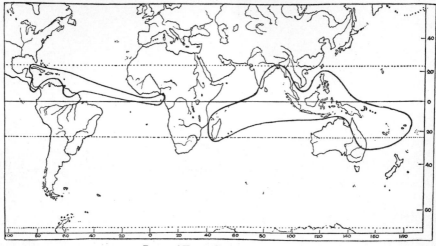

Range of Hernandia (Hernandiaceae).

paniculate cymes, bracteate or not; calyx superior, with 3-5 valvate sub-equal segments in two whorls or rarely 4-8 in one whorl; stamens 3-5 in a single whorl, when the calyx is double opposite the outer segments, often 4; anthers 2-celled, opening introrsely or laterally by *2 valves*; *staminodes gland-like*, in one or two whorls outside the stamens, or absent, those of the outer whorl in pairs at the base of the filaments, those of the inner whorl alternate with the stamens; ovary *inferior*, 1-celled; ovule solitary, pendulous; fruit dry, more or less ribbed, either with 2-4 wings on the body or with 2 terminal wings formed by enlarged perianth-segments, or wingless but enclosed in the inflated receptacle; seed solitary, *without endosperm*; testa leathery; embryo straight; cotyledons large, plano-convex or flat and twisted around the radicle. B.H.

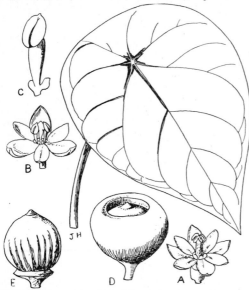

FIG. 13.—Hernandia peltata *Meisn.* (Hernandiaceae).   A and B, flowers.   C, stamen and glands.   D, fruit.   E, same with receptacle removed.

3:164; (under *Lauraceae*). E.P. 3, 2:126. Tropics.—HERNANDIA, ILLIGERA, SPARATTANTHELIUM, GYROCARPUS.

A small family, not very natural and probably of mixed derivation.

14. MYRISTICACEAE

Trees, often large and frequently aromatic ; leaves alternate, entire, penni-nerved, often with *pellucid dots* ; flowers small, dioecious, apetalous, fascicled, corymbose or capitate ; calyx 3- (rarely 2-5-) lobed, funnel-shaped to globose or saucer-shaped, lobes *valvate* ; male flower : stamens 2-30 ; filaments *united into a column* ; anthers 2-celled, free or united into a mass, dehiscing longitudinally ; rudimentary ovary absent ; female flower : staminodes absent ; ovary superior, sessile, 1-celled ; stigma subsessile ; ovule 1, almost basal ; fruit fleshy, usually

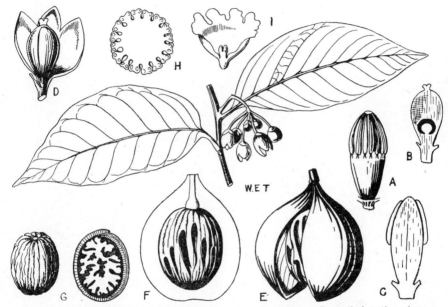

FIG. 14.—Myristica fragrans *Houtt.* (Myristicaceae). A, anther-column. B, vertical section of ovary.
C, anther. D, open female flower. E, fruit. F, section of fruit. G, seed. H, same transverse.
I, embryo.—After Köhler.

dehiscing by two valves ; seeds erect, with a thin or fleshy sometimes laciniate often coloured aril ; endosperm copious, replete with fat and often starch, mostly *ruminate* ; embryo small ; cotyledons ascending or spreading, sometimes connate. B.H. 3 : 135. E.P. 3, 2 : 40. Tropics.—MYRISTICA, PYCNANTHUS, etc.

USEFUL PRODUCTS : *Nutmeg* (Myristica fragrans *Houtt.*), Indian Archipelago, and much cultivated in Tropics.

Order 4. RANALES

Herbaceous, often with scattered vascular bundles in the stem, or softly woody ; flowers hypogynous to rarely perigynous, ⚥, hemicyclic to rarely completely cyclic ; petals mostly present ; stamens ∞, free ; apocarpous ; seeds with copious uniform endosperm and minute embryo. Leaves alternate or rarely opposite, very rarely stipulate, simple or much divided.—Cosmopolitan, but rare in the Tropics.

15. RANUNCULACEAE

Terrestrial perennials (rarely annuals), rarely aquatic herbs, with radical or alternate leaves, rarely climbing soft-wooded plants with opposite leaves (*Clematis*) ; stipules absent or very rudimentary (*Thalictrum* spp.) ; indumentum (when present) of simple hairs ; flowers ♀, rarely ♂♀, actinomorphic or zygomorphic (*Delphineae*), solitary to racemose or paniculate ; sepals 3 to many, green or coloured when petals absent, imbricate or rarely valvate ; petals few to many, free, mainly with a nectariferous claw ; stamens usually numerous, hypogynous, free ; anthers 2-celled ; carpels usually many, rarely reduced to 1, free or partly connate (*Nigella*), 1-celled ; ovules anatropous, numerous or

FIG. 15.—Ranunculus cortusaefolius *Willd*. (Ranunculaceae).   A, carpels.   B, one carpel.—Orig.

solitary ; fruit a bunch of follicles, rarely baccate, or of dry achenes often with long persistent styles ; seeds not arillate, with a very small embryo and copious endosperm.   B.H. 1 : 1.   E.P. 3, 2 : 43.   Distributed over all parts of the world, to the limits of vegetation on high mountains and towards the poles ; comparatively rare in the Southern Hemisphere and in the Tropics.—CALTHA, HELLEBORUS, TROLLIUS, NIGELLA, AQUILEGIA, DELPHINIUM, ACONITUM, PAEONIA, RANUNCULUS, THALICTRUM, ANEMONE, CLEMATOPSIS, CLEMATIS, etc.

USEFUL PRODUCTS : *Stavesacre Seeds* (Delphinium Staphisagria *L.*), S.E. Europe ; *Aconite Root* (Aconitum Napellus *L.*), Europe ; *Black Cohosh* or *Black Snake Root* (Cimicifuga racemosa *Nutt.*) ; *Hydrastis Rhizome* (Hydrastis canadensis *L.*), N. America.   Many beautiful ornamental plants.

The most primitive of herbaceous *Dicotyledons*, closely related to a certain group of *Monocotyledons* (Alismaceae, etc.), and with a great range of floral structure.

16. CABOMBACEAE

Aquatic herbs with perennial rhizomes ; stems coated with mucilage ; leaves alternate, the *submerged ones finely dissected*, the floating *peltate* ; flowers

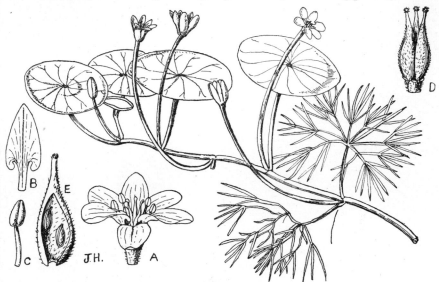

FIG. 16.—Cabomba aquatica *Aubl.* (Cabombaceae). A, flower. B, petal. C, stamen. D, carpels. E, same open.—After Bot. Mag.

axillary, solitary, *hypogynous*, actinomorphic ; sepals 3, petaloid ; petals 3 ; stamens 3-18 ; anthers extrorse, opening lengthwise ; carpels 2-18, free, 1-celled ; stigma subsessile, entire ; ovules 2-3, parietal, orthotropous ; fruits indehiscent; seeds 1-3 on the dorsal suture ; embryo at the base of fleshy endosperm ; cotyledons fleshy. B.H. 1 : 46 (under *Nymphaeaceae*). America, India, Australia.—CABOMBA, BRASENIA.

A small family formerly included in the *Nymphaeaceae*, but more closely allied to the preceding.

17. CERATOPHYLLACEAE

Aquatic *submerged herbs*, with leafy floating branches ; leaves *verticillate*, variously divided with thread-like or linear segments ; flowers *monoecious*, solitary in the whorls, the males and females at

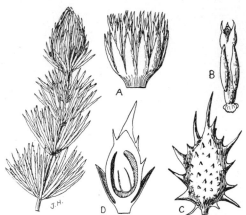

FIG. 17.—Ceratophyllum demersum *L.* (Ceratophyllaceae). A, flower. B, stamen. C, fruit. D, vertical section of same.—After Martius.

separate nodes, sessile ; calyx thinly herbaceous, many-parted into narrow subvalvate segments often dentate or lacerate at the apex. Male flowers :

stamens 10-20, crowded on a flat torus ; anthers almost sessile, erect, linear-oblong, 2-celled, cells parallel, opening lengthwise, with the connective produced beyond the cells, thick and often coloured. Female flowers : staminodes 0 ; ovary sessile, ovoid, 1-celled ; style continuous with the ovary ; ovule 1, pendulous, anatropous ; fruit a nut, ovoid or ellipsoid ; seed pendulous ; endosperm 0 ; embryo straight ; cotyledons oblong, equal ; radicle very short ; the plumule already well developed and showing several leaves in the seed. B.H. 3 : 415. E.P. 3, 2 : 10. Cosmopolitan.—CERATOPHYLLUM.

18. NYMPHAEACEAE

Aquatic herbs with peltate or cordate often floating leaves on long petioles ; flowers ♂, solitary, large and showy, often sweet-scented ; sepals 4-6, free or adnate to the torus ; petals numerous, hypogynous or perigynous, imbricate, sometimes gradually passing into the stamens, the latter numerous, with introrse

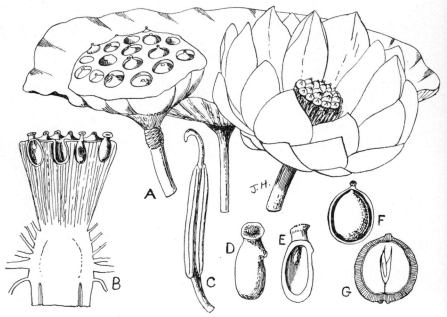

FIG. 18.—Nelumbium luteum *L.* (Nymphaeaceae). A, torus and carpels in fruit. B, section of torus. C, anther. D, carpel. E, section of carpel. F, section of fruit. G, section of seed.—After Le Maout & Decne.

anthers opening longitudinally ; carpels 8 or more, united into a many-celled ovary (*Nuphar*) or sunk in the enlarged torus (*Nelumbium*) ; ovules 1 to many, on the walls or from the apex of the carpel ; endosperm usually present ; embryo straight. B.H. 1 : 45, partly. E.P. 3, 2 : 1. Widely dispersed in ponds, streams and lakes. Tropics and N. Temperate Zone.—NUPHAR, NYMPHAEA, VICTORIA, NELUMBIUM, etc.

Several beautiful hardy NYMPHAEA spp. suitable for water gardening. *Victoria Water Lily* (Victoria regia *Lindl.*), Guiana and Brazil ; *Egyptian Lotus* (Nelumbium speciosum *Willd.*).

Order 5. BERBERIDALES

Herbaceous to shrubby or climbing ; stem often with broad medullary rays ; flowers hypogynous ; ♀ to ♂♀, cyclic ; petals present, small ; stamens mostly definite in number, free, opposite the petals ; carpels usually 1-3, free ; seeds with copious endosperm, and small to large embryo. Leaves alternate or radical, simple or compound, usually exstipulate.— Mainly North Temperate Zone.

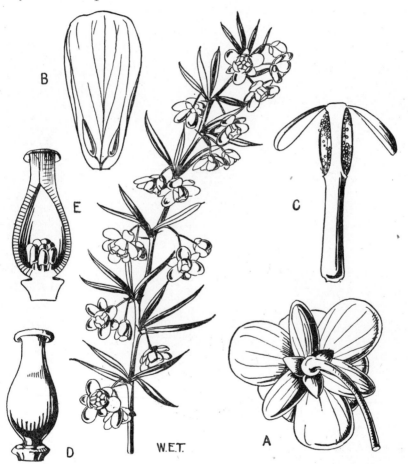

FIG. 19.—Berberis stenophylla *Hance* (Berberidaceae). A, flower from below. B, petal. C, stamen. D, ovary. E, section of ovary.—Orig.

19. BERBERIDACEAE

Herbs, undershrubs, or shrubs, herbs often with creeping rhizomes or thick tubers ; leaves alternate or radical, simple or compound, *mostly exstipulate* ; flowers ♀, solitary to paniculate ; *sepals and petals similar,* in 2 to several

H

series, free, hypogynous, imbricate or outer valvate, caducous, rarely absent ; stamens 4-9, *opposite the petals*, hypogynous, free ; anthers 2-celled, opening lengthwise or by *valves* ; *carpel 1* ; style short or absent ; ovules few, ascending, or numerous on the ventral side, anatropous ; fruit a berry or capsule ; seeds with copious endosperm, and small or long embryo ; cotyledons short. B.H. 1 : 40, partly.   E.P. 3, 2 : 70.   Mainly N. Temperate Zone.—BERBERIS, MAHONIA, NANDINA, EPIMEDIUM, ACERANTHUS, PODOPHYLLUM, etc.

USEFUL PRODUCTS : *May Apple* or *Podophyllum Roots* (Podophyllum peltatum *L.*), N. America.   Many beautiful garden shrubs.

20. CIRCAEASTERACEAE

Small *annual herb* with a rosette of obovate spinulose-dentate leaves ; flowers solitary in the upper leaf-axils, shortly pedicellate, ♀, actinomorphic ; sepals 2, membranous, valvate, persistent ; *petals absent* ; stamens 2, free, alternate

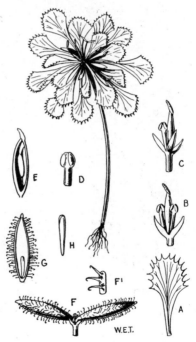

FIG. 20.—Circaeaster agrestis *Maxim.* (Circaeasteraceae).   A, leaf.   B and C, flowers.   D, anther. E, section of ovary.   F, fruit.   F¹, prickles from fruit.   G, section of fruit.   H, embryo.—After Hook. Ic. Pl.

with the sepals, erect in bud, rarely reduced to one and the other sepaloid ; anthers 2-celled, introrse, cells divergent from the apex, opening lengthwise ; ovary superior, linear, 1-celled, stigma sessile ; ovule 1, *pendulous* from the apex of the cell ; fruit indehiscent ; seed with copious endosperm ; embryo terete, straight, with short cotyledons.   N.W. Himalaya.—CIRCAEASTER.

21. LARDIZABALACEAE

Twining or rarely erect shrubs; wood with *broad primary medullary rays*; leaves alternate, *digitately compound* or rarely pinnate; petiolules swollen at

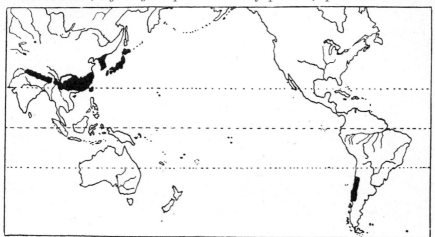

Distribution of Lardizabalaceae (shaded black).

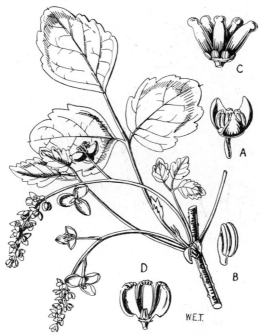

FIG. 21.—Akebia lobata *Decne.* (Lardizabalaceae). A, male flower. B, anther. C, female flower. D, fruit.—After Bot. Mag.

the base; hairs simple; flowers racemose, arising with the leaves from *perulate buds*, ♂♀, actinomorphic; sepals 3 or 6, imbricate, or the outer valvate, often petaloid ; petals 6, smaller than the sepals or absent ; stamens 6, free or connate ; anthers free, opening lengthwise ; connective often produced ; staminodes 6 or absent from the ♀ flowers ; carpels 3 (or more), soon divergent ; stigma oblique, subsessile ; ovules numerous or solitary ; mature carpels fleshy, coloured, indehiscent or opening by the adaxial suture ; seeds ovoid or sub-reniform, with fleshy copious endosperm ; embryo small. B.H. 1 : 40 (under *Berberidaceae*). E.P. 3, 2 : 67. Temperate S. America, E. Asia.—LARDIZABALA, DECAISNEA, HOLBOELLIA, AKEBIA, etc.

22. SARGENTADOXACEAE [1]

Climbers ; leaves alternate, trifoliolate ; stipules absent ; flowers unisexual ; inflorescences from axillary perulate buds, racemose ; male flowers : sepals 6, free, conspicuous in bud, biseriately imbricate ; petals 6, very small and scale-

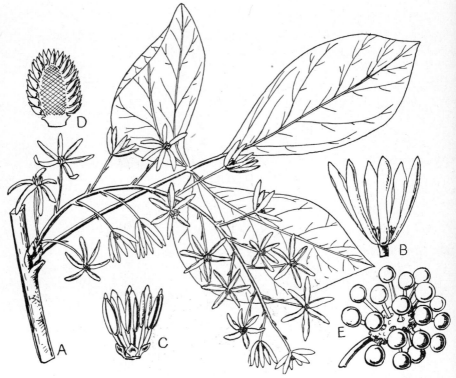

FIG. 22.—Sargentadoxa cuneata *Rehd. & Wils.* (Sargentadoxaceae). A, male shoot. B, male flower. C, petals and stamens. D, section of female without sepals and petals. E, fruit.—Partly original.

like ; stamens 6, opposite the petals ; anthers extrorse, 2-celled, connective shortly produced at the apex ; female flowers : sepals and petals as in the male ; staminodes 6 ; carpels numerous, spirally arranged, free ; ovule 1,

[1] This family is to be attributed to Dr. Stapf, to whom I am indebted for the information above, and who is describing and figuring this interesting family in another place. The family in many ways combines in its two sexes the characters of the *Lardizabalaceae* and *Schizandraceae*, with the male flowers similar to the former, and the gynaecium of the latter.

pendulous ; fruit baccate ; seeds with copious smooth endosperm and minute embryo. W. China.—SARGENTADOXA.

23. MENISPERMACEAE

Twining or rarely erect shrubs or small trees, with the wood in cross section showing *broad medullary rays* ; root bitter ; leaves petiolate, alternate, *exstipulate*, usually simple, rarely trifoliolate or palmately lobed and nerved. Inflorescence cymose, paniculate, fasciculate, or rarely the flowers solitary, axillary or borne on the older wood ; flowers small, inconspicuously coloured, *unisexual*, dioecious, actinomorphic, rarely slightly zygomorphic. Male flowers : sepals in 2-4 series, imbricate, the outer smaller ; petals usually smaller than the sepals, minute or absent, free or rarely united ; stamens usually 6 or 3, or indefinite, when few *opposite to the petals*, free or variously united ; anthers short. Female flowers : staminodes present or absent ; *carpels 3 or 6,* rarely 1 or several, *free,*

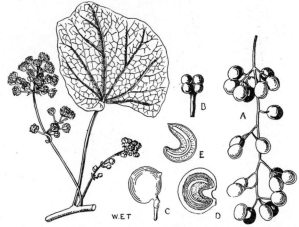

FIG. 23.—Menispermum canadense *L.* (Menispermaceae). A, fruits. B, anther. C, fruit. D, section of same. E, section of seed.—After Le Maout & Decne.

sessile or stipitate ; stigma terminal, entire or lobed ; ovules 2, soon reduced to 1 by abortion, attached to the ventral suture ; carpels drupaceous, with the scar of the style subterminal or near the base by *excentric growth*, sessile or stipitate ; exocarp membranous or subcoriaceous, mesocarp more or less pulpy, endocarp often bony and rugose, tuberculate or ribbed ; seed often curved in the form of a horseshoe, with uniform or ruminate endosperm or without endosperm ; embryo often curved, with a small radicle and flat or semi-terete cotyledons. B.H. 1 : 30. E.P. 3, 2 : 78. Mainly Tropics and Subtropics.— TINOSPORA, COCCULUS, MENISPERMUM, STEPHANIA, CISSAMPELOS, etc.

USEFUL PRODUCTS : *Levant Berries* (Anamirta paniculata *Coleb.*), E. Asia.

Order 6. ARISTOLOCHIALES

Softly woody with broad medullary rays, or parasitic or epiphytic; flowers hypogynous to epigynous, ♀ to ♂ ♀; no petals ; stamens ∞ to few ; parietal or axile placentation ; endosperm present or absent, with small to large embryo. Leaves (when present) alternate, simple, exstipulate.—Mostly Tropics.

24. ARISTOLOCHIACEAE

Climbing shrubs or rarely dwarf and erect ; stems of the woody species in cross section showing *broad medullary rays* ; roots often medicinal ; leaves petiolate, alternate, simple, mostly entire, *without stipules* ; flowers solitary or racemose, axillary or in clusters on the older wood, pedicellate, hermaphrodite, zygomorphic, or rarely actinomorphic ; calyx often enlarged and petaloid, variously produced above the ovary, often tubular, the limb either symmetrically

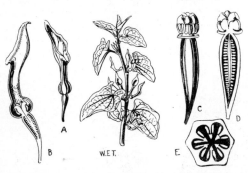

FIG. 24.—Aristolochia Clematitis *L.* (Aristolochiaceae). A, flower. B, section of same. C, fruit. D, vertical section of fruit.

3-lobed, or unilateral and entire or lobed, usually highly coloured and foetid ; stamens 6-∞, in 1-2-series *around the apex of the ovary or stylar column* ; filaments short, thick, free or scarcely distinguishable from the column ; anthers free or adnate, with 2 parallel cells, extrorse, opening longitudinally ; ovary *inferior* or rarely semi-superior, 4-6-celled or imperfectly celled ; styles thick, short, united into a column, divided into 3-∞ stigmatic lobes; ovules numerous in each cell ; fruit capsular or rarely indehiscent, sometimes dehiscing from the base upwards and hanging like an inverted parachute ; seeds numerous, often immersed in the pulpy endocarp, 3-sided or flattened, raphe sometimes thickened or winged ; endosperm copious, fleshy ; embryo small. B.H. 3 : 121.   E.P. 3, 1 : 264.   Tropics and Temperate. —ARISTOLOCHIA, ASARUM, etc.

USEFUL PRODUCTS : Several used as cures for snake bites ; *Alpam Root* (Bragantia Wallichii *R. Br.*), India ; *Virginian Snake Root* (Aristolochia Serpentaria *L.*), United States.

25. CYTINACEAE

(Rafflesiaceae)

Fleshy *parasites* with *scale-like leaves*, on the roots, stems and branches of various trees and shrubs : flowers often large, solitary, rarely spicate, diclinous by abortion, rarely polygamous or ♀ ; calyx more or less epigynous with 4-10 imbricate or very rarely valvate segments ; anthers sessile, arranged in 1-3 series around a fleshy column, 2-celled, opening lengthwise by slits or by terminal pores ; pollen often viscous ; ovary inferior or subinferior, 1-celled or the placentas reaching nearly into the middle ; stigma undivided, discoid or lobate or the stigmas numerous on the top of the ovary ; ovules very numerous on *parietal placentas* or from the apex of the cells, with a single integument ; fruit fleshy, indehiscent or opening irregularly ; seeds minute, very numerous ; endosperm cellular ; embryo minute. B.H. 3 : 116.   E.P. 3, 1 : 274 (as *Rafflesiaceae*).   Tropics and Temperate.—CYTINUS, APODANTHES, RAFFLESIA, BRUGMANSIA, etc.

The flower of *Rafflesia Arnoldii* R. Br. is the largest in the vegetable kingdom.

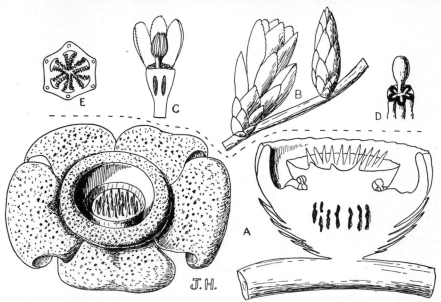

FIG. 25.—A, Rafflesia Patma *Bl.* (Cytinaceae).   B. Cytinus.   C, vertical section of flower.   D, stigma.
E, transverse section of ovary.

26. HYDNORACEAE

Parasitic herbs on the roots of various trees and shrubs ; scale-leaves 0 ; flowers
♂, solitary, subsessile, rather large ; calyx very thick, valvately 3-4-lobed ;

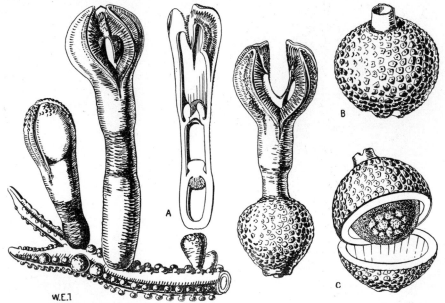

FIG. 26.—Hydnora longicollis *Welw.* (Hydnoraceae).   A, vertical section of flower.   B, fruit.
C, fruit in section.—After Welw.

anthers numerous, sessile in a single or double series on the tube of the calyx, the cells densely crowded, linear, opening lengthwise ; ovary inferior, 1-celled, crowned by the sessile stigma ; ovules very numerous from *apical or parietal placentas* often nearly meeting in the middle ; fruit baccate ; seeds numerous, small or minute, in copious endosperm. B.H. 3 : 120 (under *Cytinaceae*). E.P. 3, 1 : 282.   Tropics and Temperate.—HYDNORA, PROSOPANCHE.

27. NEPENTHACEAE

Shrubs or undershrubs, prostrate, erect or scandent ; leaves alternate, sessile or petiolate, divided when adult into petiole, blade, *tendril, ascidium*

FIG. 27.—Nepenthes Rafflesiana *Jack* (Nepenthaceae).   A, male flower.   B, fruit.—After Hook.

(pitcher) and *operculum*; flowers *dioecious*, small, actinomorphic; sepals 4-3,
separate or rarely connate at
the base, imbricate, glandular
and nectariferous inside;
stamens 4-24; *filaments connate into a column*; anthers
crowded into a mass, 2-celled,
opening lengthwise; ovary of
4 carpels very rarely 3, opposite
the sepals, 3-4-celled; style
absent or very short; stigma
discoid; ovules numerous in
many series on the central
placentas; fruit a capsule,
sessile or shortly stipitate,
loculicidally dehiscent; seeds
numerous, imbricate, ascending, filiform; endosperm fleshy
with straight cylindric embryo
in the middle. B.H. 3 : 115.

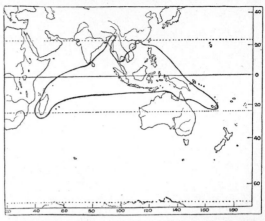

The distribution of the remarkable and distinct genus Nepenthes
emphasises the close relationship between the island of
Madagascar and Indo-Malaya.

E.P. 3, 2 : 253. Malaya to Madagascar. — NEPENTHES. Well - known
" Pitcher-Plants ".

Order 7. PIPERALES

Herbs, shrubs or trees; herbaceous stems often with scattered bundles
as in *Monocotyledones*; flowers hypogynous to epigynous; usually no calyx;

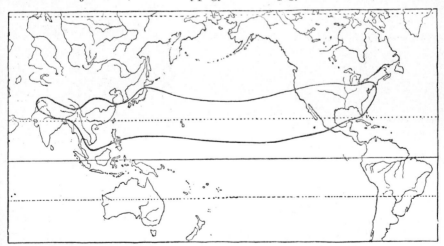

Range of Saururaceae. A distinct family common to Eastern Asia and N. America.

ovary superior to rarely inferior; carpels rarely free; placentation parietal
to subaxile; seeds with copious endosperm and minute embryo. Leaves
alternate or opposite, usually stipulate.—Mostly Tropics.

28. PIPERACEAE

Herbs or shrubs, erect or scandent ; vascular bundles more or less scattered as in *Monocotyledones* ; leaves usually alternate, entire, rarely opposite or

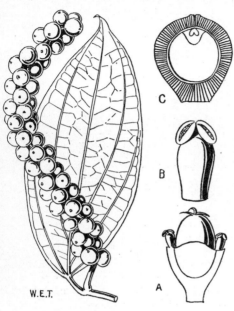

W.E.T.

FIG. 28.—Piper nigrum *L*. (Piperaceae). A, flower. B, stamen. C, section of fruit.—After Le Maout & Decne.

whorled, petiolate ; stipules *adnate to the petiole* or absent ; flowers minute, hermaphrodite or unisexual, usually densely spicate or spikes umbellate ; calyx absent; stamens 2-6, hypogynous; filaments usually free ; anthers 2-celled, distinct or confluent ; ovary superior, 1-celled, 1-ovuled ; stigmas 1-5, short ; ovule erect ; fruit baccate, small, with a succulent, thin or dry pericarp ; seeds small, with small endosperm and copious mealy perisperm ; embryo very small. B.H. 3 : 125. E.P. 3, 1 : 3. Mainly Tropics. PIPER, PEPEROMIA, etc.

USEFUL PRODUCTS : *Pepper* (Piper nigrum *L*.), Tropics; *Cubebs* (P. Cubeba *L*.), Malay Archipelago.

A family of rather doubtful origin, but probably an extreme reduction from the *Ranales*, becoming more or less woody.

29. SAURURACEAE

Perennial herbs; leaves alternate, simple ; *stipules adnate to the petiole* ; flowers ♀, in dense spikes or racemes ; bracts conspicuous ; perianth absent; stamens 6 or 8, rarely fewer by abor-

FIG. 29.—Anemopsis californica *Hk. f.* (Saururaceae). A, flower showing ovary in vertical section. B, ovary, cross section.—After Bot. Mag.

tion, free or adnate to the ovary at the base or quite epigynous; anthers 2-celled, opening lengthwise; ovary composed of 3 or 4 *free* or *connate carpels*, in the latter case the ovary 1-celled with *parietal placentas*; styles free; ovules in each free carpel 2-4, on each placenta 6-8; fruit of separate dehiscent cocci or opening at the top; seeds with small endosperm and copious mealy perisperm and small embryo. B.H. 3:127 (under *Piperaceae*). E.P. 3, 1:1. N. Temperate and Subtropical, Malaya.— SAURURUS, HOUTTUYNIA.

30. CHLORANTHACEAE

Herbs, shrubs or trees, mostly aromatic; leaves opposite, simple; *petioles more or less connate at the base*; stipules small; flowers spicate, paniculate or capitate; calyx absent from the male flowers; stamens 1-3, connate into a mass; anthers 1-2-celled, opening lengthwise; female calyx adnate to the ovary, often minutely 3-dentate at the apex; ovary inferior, 1-celled; stigma sessile or on a short style; ovule solitary, orthotropous, pendulous; drupe small, ovoid or globose, exocarp more or less succulent, endocarp

FIG. 30.—Ascarina lanceolata *Hk. f.* (Chloranthaceae). A, male flower. B, stamen. C, fruit. D, vertical section of ovary.—After Seemann.

Range of Lacistemaceae.

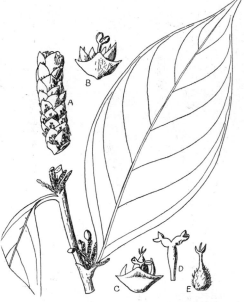

FIG. 31.—Lacistema robustum *Schnitz.* (Lacistemaceae). A, inflorescence. B, male flower. C, female flower. D, stamen. E, ovary.—After Martius.

hardened ; seed with copious fleshy endosperm and minute embryo. B.H. 3 : 133. E.P. 3, 1 : 12.   Tropics and S. Temperate. — CHLORANTHUS, ASCARINA, HEDYOSMUM.

31. LACISTEMACEAE

Shrubs or small trees ; leaves alternate, simple ; stipules absent ; flowers ☿, very small, crowded in axillary clustered spikes ; bracts imbricate, concave ; bracteoles 2 at the base of the flower ; sepals 6, unequal or absent ; petals absent ; stamen solitary, inserted on a fleshy sometimes cupular disk ; anther cells 2, *separate*, sometimes stipitate, ovoid, opening lengthwise ; ovary sessile or subsessile, superior, 1-celled, with 2-3 *parietal placentas* ; stigmas 2-3 ; ovules 1-2 on each placenta, pendulous, anatropous ; fruit a capsule, dehiscing by valves, often 3-sided ; seeds 1-3 in each capsule, pendulous ; embryo straight in the middle of and slightly shorter than the copious fleshy endosperm ; cotyledons foliaceous. B.H. 3 : 412.   E.P. 3, 1 : 14.   Tropical America (see map). —LACISTEMA.

Order 8. RHOEADALES

Herbaceous to subwoody ; flowers hypogynous to rarely subperigynous, ☿, actinomorphic to zygomorphic ; petals present ; stamens ∞ to few, free or united in two bundles ; syncarpous, with parietal placentation ; seeds with copious endosperm and minute embryo. Leaves alternate or rarely subopposite, simple or much divided, exstipulate. Mainly North Temperate regions.

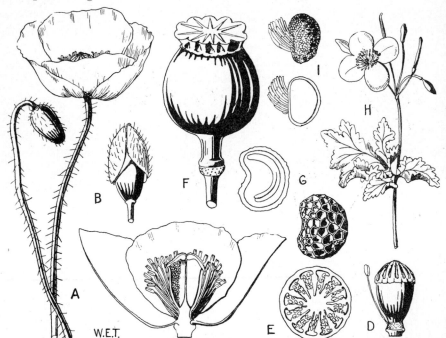

FIG. 32.—Papaver Rhoeas *L.* (Papaveraceae). A, flower. B, flower-bud showing caducous sepals. D, ovary with one stamen. E, ovary, cross section. F, capsule. G, seed. H, Chelidonium majus *L.* I, seed of same.—After Le Maout & Decne.

32. PAPAVERACEAE

Annual to perennial herbs with coloured juice, rarely shrubs (*Dendromecon*) or small trees (*Bocconia*) ; leaves alternate or the floral ones opposite or whorled (*Platystemoneae*), often much divided ; stipules 0 ; indumentum of simple or

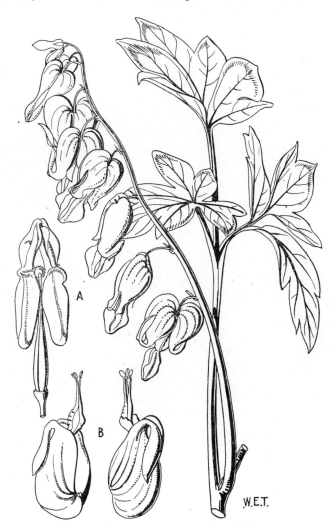

FIG. 33.—Dicentra spectabilis *Lem.* (Fumariaceae).   A, inner petals with ovary and style.
B, outer petals with stamens in bundles of 3.—After Bot. Mag.

barbellate hairs ; flowers mostly solitary, showy, actinomorphic, ♂, visited by insects for pollen ; sepals 2-3, caducous or calyptrate ; petals 4-6 or 8-12, free, biseriate, imbricate, often crumpled ; nectaries 0 ; stamens numerous, free ; anthers 2-celled, opening lengthwise ; ovary superior, composed of 2 or more united carpels, 1-celled with parietal placentas, or several-celled by the intrusive placentas reaching the middle, rarely 2-celled by a spurious wall ; carpels rarely loosely united and becoming free in fruit (*Platystemon*) ; stigmas opposite or alternate with the placentas ; ovules numerous, anatropous ; fruit capsular, opening by valves or pores ; seeds small, with a crested or smooth raphe or arillate ; embryo minute in copious fleshy or oily endosperm. B.H. 1 : 49, partly. E.P. 3, 2 : 130. Mainly N. Temperate and Subtropics.— PAPAVER, ROMNEYA, ARGEMONE, MECONOPSIS, BOCCONIA, MACLEAYA, CHELIDONIUM, ESCHSCHOLTZIA, SANGUINARIA, etc.

USEFUL PRODUCTS : *Opium Poppy* (Papaver somniferum *L.*), Eastern countries ; *Blood Root* or *Puccoon* (Sanguinaria canadensis *L.*), N. America. Many ornamental plants.

33. FUMARIACEAE

Herbaceous with brittle stems and watery juice, sometimes scandent ; leaves radical, alternate or rarely subopposite, usually much divided ; flowers ⚥, often *zygomorphic* ; sepals 2, small, deciduous ; petals 4, imbricate, more or less *connivent*, the two outer often saccate or spurred at the base, the two inner narrower and sometimes coherent to the apex ; stamens 4, *free and opposite the petals*, or 6 and *united into two bundles* ; ovary superior, 1-celled with two parietal placentas ; style slender ; ovules 1 to many, anatropous ; fruit capsular or a nut, capsule sometimes transversely septate and breaking into 1-seeded indehiscent segments or dehiscing by valves ; seeds shining, crested or nude ; endosperm fleshy with minute embryo. B.H. 1 : 54. E.P. 3, 2 : 137 (under *Papaveraceae*). Mainly N. Temperate Zone.—FUMARIA, CORYDALIS, DICENTRA, HYPECOUM, etc.

USEFUL PRODUCTS : Several handsome garden plants.

Order 9. LOASALES

Mostly herbaceous ; flowers hypogynous to epigynous, actinomorphic ; petals present ; stamens numerous to few, sometimes in bundles ; syncarpous with parietal placentation ; seeds with copious endosperm, often arillate ; embryo straight. Leaves alternate, simple to much divided, exstipulate.—Mostly Tropical and Temperate America.

34. TURNERACEAE

Herbs or rarely shrubs ; leaves entire or lobed, alternate ; stipules 0 ; flowers ⚥, actinomorphic, yellowish ; *calyx tubular*, 5-toothed, teeth imbricate ; petals 5, inserted on the calyx-tube, free, clawed, contorted in bud ; stamens 5, inserted at the base of the corolla-tube ; filaments free ; anthers 2-celled, opening lengthwise ; ovary superior, 1-*celled*, with 3 *parietal* placentas ; styles 3, terminal, slender ; stigmas fringed ; ovules numerous ; fruit a capsule opening *loculicidally* into 3 valves with the placenta in the middle of each ;

seeds *arillate*, pitted; endosperm horny or fleshy; embryo straight, large. B.H. 1 : 806. E.P. 3, 6*a* : 57. Mainly Tropical America.—TURNERA, WORMSKIOLDIA, ERBLICHIA, etc.

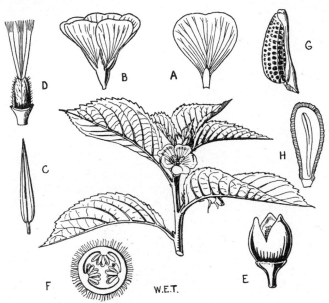

FIG. 34.—Turnera salicifolia *Camb.* (Turneraceae). A, petal with scale. B, flower. C, stamen. D, ovary with styles. E, capsule bursting from above downwards. F, ovary in cross section. G, seed with aril. H, seed in longitudinal section.—After Le Maout & Decne.

35. LOASACEAE

Herbs or rarely woody, mostly *clothed with rough bristly hairs*; leaves alternate or opposite, entire or variously divided; stipules absent; flowers ☿, solitary to cymose or capitate, often leaf-opposed, actinomorphic; calyx-tube adnate to the ovary, often ribbed, the ribs sometimes spirally twisted; lobes 4-5, contorted or imbricate, persistent; petals 4-5, inserted on the calyx, sessile or clawed, *induplicate-valvate*; sometimes petaloid scales between the petals; stamens numerous, rarely few; filaments free or collected into bundles *opposite the petals*; staminodes present or absent; *ovary inferior* or nearly completely so, 1-3-celled; style 1; ovules solitary or many, parietal or from the top of the ovary; capsule often ribbed; seeds often

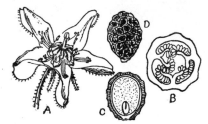

FIG. 35.—Caiophora lateritia *Bth.* (Loasaceae). A, flower. B, ovary in cross section C, seed in longitudinal section. D, seed.— After Le Maout & Decne.

minute, with or without endosperm; embryo straight, linear. B.H. 1 : 801. E.P. 3, 6*a* : 100. Mainly Tropical and Temperate America.—MENTZELIA, LOASA, BLUMENBACHIA, GRAMMATOCARPUS, etc.

Order 10. CAPPARIDALES

Herbaceous to woody ; flowers hypogynous or subperigynous, often somewhat zygomorphic; petals present or absent; stamens numerous to few, usually free ; syncarpous with parietal placentation ; ovary often stipitate, often of two carpels ; seeds without or with very little endosperm ; embryo curved or variously folded. Leaves mostly alternate, simple or digitate, rarely stipulate.—Mainly Tropics.

36. CAPPARIDACEAE

Herbs, shrubs or trees, sometimes scandent ; leaves alternate or rarely opposite, simple or digitately 3-7-foliolate ; stipules when present minute or spiny ; flowers mostly hermaphrodite, actinomorphic or rarely zygomorphic,

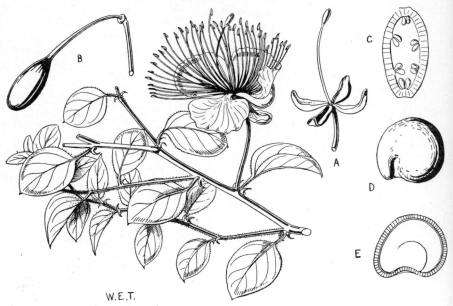

W.E.T.

FIG. 36.—Capparis spinosa L. (Capparidaceae). A, calyx with stipitate ovary. B, fruit. C, ovary in section. D, seed. E, seed in section.—Orig.

hypogynous, axillary or terminal, variously arranged ; sepals free or partially united, imbricate or valvate, usually 4 ; petals 4 to many or absent ; torus elongated or short, rarely with an appendix ; stamens few to many, sometimes some of them without anthers ; filaments sometimes partially adnate to the torus ; anthers 2-celled, longitudinally dehiscent ; ovary sessile or more usually supported on a *long or short gynophore*, 1-celled with parietal placentas or divided into 2 or more cells by spurious dissepiments ; ovules few to many ; fruit a capsule or a berry, sometimes the latter elongate or torulose ; seeds usually reniform or angular ; *endosperm none or scanty* ; embryo *arcuate* or *incurved.* B.H. 1 : 103. E.P. 3, 2 : 209. Tropics mainly.—CAPPARIS, CLEOME, POLANISIA, GYNANDROPSIS, MAERUA, CADABA, BOSCIA.

USEFUL PRODUCTS : *Capers* (flower buds of Capparis spinosa *L.*), Mediterranean region.

37. MORINGACEAE

Trees with gummy bark ; leaves deciduous, alternate, 2-3 times *pinnate,* pinnae opposite ; stipules 0, or represented by stipitate glands at the base of the petioles and pinnae ; flowers in axillary panicles, white or red, ♀, zygomorphic ; calyx-tube short, with 5 unequal spreading or reflexed imbricate lobes, the fifth posticous ; petals 5, the upper two smaller, the lateral ones ascending, the anticous larger ; disk lining the calyx-tube, with a short free margin; stamens inserted on the margin of the disk, declinate, 5 perfect alternating with the same number antherless or reduced to setae ; filaments free ; anthers dorsifixed, 1-celled, opening lengthwise by a slit ; ovary stipitate, terete, villous, curved, 1-celled, with 3 *parietal placentas* ; style terminal, slender, tubular, truncate at the apex; ovules numerous, in 2 series on each placenta, pendulous, anatropous ; capsule long, beaked, 3-6-angled, torulose, 1-celled, 3-valved; seeds 3-winged or not, the chalaza and wings hardened or membranous ; embryo without endosperm, straight.

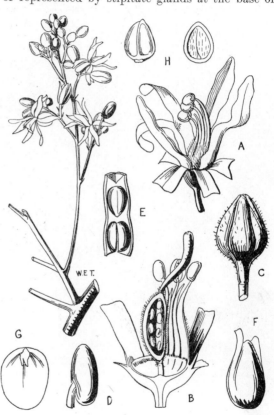

FIG. 37.—Moringa aptera *L.* (Moringaceae). A, flower. B, flower in vertical section. C, flower-bud. D, anther. E, part of fruit in longitudinal section showing seeds. F, seed. G, embryo cut vertically. H, seed entire and cut vertically.—After Le Maout & Decne.

B.H. 1 : 429. E.P. 3, 2 : 242. N. Africa to India ; also widely cultivated as an ornamental tree.—MORINGA.

USEFUL PRODUCTS : *Horse Radish Tree* (Moringa pterygosperma *Gaertn.*).

38. TOVARIACEAE

Annual herbs with a strong odour ; leaves alternate, *trifoliolate,* membranous ; stipules 0 ; flowers ♀, hypogynous, nodding in terminal many-flowered racemes,

I

8-*merous* ; sepals 8, lanceolate-subulate, imbricate, deciduous ; petals 8, *sessile* ; stamens 8, free ; filaments pilose ; anthers 2-celled, opening lengthwise ; ovary subglobose, 6-8-celled, slightly stipitate ; septa membranous ; ovules numerous on spongy *axile placentas* ; stigma sessile, 8-rayed ; fruit a small globose berry ;

FIG. 38.—Tovaria pendula *R. & P.* (Tovariaceae). A, flower. B, stamen. C, flower with petals and stamens removed. D, fruit. E, ovary in cross section. F, seed in section.—After Hk. Ic. Pl.

pericarp membranous ; seeds very numerous, small, shining ; embryo curved, enclosed in a *thick layer of endosperm.* B.H. 1 : 110 (under *Capparidaceae*). E.P. 3, 2 : 207. Tropical America, W. Indies.—TOVARIA.

Order 11. CRUCIALES

Characters more or less as for *Capparidales*, but stamens 6, tetradynamous (4 long and 2 short) ; petals 4, often clawed ; ovary with 2 parietal placentas, often divided by a false septum. Leaves mostly alternate, exstipulate.—Cosmopolitan, rarer in the Tropics.

39. CRUCIFERAE

Annual or perennial herbs, rarely somewhat shrubby, with watery juice ; indumentum of simple, *medifixed* or *stellate hairs,* rarely glandular ; leaves alternate or rarely opposite ; *stipules absent* ; flowers ⚥, mostly actinomorphic, usually racemose, rarely bracteate ; sepals 4, free, imbricate in 2 series, rarely valvate ; petals 4, rarely 0, mostly equal, often long-clawed, imbricate or contorted ; glands mostly present on the torus, often opposite the sepals ; stamens 6, *tetradynamous*, very rarely numerous or fewer, free or connate in pairs ; anthers 2- (rarely 1-) celled, opening lengthwise ; ovary sessile or rarely stipitate, usually of 2 united carpels, 1-celled with 1-2 *parietal placentas* and divided by a *spurious membranous septum*, or sometimes transversely several or many-celled ; stigmas 2 or connate ; ovules usually many ; fruit elongated (siliqua) or short (silicule), bivalved or indehiscent, rarely transversely jointed; seed without endosperm (very rarely a little endosperm present), *usually folded* ; cotyledons accumbent, incumbent or folded. B.H. 1 : 57. E.P. 3, 2 : 145. Cosmopolitan. — BRASSICA, CHEIRANTHUS, NASTURTIUM, BARBAREA, ARABIS, CARDAMINE, ANASTATICA, LUNARIA, AUBRIETIA, ALYSSUM, DRABA, COCHLEARIA, SISYMBRIUM, DIPLOTAXIS, CAPSELLA, LEPIDIUM, AETHIONEMA, ISATIS, CRAMBE, CAKILE, RAPHANUS, etc.

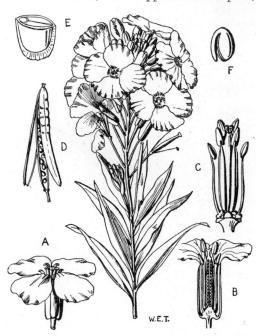

FIG. 39. — Cheiranthus Cheiri *L.* (Cruciferae). A, flower. B, flower cut vertically. C, stamens and ovary. D, fruit splitting from below. E, section of seed. F, embryo.—After Baill.

USEFUL PRODUCTS : *Cabbage* (Brassica oleracea *L.*) ; *Common Turnip* (Brassica Rapa *L.*) ; *Mustard* (Brassica alba *Boiss.*, and B. nigra *Koch*) ; *Horse Radish* (Cochlearia Armoracia *L.*) ; *Radish* (Raphanus sativus *L.*) ; *Watercress* (Nasturtium officinale *Br.*).—Many beautiful plants for the garden and rockery, including the *Wallflower* (Cheiranthus Cheiri *L.*) ; *Honesty* (Luaria rediviva *L.*).

Order 12. VIOLALES

Herbaceous to woody ; flowers hypogynous to perigynous, mostly zygomorphic ; petals present, sometimes divided ; stamens several to few, mostly free ; ovary syncarpous with parietal placentation ; seeds with or without endosperm ; embryo straight or curved. Leaves alternate, rarely opposite, stipulate.—Tropics and Temperate Regions.

40. VIOLACEAE

Herbaceous perennials or shrubs, rarely annuals ; leaves alternate, rarely opposite, simple ; *stipules leafy or small* ; flowers solitary to paniculate, actino-

morphic or zygomorphic, ☿, rarely polygamous, sometimes cleistogamous ;
sepals 5, persistent, imbricate ; petals 5, mostly unequal, the lowermost often
larger and spurred, imbricate or contorted ; stamens 5, mostly hypogynous ;
anthers erect, more or less *connivent in a ring around the ovary*, introrse, opening
lengthwise, the abaxial stamen often *spurred at the base* ; ovary free, sessile,
1-celled with 3-5 *parietal placentas* ; style simple, rarely split ; ovules numerous,
or 1-2 on each placenta, anatropous ; fruit an elastic capsule or baccate ; seeds

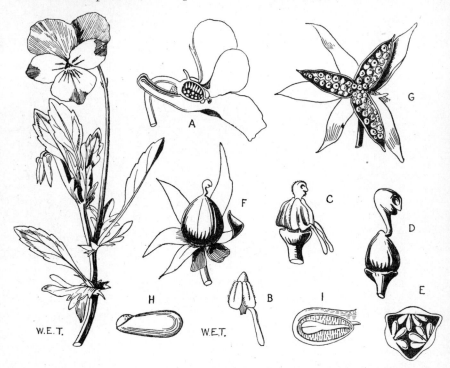

FIG. 40. — Viola tricolor *L.* (Violaceae).   A, flower cut lengthwise.   B, stamen with spurred anther.
C, ovary with 2 stamens.   D, ovary with style and stigma.   E, ovary in cross section.   F, fruit.
G, fruit-capsule splitting into 3 valves.   H, seed.   I, seed in section.—After Le Maout & Decne.

sometimes winged or tomentose ; endosperm fleshy ; embryo straight. B.H.
1 : 114, partly. E.P. 3, 6 : 322. Temperate and Tropics.—VIOLA, HYBANTHUS,
RINOREA (Alsodeia), etc.

USEFUL PRODUCTS : *False Ipecacuanha* (Hybanthus (*Ionidium*) Ipecacuanha
Baill.). Many beautiful garden plants used for bedding, etc.

41. RESEDACEAE

Annual or perennial herbs with watery juice, rarely woody ; leaves
alternate, simple or pinnately divided ; stipules small, *gland-like* ; flowers
mostly *zygomorphic*, ☿, rarely ♂ ♀, racemose or spicate ; calyx persistent,
mostly zygomorphic, 4-7-lobed, imbricate ; petals small and inconspicuous or
0, *valvate*, free or slightly coherent, *often laciniate*, sometimes with a scale at

the base ; disk present, often dilated on the adaxial side ; stamens 3-40, perigynous or on the disk, not covered by the petals in bud ; filaments free or united at base ; anthers 2-celled, introrse ; ovary of 2-6 free or connate carpels, closed or *gaping at the top*, each carpel with a *separate stigma* ; ovules numerous on parietal placentas or at the base of the ovary ; fruit a *gaping capsule* or

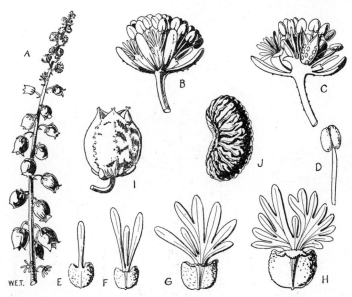

FIG. 41.—Reseda arabica *Boiss.* (Resedaceae). A, inflorescence. B, flower. C, flower cut vertically. D, stamen. E, F, G, H, petals. I, capsule open at the apex. J, seed.—After Cosson.

baccate ; seeds numerous, kidney-shaped or horse-shoe-shaped ; no endosperm ; embryo curved or folded ; cotyledons incumbent. B.H. 1 : 110. E.P. 3, 2 : 237. Mainly Mediterranean.—RESEDA, OLIGOMERIS, etc.

USEFUL PRODUCTS: Fragrant garden plants; *Mignonette* (Reseda odorata *L.*).

Order 13. POLYGALALES

Herbaceous to woody ; flowers hypogynous to subperigynous, zygomorphic ; petals present, sometimes some partially united ; stamens definite, free or monadelphous, sometimes some infertile ; syncarpous with axile or apical placentation ; seeds with or without endosperm ; embryo straight. Leaves alternate, rarely opposite ; stipules mostly absent.— Temperate and Tropical Regions.

42. POLYGALACEAE

Herbs, shrubs, climbers, or rarely small trees ; leaves alternate, rarely opposite, simple ; stipules 0 ; flowers ⚥, zygomorphic ; pedicels often articulated ; sepals 5, free, imbricate, the two inner larger *often petaloid*, wing-like ;

petals 3-5, hypogynous, declinate, outer 2 free or united with the lowermost ; upper 2 free, or minute and scale-like or 0 ; stamens 8, rarely 5 or 4, *monadelphous beyond the middle* or rarely free, the sheath split above, often adnate to the petals ; anthers erect, 1-2-celled, opening by an *apical pore*, rarely 2-valved or opening nearly to the base ; torus small or rarely expanded into an annular disk within the stamens ; ovary free, 2-celled or rarely 1-celled or

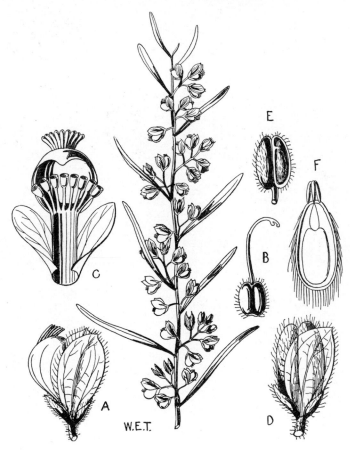

FIG. 42.—Polygala eriocarpa *D.C.* (Polygalaceae). A, flower. B, ovary with style. C, part of flower showing 2 sepals, crested keel petal and staminal tube. D, fruit with membranous inner sepals. E, fruit capsule showing one half cut vertically. F, seed cut lengthwise.—After Deless.

3-5-celled ; style simple ; ovules solitary in each cell, rarely more, pendulous ; fruit a capsule or drupaceous ; *seeds often pilose*, with a *conspicuous strophiole* ; endosperm mostly present ; embryo straight. B.H. 1 : 134. E.P. 3, 4 : 323. Temperate and Tropics. — POLYGALA, MURALTIA, SECURIDACA, MONNINA, COMESPERMA, CARPOLOBIA.

USEFUL PRODUCTS : *Senega* or *Snake Root* (Polygala Senega *L.*), United States ; *Rhatany Root* (Krameria triandra *R. & P.*, etc.), S. America.

43. TRIGONIACEAE

Trees or scandent shrubs ; leaves alternate or opposite, simple ; stipules small and caducous ; flowers ♂, racemose or paniculate ; sepals 5, imbricate, free or connate at the base, unequal ; petals 5 or 3, contorted, hypogynous or subperigynous, unequal, the posterior one often the largest and *gibbous at the base* ; stamens 3-12, sometimes *some infertile, unilateral,* opposite the anterior

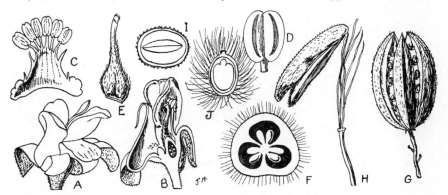

FIG. 43.—Trigonia pubescens *Camb.* (Trigoniaceae). A, flower. B, flower cut vertically. C, stamina sheath. D, anther. E, ovary with style. F, ovary in cross section. G, fruit-capsule opening loculicidally. H, old fruit. I, J, seed.—After Martius.

petal ; *filaments connate at the base* ; anthers 2-celled, opening lengthwise ; gland or a crenate crest often present opposite the posterior petal ; ovary superior, 3-celled, woolly ; style 1, truncate ; ovules 2 to many in each cell, axile ; fruit a capsule, septicidally 3-valved ; seeds compressed, enveloped in cottony hairs ; endosperm absent ; embryo straight, *transverse to the length of the seed.* B.H. 1 : 977 (under *Vochysiaceae*). E.P. 3, 4 : 309. Tropical S. America.— TRIGONIA, LIGHTIA.

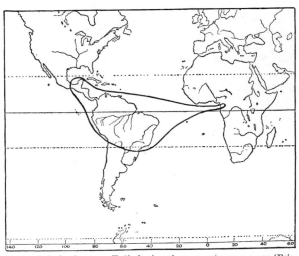

Range of Vochysiaceae. Entirely American except a new genus (Erismadelphus) recently discovered in primaeval forest in the Cameroons.

44. VOCHYSIACEAE

Large trees full of resinous juice, shrubs or climbers; leaves opposite or verticillate, rarely alternate, simple ; stipules small or absent, or reduced to glands ; flowers ♂, zygomorphic, racemose or paniculate ; sepals 5, imbricate, the posticous often the largest and gibbous or spurred at the base ; petals 1-5, contorted ; stamens hypogynous or perigynous, *only* 1 *fertile* ; *filaments free* ; anthers 2-celled, opening lengthwise ; ovary superior or rarely adnate to the calyx, often oblique, 1-3-celled ; style 1 ; ovules 2-many in each cell, axile ;

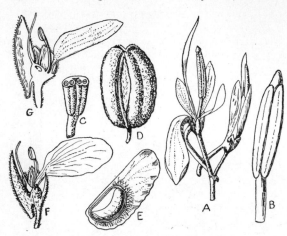

fruit capsular or samaroid, 3-valved ; seeds one or more, often winged, sometimes pilose ; endosperm absent or rarely present ; embryo straight.   B.H. 1 : 975.   E.P. 3, 4 : 312. Tropical America, one in W. Africa. — VOCHYSIA, QUALEA, ERISMADELPHUS, etc.

FIG. 44.—A-D, Vochysia guianensis.   F-G, Callisthene minor
Aubl. (Vochysiaceae).

Order 14.
SAXIFRAGALES

Herbaceous ; flowers actinomorphic, more or less perigynous or rarely epigynous ; petals present ; stamens definite, free ;   apocarpous   to   syncarpous   with   axile   placentation ;   seeds   with copious endosperm and small straight embryo.   Leaves radical, alternate or opposite, sometimes modified, exstipulate.—Cosmopolitan.

45. CRASSULACEAE

Herbs or undershrubs, usually succulent ; leaves opposite or alternate, *without stipules* ; flowers actinomorphic, hermaphrodite, usually cymose ; sepals free or united into a tube, often 4 or 5 ; petals the same number as the sepals,

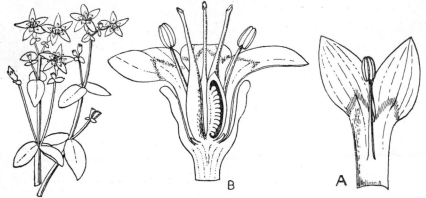

FIG. 45.—Grammanthes gentianoides *D.C.* (Crassulaceae).   A, part of corolla and stamen.
B, flower cut vertically.—After Bot. Mag.

free or variously connate, hypogynous ; stamens as many or twice as many as the petals, if few then alternate with the petals, slightly perigynous ; filaments free ; anthers 2-celled, introrse, dehiscing longitudinally ; hypogynous scales present within the stamens ; carpels superior, *the same number as the petals, free or united at the base,* 1-celled ; ovules many or rarely few, inserted on the adaxial suture ; style short or elongated ; fruit follicular, membranous or leathery, often surrounded by the persistent membranous corolla, opening on the adaxial side ; seeds minute, usually with fleshy endosperm ; embryo straight. B.H. 1 : 656. E.P. 3, 2a : 23. Mainly warm dry regions.—CRASSULA, ROCHEA, BRYOPHYLLUM, KALANCHOE, COTYLEDON, SEDUM, SEMPERVIVUM, MONANTHES, etc.

USEFUL PRODUCTS: Many curious and beautiful garden and greenhouse plants.

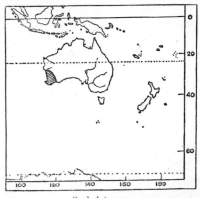

Cephalotaceae.

46. CEPHALOTACEAE

Perennial herbs with short underground rhizomes ; leaves of two kinds,

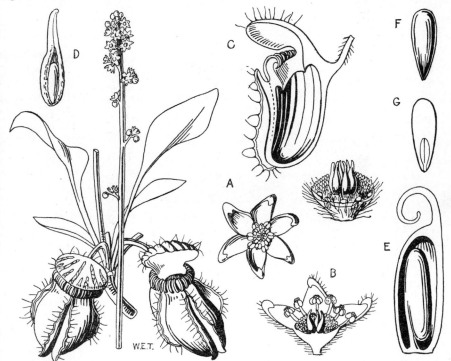

FIG. 46.—Cephalotus follicularis *Labill.* (Cephalotaceae). A, flower. B, section of same. C, section of ascidium. D, carpel. E, same in section. F, G, seeds.—After Le Maout & Decne.

some flat, elliptic, entire, nerveless, others (ascidia) *composed of a petiole dilated at the top into a lidded pitcher like* NEPENTHES ; flowers borne on a leafless narrow raceme of cymules bracteate at the base ; calyx coloured, 6-lobed ; lobes *valvate*, hooded ; petals *absent* ; stamens 12, perigynous, inserted at the top of the calyx-tube on the outer margin of a setose glandular disk, six longer than the others ; filaments free ; anthers 2-celled, opening lengthwise, connective swollen at the top and glandular ; carpels 6, free, in a single

FIG. 47.—Kirengeshoma palmata *Yatabe* (Saxifragaceae). A, petal with adherent stamens. B, part of calyx with ovary and styles. C, anthers. D, ovary in vertical section. E, ovary in cross section. —After Bot. Mag.

whorl, 1-celled and usually with 1 (rarely 2) *basal erect ovule* in each ; follicles surrounded by the accrescent calyx, shortly stipitate, thickly hairy outside, 1-seeded ; seeds with fleshy endosperm and rather small, straight embryo. B.H. 1 : 655 (under *Saxifragaceae*).   E.P. 3, 2a : 39.   Australia.—CEPHALOTUS.

47. SAXIFRAGACEAE

Herbs, not or slightly succulent ; leaves usually alternate (opposite in *Vahlia*), *not stipulate* ; flowers actinomorphic, hermaphrodite, rarely solitary ; sepals usually 5, imbricate or valvate ; petals alternate with the sepals or absent, often clawed, *perigynous or rarely epigynous* ; stamens inserted with the petals, 5-10 ; filaments free, anthers 2-celled, dehiscing longitudinally ; ovary 1-3-celled, free or adnate to the tubular receptacle ; styles usually free ; ovules numerous, on axile placentas or the latter pendulous from the apex of the cells ; fruit a capsule ; seeds numerous, small, with endosperm ; embryo minute, straight. B.H. 1 : 629. E.P. 3, 2a : 41 (partly). Mainly Cold and Temperate Regions.—SAXIFRAGA, ASTILBE, ROGERSIA, BERGENIA, HEUCHERA, CHRYSO-SPLENIUM, PARNASSIA, FRANCOA, etc.

USEFUL PRODUCTS : Many plants for the herbaceous border, rock garden and greenhouse.

Order 15. SARRACENIALES

Characters more or less as in *Saxifragales*, but adapted for entrapping insects ; leaves tubular or covered with viscid glands, usually radical ; stamens numerous to few ; syncarpous with parietal or axile placentation. —Cosmopolitan.

48. DROSERACEAE

Herbs, often stemless with rosettes of leaves, the latter often circinate in bud and usually covered with sticky stipitate glands which entrap insects ;

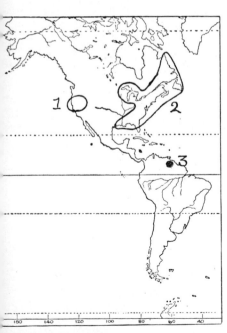

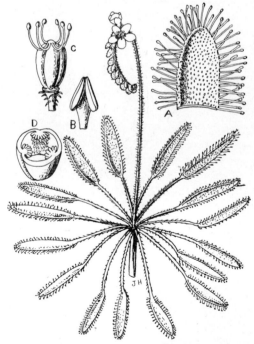

Distribution of Sarraceniaceae. 1, Darlingtonia ; 2, Sarracenia ; 3, Heliamphora.

FIG. 48.—Drosera capensis *Harv.* (Droseraceae). A, portion of leaf with gland-tipped tentacles. B, stamen. C, ovary with styles. D, ovary in cross section.

flowers actinomorphic, hermaphrodite, in usually simple circinate cymes; sepals 5-4, more or less connate at the base, imbricate, persistent; petals 5, hypogynous, very rarely perigynous, nervose; stamens 4-20, often 5, hypogynous, free or rarely united at the base; anthers 2-celled, extrorse, opening by longitudinal slits; ovary free, 1-*celled*, with *parietal* or *subbasal* placentas; ovules many or rarely few; styles 3-5, mostly free; fruit a loculicidal capsule; seeds numerous, with fleshy endosperm; embryo straight; cotyledons short. B.H. 1 : 661.   E.P. 3, 2 : 261.   Cosmopolitan in sandy and boggy places.— DROSERA, DIONAEA, DROSOPHYLLUM, ALDROVANDA.

49. SARRACENIACEAE

Herbs with radical tubular leaves with small lamina; flowers scapose, solitary or few in racemes, nodding, ♀; sepals 4-5, free, hypogynous, imbricate, *often coloured, persistent*; petals 5, free, imbricate, or absent; *stamens numerous,*

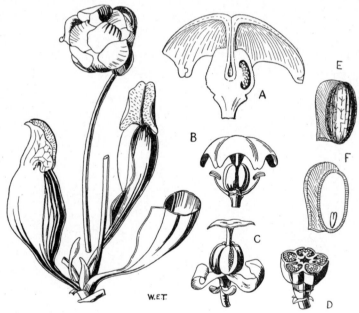

FIG. 49.—Sarracenia purpurea *L.* (Sarraceniaceae).   A, section of flower.   B, stamens and pistil. C, fruit.   D, section of fruit.   E, F, seed.—After Le Maout & Decne.

hypogynous, free; anthers 2-celled, opening lengthwise; ovary free, 3-5-celled, with axile placentas and numerous anatropous ovules; style simple, often *peltately dilated* at the apex; fruit a capsule, *loculicidally* 3-5-valved; seeds numerous, small, with fleshy endosperm and small embryo.   B.H. 1 : 48.   E.P. 3, 2 : 244.   America.—SARRACENIA, DARLINGTONIA, HELIAMPHORA.

Order 16. PODOSTEMONALES

Submerged freshwater herbs like mosses, hepatics or algae; petals absent; stamens 1-4, free or partly connate; syncarpous with parietal or central placentation ; seeds minute, without endosperm.—Tropics and Subtropics.

50. PODOSTEMONACEAE

Submerged fresh-water herbs often greatly resembling mosses, hepatics and algae ; flowers ⚥, small, solitary or cymose, actinomorphic, often enclosed when young in a spathe composed of partially connate bracts ; sepals 2-3, usually small, connate in the lower part ; petals absent ; stamens 1-4, hypogynous ; filaments free or partially connate ; anthers 2-celled, small, opening

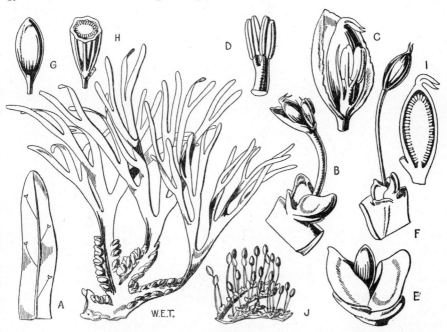

FIG. 50.—Dicraea algaeformis *Bedd.* (Podostemonaceae). A, portion of frond enlarged. B, expanded flower with involucre. C, flower itself magnified. D, stamen. E, bud in involucre. F, fruit. G, bud enclosed in involucre. H, fruit in cross section. I, ovary in vertical section. J, portion of fruiting frond.—After Fitch.

lengthwise ; ovary sessile or shortly stipitate, superior, 1-3-celled with a *central placenta* ; styles 2-3, slender ; ovules numerous ; fruit a septicidal capsule ; seeds minute, without endosperm.   B.H. 3 : 105.   E.P. 3, 2a : 1.   Mainly Tropics.—TRISTICHA, TERNIOLA, MARATHRUM, RHYNCHOLACIS, LIGEA, APINAGIA, PODOSTEMON, DICRAEA, etc.

51. HYDROSTACHYACEAE

Submerged fresh-water herbs ; stems thick, *tuber-like* ; leaves simple to 2 or 3 times pinnatisect, dilated and ligulate at the base ; *flowers dioecious*, densely spicate, solitary and sessile in the axil of each bract ; *calyx and petals absent* ; stamen 1 ; anthers 2-celled, opening lengthwise ; ovary 1-celled, with 2 *parietal placentas* ; styles 2, divergent ; fruit a small capsule ; ovules numerous ; seeds

numerous, without endosperm.   B.H. 3 : 115 (under *Podostemonaceae*).   E.P.
3, 2a : 1.   Madagascar and S. Africa.—HYDROSTACHYS.

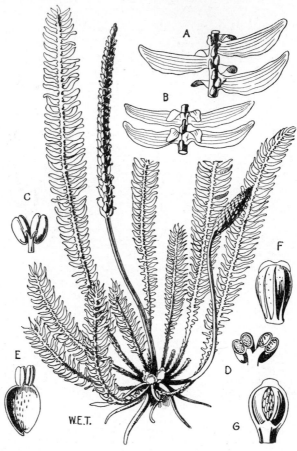

FIG. 51.—Hydrostachys distichophylla *A. Juss.* (Hydrostachyaceae).   A and B, parts of leaf.   C, stamen.
D, section of anther.   E, stamen.   F, fruit.   G, section of fruit.—After Deless.

Order 17. CARYOPHYLLALES

Herbaceous, becoming fleshy ; flowers hypogynous to perigynous, ♀,
actinomorphic ; petals usually present ; stamens mostly definite ; syncarpous ; axile to free-central placentation ; seeds with copious endosperm
and curved embryo.   Leaves mostly opposite or verticillate, stipulate or
not.—Mainly Temperate Regions.

52. ELATINACEAE

Herbs or low shrubs ; leaves *opposite or verticillate*, simple ; stipules present,
paired ; flowers small, actinomorphic, hermaphrodite, axillary, solitary or

cymose ; sepals 3-5, free, imbricate ; petals as many, hypogynous, imbricate, persistent ; stamens from as many to twice as many as the petals, free, hypogynous ; anthers 2-celled, opening by longitudinal slits ; ovary superior, 3-5-celled ; placentation axile ; styles 3-5, free ; ovules numerous ; fruit a

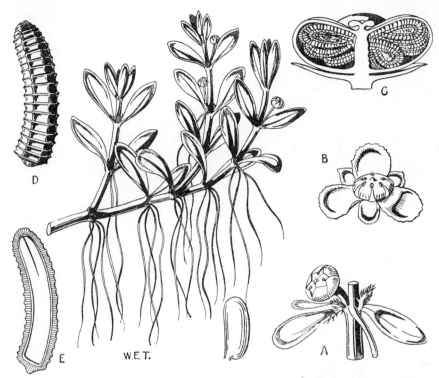

FIG. 52.—Elatine hexandra L. (Elatinaceae). A, portion of stem with flower. B, flower opened.
C, ovary in vertical section. D, seed. E, seed cut lengthwise.—After Le Maout & Decne.

septicidal capsule ; seeds without endosperm ; embryo straight or curved, with short cotyledons. B.H. 1 : 162. E.P. 3, 6 : 277. Cosmopolitan.—
ELATINE, BERGIA.

53. CARYOPHYLLACEAE

Herbs, annual or perennial ; leaves *opposite*, simple, often connected at the base by a *transverse line* ; stipules absent or if present often scarious ; flowers actinomorphic, mostly hermaphrodite, solitary or in cymes ; sepals free or united into a tube, imbricate, often with membranous margins ; petals as many as the sepals, often small or absent ; stamens up to 10, free from one another ; anthers 2-celled, dehiscing longitudinally ; ovary superior, sessile or shortly stipitate, 1-*celled* or imperfectly divided at the base, with *free-central placentation* ; styles free or variously connate ; ovules mostly numerous ; fruit a dry capsule, usually opening by valves or apical teeth ; seeds with endosperm and a more or less *curved peripheral or excentric embryo* ; funicle sometimes conspicuous. B.H. 1 : 141. E.P. 3, 1b : 61. Mainly N. Temperate and Cold

Regions.—Dianthus, Tunica, Gypsophila, Saponaria, Silene, Lychnis, Cerastium, Stellaria, Arenaria, Sagina, Drymaria, Polycarpaea, etc.

Useful Products : Many beautiful garden plants, *Pinks, Sweet William* (Dianthus barbatus *L.*) ; *Gypsophila* (G. elegans *Bieb.*), Asia Minor, etc.

FIG. 53.—Dianthus Seguieri *Vill.* (Caryophyllaceae).   A, petal.   B, ovary with styles.
C, cross section of ovary.   D, fruit dehisced.

54. Molluginaceae

Herbs, sometimes with fleshy leaves ; leaves opposite, subopposite, alternate or subverticillate ; stipules none or small and fugacious ; flowers actinomorphic,

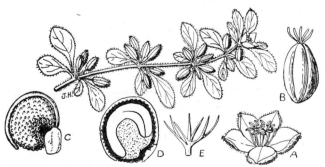

FIG. 54.—Glinus lotoides *Loefl.* (Molluginaceae).   A, flower.   B, ovary.   C, seed.   D, seed cut vertically.
E, hair.—Partly original.

hermaphrodite, solitary or cymose, usually small and inconspicuous ; sepals free or united at the base, imbricate, persistent ; petals small or absent ; stamens hypogynous or slightly perigynous, definite or indefinite ; filaments free or variously connate at the base ; anthers 2-celled, opening by longitudinal slits ; disk absent or annular ; ovary syncarpous (except *Gisekia*), usually several-celled ; style or stigmas as many as the cells ; ovules curved or inverted ; fruit dry, dehiscing loculicidally or by a transverse slit, rarely indehiscent, usually surrounded by the persistent calyx ; seeds with endosperm, the embryo curved or round the periphery. B.H. 1 : 856 (under *Ficoidaceae*). E.P. 3, 1b : 33 (under *Aizoaceae*). Mainly Tropics and Subtropics.—MOLLUGO, PHARNACEUM, ADENOGRAMMA, GISEKIA, LIMEUM, etc. Mostly weedy plants of dry places.

55. FICOIDACEAE

(Aizoaceae)

Herbs or low shrubs, erect or prostrate, often *fleshy* ; leaves alternate or opposite, sometimes minute, stipulate or not ; flowers usually hermaphrodite, actinomorphic ; calyx-tube free or adnate to the ovary ; lobes 5-8, imbricate,

FIG. 55.—Mesembryanthemum crystallinum *L.* (Ficoidaceae). A, fruit.

or rarely valvate, herbaceous ; petals numerous or absent, 1- or more-seriate, inserted in the calyx-tube, linear ; stamens perigynous, many in several series or few, rarely 1, free or united at the base into bundles ; anthers 2-celled, small, opening lengthwise ; ovary superior or inferior, 1-several-celled ; ovules solitary to many, basal, apical or axile ; fruit a capsule or nut-like and drupaceous, often clasped by the persistent calyx. B.H. 1 : 851, partly. E.P. 3, 1b : 33 (as *Aizoaceae*). Mainly S. African and Mediterranean ; a few in Australia and West Indies, S. America ; often on sandy seashores or desert places.— MESEMBRYANTHEMUM, TETRAGONIA, AIZOON, GALENIA, GUNNIA, SESUVIUM, TRIANTHEMA, CYPSELEA.

USEFUL PRODUCTS : Numerous species of *Mesembryanthemum* suitable for cool greenhouses ; a few naturalised in the S.W. coast of Britain.

K

56. Portulacaceae

Herbs or undershrubs, often succulent ; leaves alternate or opposite, with scarious or setose stipular appendages ; flowers actinomorphic, hermaphrodite,

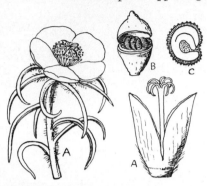

solitary or variously cymose or racemose; sepals 2, imbricate, free or united at the base ; petals 4-6, imbricate, free or connate at the base, soon falling ; stamens as many as and opposite the petals or more numerous, free ; anthers 2-celled ; ovary superior or half inferior, 1-celled with basal placenta ; ovules 1 to many; style usually variously divided ; fruit a capsule dehiscing by valves or by a transverse split (circumscissile), rarely a nut and indehiscent ; seeds globose-reniform ; embryo surrounding the copious mealy endosperm. B.H. 1 : 155. E.P. 3, 1b : 51. Mainly America.—Portulaca, Anacampseros,

Fig. 56.—A, Portulaca grandiflora *L.* B, C, Portulaca oleracea *L.* (Portulacaceae).—Orig.

Talinum, Calandrinia, Claytonia, Lewisia, etc. Some ornamental garden plants.

Order 18. POLYGONALES

Herbaceous, etc., as in *Caryophyllales*, but without petals ; ovary 1-celled, 1-ovuled ; seeds with straight or curved embryo in copious endosperm. Leaves alternate or opposite ; stipules mostly present, often intrapetiolar or sheathing and membranous or scarious.

57. Polygonaceae

Herbs, shrubs or climbers, rarely trees ; leaves alternate or rarely opposite, the base of the petiole often dilated into a *membranous sheath* (ochrea) ; flowers ♀ or ♂ ♀, actinomorphic, small ; sepals 3-6, imbricate, often enlarged and becoming membranous in fruit ; petals absent ; stamens usually 6-9, rarely more ; filaments free or united at the base ; anthers 2-celled, opening lengthwise ; disk annular or central ; ovary superior, sessile, 1-celled ; styles 2-4, usually free ; ovule *solitary, basal,* sessile or stalked ; fruit an indehiscent trigonous or 2-sided nut ; seeds with abundant mealy endosperm and often excentric embryo. B.H. 3 : 88. E.P. 3, 1a : 1. Cosmopolitan.—Eriogonum, Chorizanthe, Calligonum, Atraphaxis, Oxygonum, Polygonum, Rheum, Rumex, Muehlenbeckia, Coccoloba, Triplaris, Ruprechtia, etc.

Useful Products : *Rhubarb* (Rheum Rhaponticum *L.*) ; *Buckwheat* (Fagopyrum esculentum *Moench*).

58. Illecebraceae

Herbs, rarely subshrubs ; leaves mostly *opposite*, small, simple, often connate at the base, mostly entire ; *stipules scarious*, simple or connate, rarely 0 ; flowers small, herbaceous, green or white, often with *scarious bracts*, mostly ♀, actinomorphic ; calyx herbaceous or leathery, persistent, 4-5-lobed or parted,

FIG. 57.—Rheum nobile *Hk. f.* (Polygonaceae). A, plant showing habit. B, flower. C, stamen. D, ovary. E, ovary cut vertically. F, cross section of fruit. G, fruit.—After Hook.

FIG. 58.—Scleranthus annuus *T.* (Illecebraceae). A, flower. B, stamen. C, ovary. D, seed cut lengthwise.—Orig.

lobes imbricate ; petals 0 or sometimes replaced by small staminodes ; stamens the same number as and opposite the calyx-lobes, rarely fewer or more, mostly perigynous ; filaments free or connate at the base into a ring ; anthers 2-celled, opening lengthwise ; ovary free, sessile, 1-celled ; style 1, terminal, or styles 2-3 ; ovule 1, rarely 2, erect or pendulous from a basal funicle ; fruit a utricle or nut, mostly indehiscent, 1-seeded, included by the calyx ; seed with copious or small endosperm ; embryo annular to straight. B.H. 3 : 12. E.P. 3, 1b : 91 (under *Caryophyllaceae*). Dry arid regions mainly.—ILLECEBRUM, PARONYCHIA, HERNIARIA, SCLERANTHUS, etc.

USEFUL PRODUCTS : *Thé Arabe* or *Algerian Tea* (flowers of Paronychia argentea *Lam.* and P. capitata *Lam.*) ; *Sergena Root* (Corrigiola littoralis *L.*).

Order 19. CHENOPODIALES

More or less as in *Polygonales* but stipules absent or very small ; carpels numerous to solitary, free or connate ; seeds with curved embryo around the endosperm, rarely the embryo straight. Leaves alternate or opposite. Mostly dry regions.

59. PHYTOLACCACEAE

Herbs, shrubs or trees ; leaves alternate, entire ; stipules absent or minute ; flowers hermaphrodite or unisexual, actinomorphic or nearly so, hypogynous, in simple or compound terminal or axillary racemes ; sepals free or some connate,

FIG. 59.—Didymotheca thesioides *Hk. f.* (Phytolaccaceae). A, male plant. B, male flower. C, stamen. D, fruiting plant. E, female flower. F, fruit. G, section of fruit. H, seeds.

imbricate, equal or unequal ; petals absent ; stamens 3 to many, often inserted on a hypogynous disk ; filaments free or slightly connate at the base ; anthers 2-celled, cells parallel and dehiscing longitudinally : ovary superior, composed

of 1 or several carpels either free or variously connate ; style almost none or
short ; ovule solitary in each carpel, basal ; fruit of 1 or many carpels, fleshy
or dry ; seed erect, with the large embryo in the periphery and enclosing the
endosperm.   B.H. 3 : 78.   E.P. 3, 1b : 1.   Mainly Tropics and Subtropics.—
RIVINA, MOHLANA, PETIVERIA, MICROTEA, PHYTOLACCA, etc.

USEFUL PRODUCTS : *Bella Sombra* (Phytolacca dioica *L.*, a shade tree in
Spanish countries).

60. CYNOCRAMBACEAE

Fleshy annual herb ; lower leaves opposite, upper alternate, succulent ;
stipules uniting the base of the petioles ; flowers *monoecious*, in small sessile cymes
opposite the upper leaves, abortive in the lower opposite leaves ; male flowers
2-3 together, subsessile, female 1-3 from the same or different nodes, shortly
pedicellate ; male calyx closed in bud, at length valvate, 2-partite, segments

FIG. 60.—Cynocrambe prostrata *Gaertn.* (Cynocrambaceae).   A, male flower.   B, female flower.   C, fruit.
D, vertical section of fruit.   E, section of seed.

spreading, 5-nerved ; stamens up to about 20 in the centre ; filaments free,
slender ; anthers erect in bud, linear, opening lengthwise ; female flower with
a very oblique tubular calyx enclosing the ovary at the base and becoming
lateral by the enlargement of the latter, slightly 3-lobulate ; style simple,
becoming basal by the lateral enlargement of the ovary ; ovule solitary, erect
from the base ; fruit a subglobose nut included in the thin membranous calyx ;
seed sessile, erect ; endosperm fleshy.   B.H. 3 : 395 (under *Urticaceae*).   E.P.
3, 1a : 121.   Mediterranean, China and Japan.—CYNOCRAMBE (*Thelygonum*).

61. CHENOPODIACEAE

Annual or perennial herbs or shrubs, often glaucous ; stems sometimes jointed ; *leaves alternate* or rarely opposite, simple ; stipules absent ; flowers small or minute, often green, ♀ or ♂ ♀, mostly actinomorphic, often bracteate ; calyx 3-5-lobed, rarely absent (in the ♀ flowers), often accrescent in fruit ; lobes imbricate or subvalvate ; petals absent ; stamens often the same number as the calyx-lobes and opposite to them, hypogynous or inserted on a disk or on the calyx ; staminodes rare ; filaments usually free ; anthers 2-celled, incurved in bud, opening lengthwise ; disk present or absent ; ovary superior

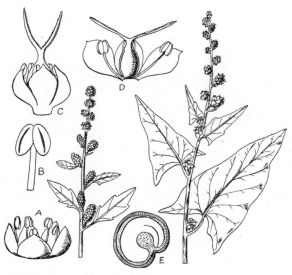

FIG. 61.—Chenopodium rubrum *L.* (Chenopodiaceae). A, male flower. B, stamen. C, perfect flower. D, flower showing ovary. E, section of seed.

or immersed in the base of the calyx, 1-celled ; style terminal, solitary or 2-3 ; *ovule solitary*, erect or suspended from a basal funicle ; fruit a nut, indehiscent, rarely circumscissile ; seed often erect ; endosperm present or absent ; *embryo peripheral, surrounding the endosperm.* B.H. 3 : 43. E.P. 3, 1a : 36. Cosmopolitan.—RHAGODIA, CHENOPODIUM, BETA, ATRIPLEX, CORISPERMUM, CHENOLEA, KOCHIA, ARTHROCNEMUM, SALICORNIA, SUAEDA, CORNULACA, SALSOLA, ANABASIS, etc.

USEFUL PRODUCTS : *Spinach* (Spinacia oleracea *L.*) ; *Beet-root* (Beta vulgaris *L.*).

62. BATIDACEAE

Littoral straggling plants ; leaves *opposite*, simple, fleshy ; stipules 0 ; flowers dioecious, densely spicate ; spikes bracteate and cone-like ; ♂ flowers subtended by closely imbricate bracts ; calyx membranous, campanulate, 2-*lipped* ; petals 4, clawed, claws united at the base ; stamens 4, alternate with the petals ; filaments free ; anthers 2-celled, opening lengthwise ; ovary rudimentary or 0 ; female flowers united into a fleshy spike ; bracts smaller than in the male ; calyx and petals absent ; ovaries 8-12, coherent, 4-celled ; stigma capitate, sessile ; ovules solitary, erect, anatropous ; fruits united and forming

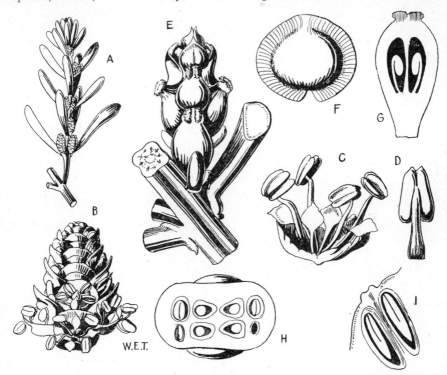

Fig. 62.—Batis maritima *L.* (Batidaceae). A, male branch. B, male inflorescence. C, male flower. D, stamen. E, female inflorescence. F, seed. G, vertical section of ovary. H, cross section of same. I, section of fruit.—After Martius.

a fleshy ovoid mass ; seed oblong, straight, without endosperm ; embryo straight.   B.H. 3 : 88.   E.P. 3, 1a : 118.   Tropical America and Pacific Islands.—Batis.

63. Amarantaceae

Annual or perennial herbs, rarely undershrubs or climbers ; leaves alternate or opposite, simple, *exstipulate* ; flowers actinomorphic, usually hermaphrodite, small, in spikes, heads or racemes with often scarious bracts and bracteoles, the latter sometimes hooked ; sepals 3-5, free or nearly so, imbricate, more or less dry and membranous ; petals absent ; stamens mostly 5, *opposite the sepals*, hypogynous ; filaments united at the base *into a short tube*, often with staminodes between ; anthers 1- or 2-celled, opening by longitudinal slits ; ovary superior, 1-celled ; style short or long ; stigma capitate or 2-3-fid ; ovules solitary or rarely several, on a basal funicle ; fruit dehiscing by a lid, or indehiscent ; seeds globose, compressed or ellipsoid, smooth ; embryo annular, surrounding the copious endosperm.   B.H. 3 : 20.   E.P. 3, 1a : 91.   Widely dispersed.— Celosia, Amarantus, Sericocoma, Cyathula, Pupalia, Ptilotus, Trichi-

NIUM, AERVA, ACHYRANTHES, PFAFFIA, TELANTHERA, ALTERNANTHERA, GOM-
PHRENA, HEBANTHE, IRESINE, etc.

SOME ORNAMENTAL PLANTS : *Cockscomb* (Celosia cristata *L.*), Asia.

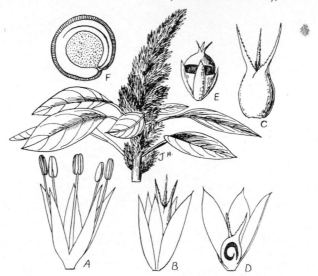

FIG. 63.—Amarantus reflexus *L.* (Amarantaceae). A, male flower. B, female flower. C, ovary.
D, vertical section of female flower. E, fruit. F, section of seed.

64. BASELLACEAE

Twiners with slender stems and rather fleshy, alternate, entire, petiolate
leaves ; stipules absent ; flowers hermaphrodite, actinomorphic, in spikes,
racemes or panicles ; bracts small ; bracteoles 2, often united to the base of
the calyx ; sepals 5, often coloured, almost free or united into a 5-lobed tube,
imbricate, persistent in fruit ; petals absent ; stamens 5, inserted opposite to
and at the base of the sepals ; filaments free, short ; anthers with 2 parallel
cells opening longitudinally ; ovary superior, 1-celled, with a solitary basal
shortly stalked campylotropous ovule ; style terminal, often deeply divided
into 3 stigmas ; fruit indehiscent, surrounded by the *persistent, often fleshy,
calyx* ; seed solitary, almost spherical, with a membranous testa ; endosperm
copious, surrounded by the *spirally twisted embryo.* B.H. 3 : 76 (under *Chenopodiaceae*). E.P. 3, 1a : 124. Tropics.—BASELLA, TOURNONIA, ULLUCUS.

Order 20. GERANIALES

Herbs or undershrubs, very rarely arborescent ; flowers hypogynous,
♀, actinomorphic to zygomorphic ; sepals imbricate or rarely valvate ;
petals present and often clawed ; stamens as many to twice as many as
the petals ; disk-glands often present ; syncarpous with axile placentation ;
ovules solitary to few ; seeds mostly without endosperm and straight
embryo. Leaves alternate or radical, rarely opposite, simple to much-
divided or pinnate ; stipules mostly present. General distribution.

FIG. 64.—Ullucus tuberosus *Caldas* (Basellaceae). A, flowers. B, anthers showing dehiscence. C, ovary. D, fruit.—After Bot. Mag.

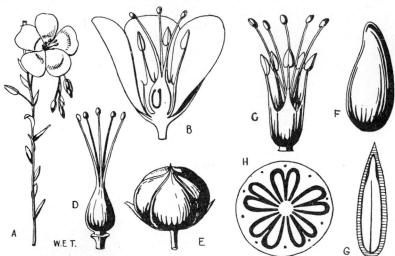

FIG. 65.—Linum usitatissimum *L.* (Linaceae). A, shoot with flower. B, vertical section of flower. C, stamens and ovary. D, ovary. E, fruit. F, seed. G, section of same. H, cross section of ovary. —After Le Maout & Decne.

65. Linaceae

Herbs or shrubs ; leaves simple, alternate or opposite ; stipules present or absent, sometimes gland-like or intrapetiolar ; flowers ⚥, actinomorphic-; sepals 4-5, free or partially united, imbricate ; petals contorted, fugacious, free, often clawed, claw naked or crested ; stamens the same number as the petals and alternate with them, sometimes alternating with *small staminodes* ; filaments *connate at the base* ; anthers introrse, 2-celled, opening lengthwise ; ovary superior, 3-5-celled, cells often again *subdivided nearly to the placentas* ; ovules 2 in each cell ; styles 3-5, filiform, *free*, with simple subcapitate stigmas ; fruit a capsule, *septicidally dehiscent* ; seeds compressed, shining ; endosperm copious, scanty or absent ; embryo straight, with flat cotyledons. B.H. 1 : 241 (partly). E.P. 3, 4 : 27. Mainly Temperate Regions.—Linum, Reinwardtia, etc.

Useful Products : *Flax* (Linum usitatissimum *L.*), generally cultivated. *Linseed* (seeds of same) from which *linseed oil* is obtained, and *oil-cake* for cattle.

66. Zygophyllaceae

Shrubs or herbs woody at the base, rarely trees ; branches often jointed at the nodes ; leaves opposite or alternate, 2-*foliolate or pinnate*, rarely 3-foliolate, not gland-dotted ; *stipules paired*, persistent, often spinescent ; flowers rarely blue, ⚥, actinomorphic or zygomorphic ; sepals 5, rarely 4, free or rarely connate at the base, imbricate, rarely valvate ; petals 4-5, rarely absent, hypogynous, free, imbricate or contorted, rarely valvate ; *disk mostly present* ; stamens the same number as to triple the number of the petals, often unequal in length ; filaments free, often *with a scale inside* ; anthers 2-celled, opening lengthwise ; ovary superior, sessile or rarely stipitate, usually 4-5-celled, cells rarely transversely locellate ; style simple, short, or stigmas sessile ; ovules 2 or more in each cell, axile ; fruit various but *never baccate* ; seeds mostly with some endosperm; embryo as long as the seed, straight or slightly curved. B.H. 1 : 262. E.P. 3, 4 : 74. Mainly Tropical and Subtropical Regions, often in dry desert places.—Tribulus, Zygophyllum, Fagonia, etc.

Useful Products : *Guaiacum Wood* or *Lignum Vitae* (Guaiacum officinale *L.* and G. sanctum *L.*), America and West Indies.

67. Geraniaceae

Annual herbs or undershrubs, rarely arborescent ; leaves alternate or opposite, mostly lobate, dissected or compound ; stipules often paired ; flowers often handsome, ⚥, actinomorphic or slightly zygomorphic, axillary, solitary to subumbellate ; sepals persistent, 4-5, free or connate to the middle, *imbricate* or rarely valvate, the dorsal one *sometimes spurred* ; petals 5, rarely 4, very rarely absent, hypogynous or subperigynous, *imbricate*, rarely contorted ; stamens 2-3 times the number of the sepals, sometimes a few without anthers, filaments mostly more or less *connate at the base* ; anthers 2-celled, opening lengthwise ; *ovary 3-5-lobed* ; ovules 1-2 in each cell, superposed, pendulous, rarely more than 2 ; fruit lobed, lobes 1-seeded, rarely more-seeded, *often beaked* ; seeds pendulous, with thin or no (rarely copious) endosperm and mostly curved embryo. B.H. 1 : 269. E.P. 3, 4 : 1. Mainly North Temperate Zone ; great concentration in S. Africa.—Monsonia, Geranium, Erodium, Pelargonium.

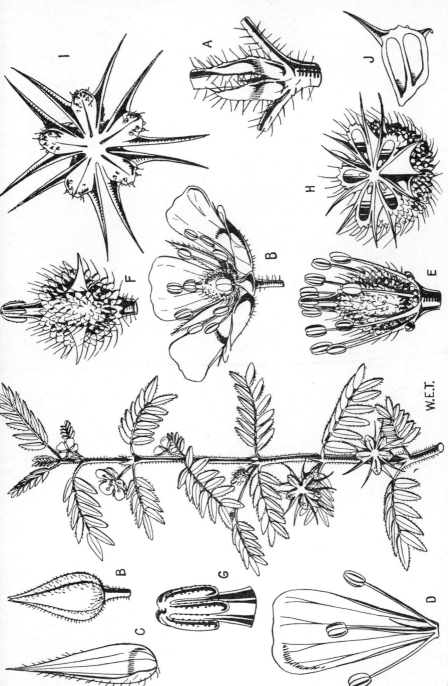

W.E.T.

FIG. 66.—Tribulus terrestris *L.* (Zygophyllaceae). A, stipules. B, flower. C, sepal. D, petal and stamens. E, stamens and ovary. F, young fruit. G, stigma. H, cross section of fruit from side. I, same from above. J, segment of fruit.

Useful Products : Chiefly cultivated for their handsome flowers and scented leaves. The so-called bedding and greenhouse "Geranium" is a *Pelargonium*.

FIG. 67.—Erodium macradenium *L'Hérit.* (Geraniaceae). A, flower. B, calyx and ovary.

68. Limnanthaceae

Annual succulent marsh herbs ; leaves alternate, much-divided ; *stipules absent* ; flowers ⚥, actinomorphic, solitary on long stalks, axillary ; sepals 3-5, *valvate* or slightly imbricate ; petals 3-5, *contorted*, slightly perigynous ; stamens 6 or 10, subperigynous, free, some with a gland at the base ; anthers 2-celled, opening lengthwise ; carpels 5 or 3, *free* or nearly so, but connected by a *common gynobasic style* with 3-5 short lobes ; ovule solitary in each carpel, *ascending* ; *ripe carpels free*, indehiscent ; seed erect, without endosperm ; embryo straight, with large cotyledons and small radicle. B.H. 1 : 274 (under *Geraniaceae*). E.P. 3, 5 : 136. N. America.—Limnanthes, Floerkea.

69. Oxalidaceae

Herbaceous or suffrutescent, rarely arborescent ; leaves alternate, digitately or pinnately compound, sometimes simple by suppression of the leaflets ; leaflets spirally coiled when young, usually closing at night ; *stipules absent* ; flowers ⚥, actinomorphic, sometimes of *two kinds*, some perfect and others minute and apetalous ; flowers solitary or subumbellate, rarely racemose or cymose ; calyx 5-fid or partite, *imbricate* ; petals 5, shortly clawed, free or shortly connate at the base, *contorted* ; stamens 10, hypogynous, connate at the base, sometimes five *without anthers* ; anthers 2-celled, opening length-

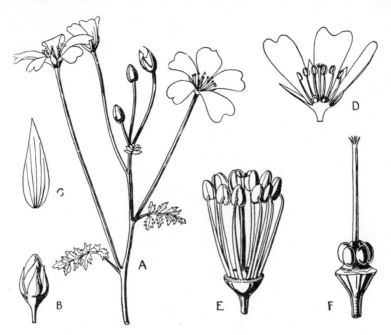

FIG. 68.—Limnanthes Douglasii *Nutt.* (Limnanthaceae).   A, branch with flowers.   B, flower-bud.
C, sepal.   D, vertical section of flower.   E, stamens.   F, ovary.—After Le Maout & Decne.

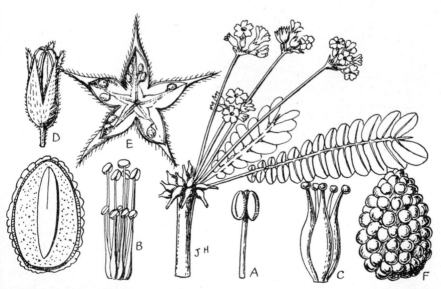

FIG. 69.—Biophytum sensitivum *D.C.* (Oxalidaceae).   A, stamen.   B, stamens.   C, ovary.
D, flower in bud.   E, fruit.   F, seed.   G, section of same.—Orig.

wise ; ovary 5-celled, superior ; styles 5, *free*, persistent ; stigmas capitate or shortly divided ; ovules 1 or more, axile ; fruit mostly a capsule ; seeds often with an elastic testa ; endosperm fleshy, copious ; embryo straight. B.H. 1 : 276 (under *Geraniaceae*). E.P. 3, 4 : 15. Tropics and Subtropics ; large number in S. Africa.—OXALIS, AVERRHOA, BIOPHYTUM, HYPSEOCHARIS, CONNAROPSIS.

Range of Tropaeolum (Tropaeolaceae).

USEFUL PRODUCTS : *Oxalic Acid* (Oxalis Acetosella *L.*) ; *Bilimbi fruit* (Averrhoa Bilimbi *L.*) ; *Carambola fruit* (Averrhoa Carambola *L.*), India and China.

70. TROPAEOLACEAE

Succulent prostrate or twining herbs with watery juice ; root often tuberous ; leaves alternate or the lower opposite, simple, *peltate*, sometimes dotted ; *stipules absent* ; flowers ⚥, *zygomorphic*, solitary, axillary ; calyx coloured, 2-*lipped* ; sepals imbricate or valvate, the lateral often broader, the dorsal *produced into a spur* (sometimes regarded as a part of the axis) ; petals 5 or rarely fewer by abortion, slightly perigynous, imbricate, the upper two exterior and often more

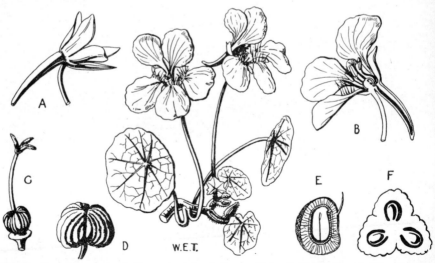

FIG. 70.—Tropaeolum majus *L.* (Tropaeolaceae). A, flower. B, longitudinal section of same. C, ovary. D, fruit. E, section of same. F, cross section of ovary.—After Le Maout & Decne.

or less different from the others ; *stamens 8, free, declinate* ; anthers 2-celled, opening lengthwise laterally ; ovary superior, sessile, 3-celled, cells 1-ovulate ; ovule pendulous ; style one, apical, with 3 stigmas ; carpels separating from the short central axis, indehiscent, hardening, rugose ; seeds without endosperm ; embryo straight, with thick fleshy cotyledons.   B.H. 1 : 274 (under *Geraniaceae*). E.P. 3, 4 : 23.   Central and S. America.—TROPAEOLUM.

USEFUL PRODUCTS : Several commonly cultivated.   *Canary Creeper* (Tropaeolum peregrinum *L.*), Peru, and other species used as bedding plants.

71. BALSAMINACEAE

Succulent herbs ; leaves alternate or opposite, simple, penninerved ; *stipules absent* ; flowers zygomorphic, ⚥, brightly coloured, solitary to subumbellate ; sepals 3, rarely 5, often coloured, imbricate, unequal, the lowermost elongated

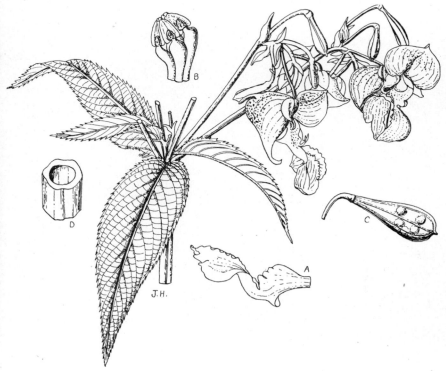

FIG. 71.—Impatiens Roylei *Hk. f.* (Balsaminaceae).   A, lateral petals.   B, stamens.   C, fruit.
D, section of stem.—After Bot. Mag.

into a *tubular spur* ; petals 5, the upper one exterior, usually erect, concave, the lateral ones united ; stamens 5 ; filaments short and broad, connate towards the top ; anthers 2-celled, *connate around the ovary* ; ovary superior, 5-celled, with axile placentas ; stigmas 1-5, more or less sessile ; ovules numerous ; fruit a succulent capsule *opening elastically* into 5 *twisted* valves, rarely a berry ; seeds without endosperm and with straight embryo.   B.H. 1 : 277 (under *Geraniaceae*).   E.P. 3, 5 : 383.   Mainly Tropical Asia and Africa.—IMPATIENS, HYDROCERA.

USEFUL PRODUCTS : Several cultivated *Impatiens*.

Order 21. LYTHRALES

Herbaceous to woody, reduced forms often aquatic ; flowers perigynous to epigynous ; ⚥, actinomorphic ; calyx tubular, lobes valvate ; petals present, often clawed ; stamens as many or twice as many as the petals, sometimes in two distinct whorls ; placentation axile ; seeds usually with no endosperm. Leaves simple, usually opposite and without stipules.

72. LYTHRACEAE

Herbs, shrubs or trees ; leaves *opposite or verticillate*, rarely alternate ; stipules *absent* or very small ; flowers usually actinomorphic, ⚥, solitary to paniculate ; sepals *united into a tube, valvate*, often with *appendages* between the lobes ; petals present or absent, inserted towards the top of the calyx-tube,

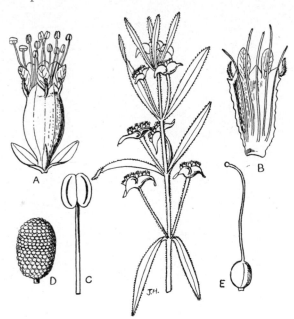

FIG. 72.—Nesaea erecta *Guill. & Perr.* (Lythraceae). A, flower. B, corolla cut open. C, stamen. D, seed. E, ovary.—After Guill. & Perr.

crumpled in bud ; stamens usually 4 or 8, rarely more, inserted below the petals ; filaments *variable in length*, usually *inflexed* in bud ; anthers 2-celled, opening lengthwise ; ovary superior, sessile or shortly stipitate, completely or incompletely 2-6-celled (rarely 1-celled) ; style simple, variable in length ; ovules numerous on an axile placenta sometimes not reaching the top of the ovary ; fruit usually capsular, opening by a transverse slit, by valves, or irregularly ; seeds numerous, without endosperm ; embryo straight. B.H. 1 : 773. E.P. 3, 7 : 1. Widely spread. — AMMANNIA, PEPLIS, CUPHEA, LYTHRUM, NESAEA, DIPLUSODON, LAGERSTROEMIA, etc.

USEFUL PRODUCTS : *Tulip Wood* (Physocalymma scaberrimum *Pohl*), Brazil ; *Henna* leaves (Lawsonia alba *Lamk.*), Tropical Asia ; Red-dye from flowers of Woodfordia floribunda *Salisb.* ; *Lagerstroemia Flos-reginae* Retz., an important timber of E. India.

73. CRYPTERONIACEAE

Trees with 4-angled branches ; leaves opposite, entire, exstipulate ; flowers in axillary spiciform racemes or panicles, very small, white or green, actinomorphic, polygamo-dioecious ; calyx-tube 4-5-lobed, lobes valvate ; petals absent ; stamens 4-5, *alternate* with the calyx-lobes ; anthers didymous ; disk none ; ovary superior, 2-celled ; style slender ; ovules numerous, axile ; fruit

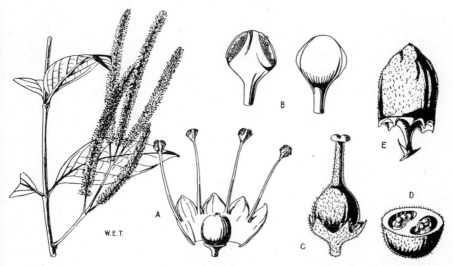

FIG. 73.—Crypteronia paniculata *Bl.* (Crypteroniaceae).   A, flower, dissected.   B, anthers.   C, ovary. D, cross section of same.   E, fruit.—Orig.

a capsule, loculicidally 2-valved, valves connected by the persistent style ; seeds minute, elongated, winged or not ; endosperm none ; embryo cylindric. B.H. 1 : 782 (under *Lythraceae*).   Engler and Gilg, *Syllabus*, eds. 9 and 10 : 299 (1924).   India, Malay Archipelago.—CRYPTERONIA.

Although I retain this family near *Lythraceae*, whence it has been separated by Engler and Gilg in their latest *Syllabus*, there is also some relationship with the *Escalloniaceae*, perhaps due to parallel development.

74. SONNERATIACEAE

Trees ; leaves *opposite*, simple, entire ; *stipules absent* ; flowers solitary or 3 together, axillary or terminal, ⚥, actinomorphic ; calyx-tube campanulate, thick and leathery ; lobes 4-8, *valvate* ; petals 4-8, small, or absent ; *stamens numerous*, inserted on the calyx in several series ; filaments free, at length reflexed ; anthers reniform, versatile, opening lengthwise ; ovary free or adnate at the base to the calyx-tube, *many-celled* ; septa thin ; style long, simple ;

L

ovules numerous, on thick axile placentas, ascending ; fruit a berry, with
numerous cells and seeds ; seeds *without endosperm* ; embryo with short leafy

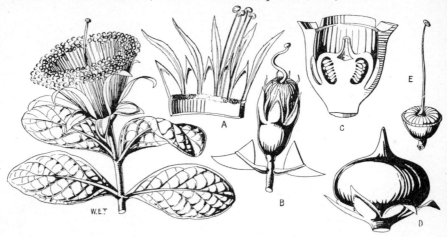

FIG. 74.—Sonneratia acida *Roxb.* (Sonneratiaceae).   A, perianth and stamens.   B, young fruit.
C, vertical section of ovary.   D, fruit.   E, ovary.—Orig.

cotyledons.   B.H. 1 : 784 (under *Lythraceae*).   E.P. 3, 7 : 17.   Tropical coasts
from East Africa to Australia.—SONNERATIA, DUABANGA.

75. PUNICACEAE

Woody and sometimes spiny ; leaves mostly *opposite* or fascicled, simple,
not glandular ; stipules absent ; flowers ⚥, terminal, solitary or clustered ;

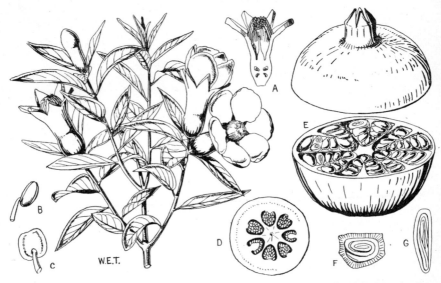

FIG. 75.—Punica Granatum *L.* (Punicaceae).   A, vertical section of flower.   B and C, views of anther.
D, cross section of ovary.   E, fruit to show seeds.   F and G, sections of seed.

calyx coloured, tubular, *adnate to the ovary*, 5-7-lobed, lobes *valvate*; petals 5-7, imbricate and *crumpled* in bud; stamens numerous, epigynous; filaments slender, free; anthers 2-celled, dorsifixed, opening lengthwise; ovary *inferior*, many-celled, cells *superposed in two series*, the lower with *axile*, the upper with *parietal* placentation; style slender, simple; ovules numerous on each placenta; fruit a spherical berry crowned by the calyx-limb; seeds numerous, covered with pulp; endosperm absent; cotyledons convolute. B.H. 1 : 784 (under *Lythraceae*). E.P. 3, 7 : 22. Orient to N.W. India; widely cultivated.—PUNICA.

USEFUL PRODUCTS : *Pomegranate* (Punica Granatum *L.*), Tropics and Subtropics, cultivated.

76. OLINIACEAE

Shrub or small tree; branches *quadrangular*; leaves *opposite*, simple penninerved; stipules 0; calyx-tube adnate to the ovary; limb produced *beyond* the ovary, tubular, 4-5-toothed, deciduous; petals 5, rarely 4, inserted at the mouth of the calyx, spathulate, pilose within the base, alternating with as many *incurved scales*; stamens 4-5, inserted on the calyx - tube; filaments short; anthers small, didymous, with thickened connective; ovary *inferior*, 3-5-celled; style with a thickened stigma; ovules up to 3 in each cell, axile, pendulous; fruit drupaceous, each cell 1-seeded; seeds without endosperm; cotyledons irregularly convolute; radicle short. B.H.

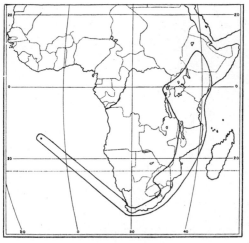

Distribution of Oliniaceae.

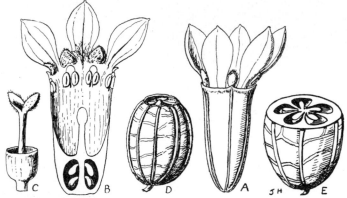

FIG. 76.—Olinia cymosa *Thumb.* (Oliniaceae).   A, flower.   B, vertical section of same.   C, ovary.
D, fruit.   E, cross section of same.—Orig.

1 : 785 (under *Lythraceae*).   E.P. 3, 6a : 213.—St. Helena, S. and E. Tropical Africa.—OLINIA.

77. ONAGRACEAE
(Oenotheraceae)

Herbs or rarely shrubs, often aquatic ; leaves simple, opposite or alternate ; stipules mostly absent or deciduous ; flowers ☿, actinomorphic, often solitary ; calyx adnate to the ovary ; lobes 4-5, *valvate* ; petals 4-5, free, contorted or imbricate, rarely absent ; stamens as many or twice as many as the calyx-lobes ; anthers 2-celled, opening lengthwise ; ovary inferior or rarely semisuperior, 2-6-celled, rarely incompletely celled ; ovules 1 to many, on axile placentas ;

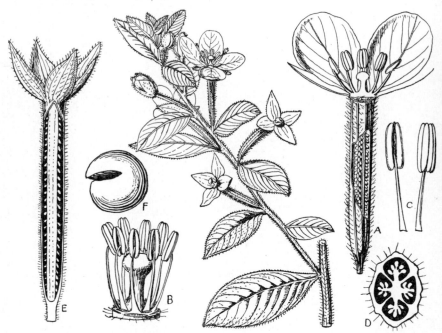

FIG. 77.—Jussiaea suffruticosa *L.* (Onagraceae). A, flower dissected to show parts. B, stamens and ovary. C, stamens. D, cross section of ovary. E, fruit. F, seed.—After Baill.

style simple ; fruit a capsule or nut ; seeds numerous or rarely solitary, without endosperm ; embryo straight or nearly so ; including *Hydrocaryaceae.* B.H. 1 : 785. E.P. 3, 7 : 199. Temperate and Subtropics.—EPILOBIUM, JUSSIAEA, LUDWIGIA, CLARKIA, OENOTHERA, FUCHSIA, LOPEZIA, GAURA, CIRCAEA, TRAPA, etc.

USEFUL PRODUCTS : Ornamental plants, " Clarkias ", " Fuchsias ". *Evening Primrose* (Oenothera), etc. ; *Singhara flour* (fruits of Trapa bispinosa *Roxb.*), a valuable food in N.W. India.

78. HALORRHAGACEAE

Herbs or undershrubs, often aquatic ; leaves alternate, opposite or verticillate, sometimes very large, the submersed ones often much divided ; *stipules absent* ; flowers ☿ or ♂ ♀, solitary to paniculate or corymbose, often very small ;

calyx-tube *adnate* to the ovary ; lobes 2-4 or absent ; petals 2-4 or absent, *valvate* or slightly imbricate ; stamens 2-8, rarely 1, large ; anthers basifixed, 2-celled, opening lengthwise ; ovary *inferior*, 1-4-celled ; styles 1-4 ; ovules as

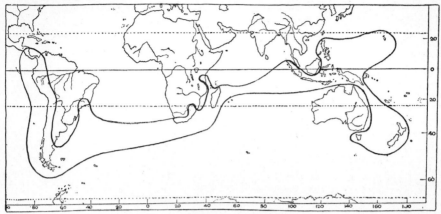

Range of Gunnera (Halorrhagaceae).

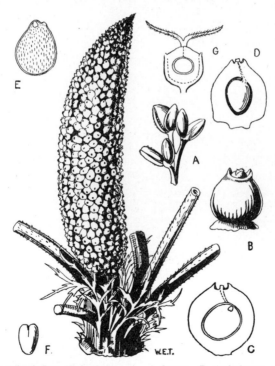

FIG. 78.—Gunnera chilensis *Lam.* (Halorrhagaceae).   A, flowers.   B, single flower.   C, section of fruit. D, section of ovary.   E, seed.   F, embryo.   G, ovary.—After Le Maout & Decne.

many as the styles, pendulous from the apex of the cells ; fruit small, a nut or drupe, sometimes winged, indehiscent or rarely breaking up into cocci ; seeds pendulous, with copious endosperm and straight fairly large (rarely small) embryo. B.H. 1 : 673. E.P. 3, 7 : 226. Mostly *aquatic* and scattered throughout the world.—HALORRHAGIS, HIPPURIS, GUNNERA, MYRIOPHYLLUM, etc.

USEFUL PRODUCTS : *Gunnera* spp., with large handsome foliage, often planted near lakes and ponds.

79. CALLITRICHACEAE

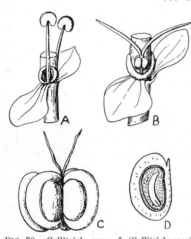

Annual herbs, terrestrial or aquatic, with slender stems ; leaves *opposite*, linear, entire ; stipules absent ; flowers minute, *unisexual*, axillary, solitary or rarely the male and female in the same axil ; calyx and corolla absent ; *stamen* 1, subtended by 2 bracts ; filament slender ; anther 2-celled, opening lengthwise at the side, the slit becoming confluent at the top ; ovary subsessile, 4-lobed, 4-celled ; styles 2, elongated, *free*, papillose ; ovules solitary and pendulous from the apex of each cell ; fruit 4-lobed, lobes margined or winged ; seeds with a membranous testa, fleshy endosperm and terete straight embryo. B.H. 1 : 676 (under *Halorrhagaceae*). E.P. 3, 5 : 120. Cosmopolitan. —CALLITRICHE.

FIG. 79.—Callitriche verna *L.* (Callitrichaceae). A, male flower. B, female flower. C, fruit. D, section of same to show seed.

Order 22. THYMELAEALES

Very similar to *Lythrales,* but more woody and apetalous ; calyx often corolline ; mostly monocarpellary ; ovules few to solitary ; seeds with or without endosperm and usually straight embryo. Leaves alternate or opposite ; stipules absent. Flowers often in heads surrounded by an involucre of leafy bracts.

80. GEISSOLOMATACEAE

Low shrub ; leaves *opposite*, decussate, sessile, entire ; stipules absent ; flowers ⚥, actinomorphic, in short much reduced bracteate axillary racemes ; bracts 6, decussate, persistent ; calyx hypogynous, persistent, shortly tubular, 4-*partite* nearly to the base, segments petaloid, obovate, imbricate ; stamens 8, inserted at the base of the calyx, opposite and alternate with the calyx-segments ; filaments slender, free ; anthers 2-celled, opening lengthwise ; ovary superior, sessile, 4-*celled*, cells narrowly winged ; styles 4, loosely united at the *apex* ; ovules 2 in each cell, pendulous from the apex ; fruit a 4-celled capsule ; seeds often solitary with scanty endosperm and straight central embryo ; cotyledons long and linear. B.H. 3 : 203 (under *Penaeaceae*). E.P. 3, 6a : 205. S. Africa.—GEISSOLOMA.

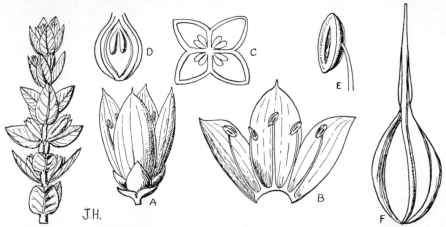

FIG. 80.—Geissoloma marginatum *Juss.* (Geissolomataceae). A, flower. B, corolla and stamens. C, cross section of ovary. D, vertical section of same. E, anther. F, fruit.—Orig.

81. THYMELAEACEAE

Trees, shrubs or rarely herbs ; leaves opposite or alternate, *simple,* mostly small ; *stipules absent* ; flowers often in terminal bracteate or ebracteate heads, spikes or racemes, rarely solitary, ☿ or dioecious, actinomorphic or slightly zygomorphic; calyx hypogynous, tubular, sometimes *petaloid*, often swollen below ; lobes 4-5, *imbricate* ; petals or staminodes 4-12, or absent, scale-like, inserted at the mouth or within the calyx - tube ; stamens 2 to many, mostly the same number as the calyx-lobes and opposite to them or a second series alternate with them ; anthers 2-celled, introrse, opening lengthwise ; hypogynous *disk* annular, cupular, or of separate scales, or absent ; ovary superior, 1-2-celled, entire ; style in the 1-celled ovary often *excentric* ; stigma more or less capitate : ovule *solitary* in each ovary or cell, pendulous from near the apex, anatropous ; fruit indehiscent, rarely capsular ; seed with copious to no endosperm, and straight embryo. B.H. 3 : 186. E.P. 3, 6a : 216. Mainly S. Africa, Australia and Mediterranean ; rarer in the Tropics. — PIMELEA, DAPHNE, DIRCA, THYMELAEA, DAPHNOPSIS, WIK-STROEMIA, STELLERA, ARTHROSOLEN, PASSERINA, LACHNAEA, STRUTHIOLA, GNIDIA, LASIOSIPHON, PHALERIA, AQUILARIA, etc.

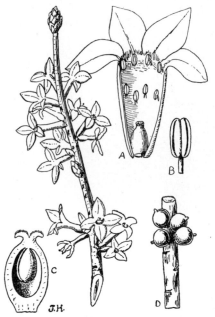

FIG. 81.—Daphne Mezereum *L.* (Thymelaeaceae). A, dissection of flower. B, anther. C, vertical section of ovary. D, fruits.—Orig.

USEFUL PRODUCTS : *Mezereon Bark* (Daphne Mezereum *L.*). Several beautiful sweet-scented garden plants.

82. PENAEACEAE

Small shrubs of ericoid habit ; leaves *opposite*, decussate, often *imbricate*, entire, mostly sessile ; stipules when present very minute or glandular ; flowers

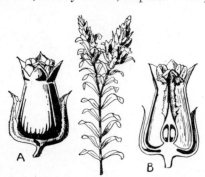

⚥, actinomorphic, solitary in the upper leaf-axils, often crowded ; bracts leafy or coloured ; bracteoles opposite, in one or more pairs ; calyx hypogynous, tubular ; lobes 4, *valvate* ; petals absent ; stamens 4, inserted in the throat of the calyx and *alternate* with its lobes ; filaments short ; anthers 2-celled, introrse, opening lengthwise ; disk absent ; ovary superior, sessile, 4-celled ; style terminal, with a 4-lobed capitate stigma ; ovules 2-4 in each cell, anatropous, ascending or pendulous ; fruit a *loculicidal capsule* included in the persistent calyx ; seeds often solitary in

FIG. 82.—Penaea myrtifolia *Endl.* (Penaeaceae). A, flower. B, dissection of same.—After Baill.

each cell ; endosperm none ; embryo thick, with large hypocotyl and 2 minute cotyledons. B.H. 3 : 202. E.P. 3, 6a : 208. Entirely S. African.—PENAEA, SARCOCOLLA, ENDONEMA.

83. NYCTAGINACEAE

Herbs, shrubs or trees ; leaves alternate or opposite, simple ; stipules absent ; flowers ⚥ or ♂♀, usually cymose, sometimes surrounded by brightly *coloured bracts*, the latter occasionally *simulating a calyx* ; calyx tubular, often *petaloid*, *valvate* or *plicate* in bud ; petals absent ; stamens 1 to many, hypogynous, free or connate at the base, *involute in bud* ; anthers 2-celled, opening l e n g t h w i s e ; ovary superior, 1-celled ; style slender ; ovule solitary, erect and inverted ; fruit indehiscent, sometimes enclosed in the persistent base of the calyx, often glandular ; seeds with copious or scanty endo-

FIG. 83.—Abronia fragrans *Nutt.* (Nyctaginaceae). A, flower. B, stamens and ovary. C, ovary. D, fruit.—After Bot. Mag.

sperm and straight or curved embryo. B.H. 3 : 1.   E.P. 3, 1b : 14.   Mainly
Tropical and Temperate America.—MIRABILIS, OXYBAPHUS, NYCTAGINIA,
BOERHAAVIA, BOUGAINVILLAEA, ABRONIA, PISONIA, NEEA, etc.

USEFUL PRODUCTS : A few cultivated plants ; *Marvel of Peru* (Mirabilis
Jalapa *L.*) ; *Bougainvillaea*, etc.

Order 23. PROTEALES

Trees or shrubs, rarely subherbaceous ; flowers perigynous ; calyx
valvate, tubular, often coloured ; stamens 4, opposite the calyx-lobes ;
ovary 1-celled ; seeds without endosperm. Leaves alternate or rarely
opposite, without stipules.

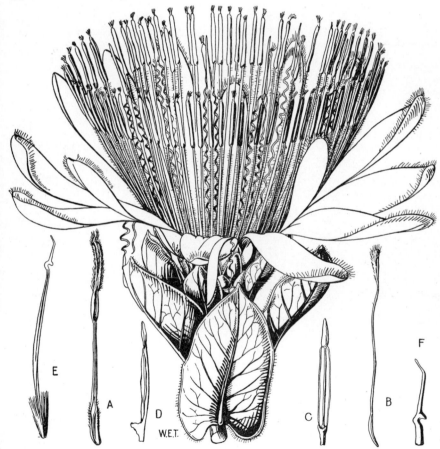

FIG. 84.—Protea latifolia *R. Br.* (Proteaceae). A, larger perianth-segment.   B, smaller perianth-segment.
C, front view of anther. D, side view of same. E, ovary. F, stigma.—After Bot. Mag.

84. PROTEACEAE

Trees or shrubs, rarely subherbaceous ; leaves alternate, rarely verticillate
or opposite, simple or variously divided ; *stipules absent* : flowers ♀ or ♂ ♀,

sometimes dioecious, racemose to capitate, the latter often involucrate ; *calyx corolla-like, coloured, tetramerous, valvate,* usually tubular in bud, variously *split when open* ; stamens 4, *opposite* the calyx-lobes ; filaments *adnate* to the lobes, rarely free ; anthers free, 2-celled, opening lengthwise ; ovary sessile or stipitate, with or without hypogynous scales or disk at the base, 1-celled ; style simple ; ovules 1 or more, pendulous or laterally attached ; fruit a nut, drupe, follicle or capsule ; seeds often winged ; endosperm 0. B.H. 3 : 165. E.P. 3, 1 : 119. Mostly S. Africa and Australia ; a few in the Tropics and in Temperate S. America.—LEUCADENDRON, PROTEA, LEUCOSPERMUM, FAUREA, SERRURIA, MIMETES, PETROPHILA, ISOPOGON, CONOSPERMUM, PERSOONIA, PANOPSIS, EUPLASSA, ROUPALA, HELICIA, GREVILLEA, HAKEA, STENOCARPUS, LOMATIA, EMBOTHRIUM, TELOPEA, BANKSIA, DRYANDRA, etc.

USEFUL PRODUCTS : *Terblanz* wood (Faurea MacNaughtonii *Phillips*), Tropical and S. Africa ; *Silky Oak* wood (Grevillea robusta *A. Cunn.*), Australia ; *Silver Tree* (Leucadendron argenteum *R. Br.*), Cape of Good Hope. Many beautiful ornamental trees and shrubs.

Order 24. DILLENIALES

Trees or shrubs, rarely herbs ; flowers hypogynous, ⚥, actinomorphic ; calyx imbricate ; petals imbricate, often crumpled in bud ; stamens numerous, free ; apocarpous ; seeds with copious plain endosperm and small to fairly large embryo, often arillate. Leaves alternate with marked pinnate nervation ; stipules absent or adnate to the petiole.

85. DILLENIACEAE

Trees, shrubs or twiners, rarely undershrubs or herbs with radical leaves ; leaves alternate, entire or dentate, rarely pinnatifid or trilobed, usually with

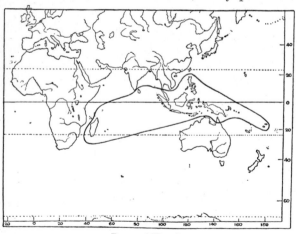

Range of Wormia.

numerous prominent *parallel lateral nerves* ; stipules absent or wing-like and *adnate* to the petiole, mostly deciduous ; flowers small to medium - sized, rarely large, ⚥ or ♂ ♀ ; sepals 5, *much imbricate, persistent* ; petals 5 or fewer, i m b r i c a t e, o f t e n *crumpled* in bud, deciduous; s t a m e n s *numerous*, rarely definite, *hypogynous*, free or variously united into bundles at the base, *usually persistent* ; anthers with lateral or introrse cells, opening lengthwise or by apical pores ; carpels free, rarely one ; ovules 1 or more, erect from the base or from the inner angle of the carpel ; styles free ; carpels dehiscent or baccate ; seeds

mostly with a *crested or laciniate aril* ; *endosperm copious,* fleshy ; *embryo minute.*
B.H. 1 : 10.   E.P. 3, 6 : 100.   Mostly Tropical and Subtropical Regions.—

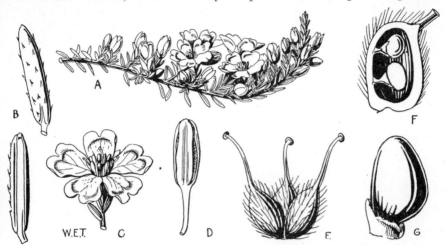

FIG. 85.—Hibbertia ericaefolia *Hk. f.* (Dilleniaceae).   A, branch with flowers.   B, leaves.   C, flower.
D, stamen.   E, ovary.   F, vertical section of same.   G, fruit.—After Hook.

DAVILLA,   DOLIOCARPUS,   TETRACERA,   ACROTREMA,   WORMIA,   DILLENIA,
HIBBERTIA,   CANDOLLEA, etc.

86. CROSSOSOMATACEAE

Small shrub ; leaves alternate, simple ; flowers solitary, terminal, showy,
♀ ; sepals 5, *connate* at the base into a turbinate tube ; petals 5, imbricate,

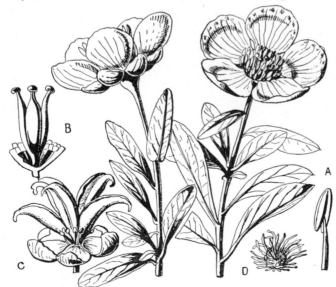

FIG. 86.—Crossosoma californica *Nutt.* (Crossosomataceae).   A, stamen.   B, ovary.   C, fruit.
D, seed.—Orig.

nervose, orbicular ; stamens *numerous*, free, inserted on the calyx-tube ; filaments slender, anthers oblong, 2-celled, opening lengthwise ; carpels 3-5, *free
from one another*, with 1-2 series of ovules, narrowed into a short style ; stigma
oblique, discoid ; fruit a bivalved capsule ; seeds numerous, globose, girt by a
multifid aril ; testa shining ; endosperm thin and fleshy ; embryo medium-
sized, slightly curved. B.H. 1 : 15 (under *Dilleniaceae*). E.P. Nachtr. 185.
California.—CROSSOSOMA.

Order 25. CORIARIALES

Shrubs with scaly buds ; flowers hypogynous, ♀ or ♂ ♀, actinomorphic ; sepals imbricate ; petals persistent ; stamens 10, free ; apocarpous, with solitary pendulous ovule ; seeds with straight embryo and
thin endosperm. Leaves opposite or verticillate, simple, without stipules.

87. CORIARIACEAE

Shrubs with *angular* branchlets and *opposite* or verticillate simple leaves
and *scaly buds* ; stipules 0 ; flowers ♀ or ♂ ♀, small, green, axillary or racemose ;
sepals 5, imbricate ; petals 5, shorter than the sepals, *keeled inside* ; stamens

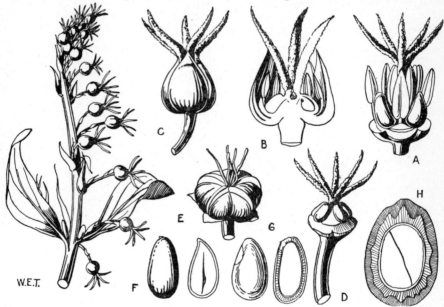

FIG. 87.—Coriaria myrtifolia *L.* (Coriariaceae).   A, flower with perianth removed.   B, vertical section of
flower.   C, flower.   D, ovary.   E, fruit.   F, G, seeds.   H, section of seed.—After Le Maout & Decne.

10, hypogynous, free, or those opposite the petals adnate to the keel ; anthers
large, exserted, opening lengthwise ; carpels 5-10, *free*, 1-celled ; *styles free*,
long ; ovules solitary in each carpel, pendulous from the apex, anatropous ;
cocci 5-8, enclosed by the much *accrescent* petals ; seed compressed, with thin
endosperm and straight embryo. B.H. 1 : 429.   E.P. 3, 5 : 128.   Warm
Temperate Regions.—CORIARIA.

Order 26. PITTOSPORALES

Trees, shrubs or climbers; flowers hypogynous, mostly ♀, actinomorphic; sepals and petals imbricate or valvate; stamens the same as or double the number of the petals, free; anthers opening lengthwise or by pores; syncarpous with parietal to axile placentation; seeds with copious endosperm and minute embryo. Leaves alternate to verticillate, simple, exstipulate.

88. PITTOSPORACEAE

Trees, shrubs or climbers sometimes spiny; leaves alternate or whorled, simple; *stipules absent*; flowers ♀, rarely ♂ ♀, actinomorphic, from solitary to corymbose: sepals 5, free or connate below, *imbricate*; petals 5, *imbricate*, with erect claws, the claws sometimes more or less *connivent*; stamens 5,

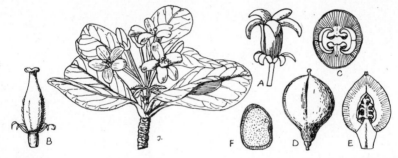

FIG. 88.—Pittosporum viridiflorum *Sims* (Pittosporaceae); branch with flowers (P. phyllyraeoides). A, flower. B, ovary. C, cross section of same. D, fruit. E, section of same. F, seed.—After Le Maout & Decne.

alternate with the petals, hypogynous, free or somewhat connivent; anthers 2-celled, introrse, opening lengthwise or by *pores*; ovary superior, completely or incompletely 2-5-celled with *parietal* or *axile* placentas; style simple; ovules numerous; fruit a capsule or berry; seeds mostly immersed in a viscid pulp, rarely winged; embryo very minute with copious endosperm. B.H. 1 : 130. E.P. 3, 2a : 106. Warmer regions of the Old World; absent from America.— PITTOSPORUM, MARIANTHUS, BILLARDIERA, SOLLYA, CHEIRANTHERA.

USEFUL PRODUCTS: *Pittosporum* furnishes useful close-grained timber in Western Australia; some ornamental plants.

89. BYBLIDACEAE

(Roridulaceae)

Herbs or undershrubs with rather crowded linear *glandular-pilose* alternate leaves; stipules absent; flowers ♀, actinomorphic, solitary or few in racemes; sepals 5, free, *imbricate*; petals 5, very shortly united at the base, *imbricate* or *contorted*; stamens 5, hypogynous or slightly united to the base of the petals;

anthers 2-celled, erect or *inflexed* in bud, opening by *apical pores* or very short pore-like slits ; ovary superior, 2-3-celled, with 1-2 ovules pendulous from the apex, or numerous and axile ; style simple, with a *capitate* stigma ; fruit a

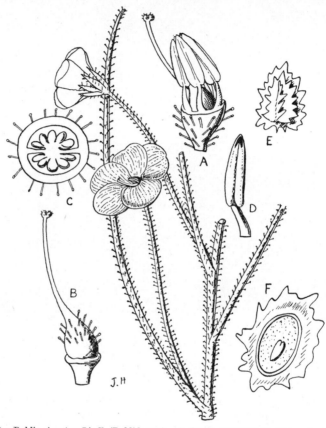

FIG. 89.—Byblis gigantea *Lindl.* (Byblidaceae). A, flower with perianth removed. B, ovary. C, cross section of same. D, stamen. E, seed. F, section of same.—After Bot. Mag.

loculicidal capsule ; seeds with endosperm and straight embryo. B.H. 1 : 664. E.P. 3, 2 : 272 (under *Droseraceae*). Australia, S. Africa.—BYBLIS, RORIDULA.

A small group, recently raised to family rank by Domin,[1] with whom I agree in placing it near *Pittosporaceae*. There is also a close general similarity with *Tremandraceae*. The supposed affinity with *Droseraceae* was based on superficial characters.

90. TREMANDRACEAE

Slender *heath-like* shrublets, sometimes with winged stems and *reduced* foliage ; indumentum often *glandular* or rarely stellate ; leaves alternate, opposite or verticillate, simple ; flowers axillary, solitary, ♀, actinomorphic ; sepals 4-5 (rarely 3) free, *valvate* ; petals the same number, hypogynous,

[1] Domin in Act. Bot. Bohem. 1 : 3 (1922).

induplicate-valvate; stamens double the number of petals, hypogynous, free; anthers 2-4-celled, opening by a single *apical pore*; torus sometimes enlarged and glandular-lobulate between the petals and stamens; ovary sessile, 2-celled; style slender; ovules 1-2 (rarely 3), pendulous, anatropous; fruit a *compressed capsule*, 2-celled, dehiscing by the margins; seed with a conspicuous appendage

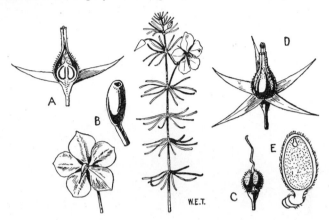

FIG. 90.—Platytheca verticillata *Baill.* (Tremandraceae).   A, vertical section of flower.   B, stamen.
C, pistil.   D, pistil and calyx.   E, section of seed.—After Baill.

to the chalaza, glabrous or pilose; endosperm copious, with rather small or minute straight embryo.   B.H. 1 : 133.   E.P. 3, 4 : 320.   Extratropical Australia.—TETRATHECA, PLATYTHECA, TREMANDRA.   Some graceful greenhouse plants.

Order 27. BIXALES

Trees or shrubs; flowers hypogynous to rarely perigynous, ☿ to ♂ ♀, actinomorphic; sepals imbricate to valvate; petals present or absent; stamens numerous to few, mostly free; ovary superior with parietal placentation; seeds with copious endosperm and small embryo.   Leaves mostly alternate and stipulate, simple.

91. BIXACEAE

Shrubs or small trees with *coloured juice*; leaves alternate, simple, *palminerved*, stipulate; flowers ☿, medium-sized, showy, paniculate; sepals 5, *imbricate*, deciduous; petals 5, large, imbricate, without a *scale* at the base; disk none; stamens numerous, hypogynous; filaments free; anthers *horseshoe-shaped*, opening by short slits at the top; ovary superior, 1-celled, with 2 *parietal* placentas; ovules numerous; style slender, recurved in bud; stigma 2-lobed; fruit a densely echinate-setose or smooth capsule, 2-valved, valves thick with the placentas in the middle; seeds obovoid; testa rather fleshy, red; endosperm copious; embryo large; cotyledons broad, incurved at the apex. B.H. 1 : 122, partly. E.P. 3, 6 : 307. Widely distributed in the Tropics.—BIXA.

USEFUL PRODUCT : *Annatto dye* (seeds of Bixa Orellana *L.*), Tropics generally.

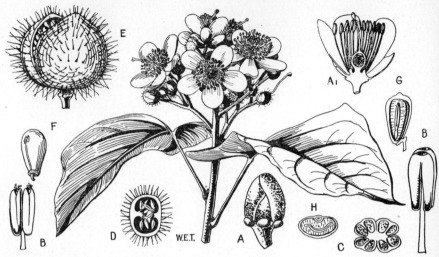

FIG. 91.—Bixa orellana *L.* (Bixaceae). A, flower-bud and glands. A₁, vertical section of flower. B, anthers. C, section of same. D, cross section of ovary. E, fruit. F, seed. G, section of seed. H, cross section.—After Le Maout & Decne.

92. COCHLOSPERMACEAE

Trees, shrubs or rhizomatous subshrubs with *coloured juice* ; leaves alternate, palmatilobed, *stipulate* ; flowers ☿, showy, paniculate or racemose ; sepals 5,

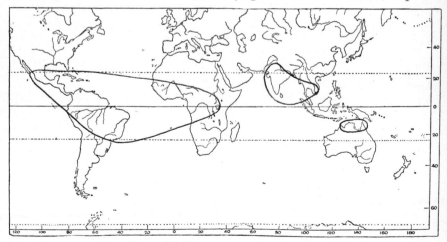

Range of Cochlospermum (Cochlospermaceae).

imbricate, deciduous ; petals 5, imbricate or subcontorted ; stamens numerous, the filaments free, equal or some longer than others ; anthers 2-celled, linear, opening by terminal short, often confluent, *pore-like slits* ; ovary 1-celled with *parietal placentas* projecting into the cell, or perfectly 3-celled ; ovules numerous ; style simple with minutely denticulate stigma ; fruit a 3-5-valved capsule ; seeds glabrous or covered with *woolly hairs*, straight or *cochleate - reniform* ;

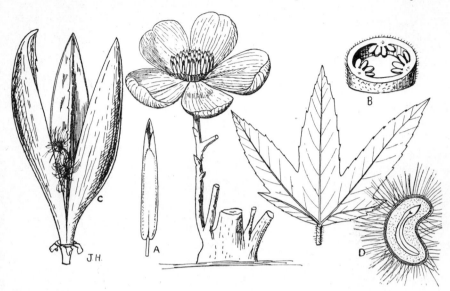

FIG. 92.—Cochlospermum tinctorium *Rich.* (Cochlospermaceae). A, stamen. B, cross section of ovary.
C, fruit. D, seed.—Orig.

endosperm copious ; embryo conforming to the shape of the seed, large ; cotyledons broad. B.H. 1 : 122 (under *Bixaceae*). E.P. Nachtr. 251. Tropics. —COCHLOSPERMUM, AMOREUXIA.

USEFUL PRODUCTS : *Kuteera Gum* (Cochlospermum Gossypium *D.C.*), India.

93. FLACOURTIACEAE

Trees or shrubs ; leaves simple, alternate ; stipules often soon falling off ; flowers ♀ or ♂♀, often *dioecious* or polygamous, variously arranged ; sepals sometimes not distinguishable from the petals, imbricate or open in bud ; petals sometimes *not arranged regularly* in relation to the sepals, large, small or absent, with or without an opposite *scale* inside the base, imbricate ;

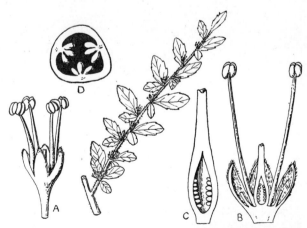

FIG. 93.—Azara microphylla *Hk. f.* (Flacourtiaceae). A, flower. B, vertical section of same. C, vertical section of ovary. D, same, cross section. —After De Wild.

M

stamens numerous, rarely few, *hypogynous*, free ; anthers 2-celled, often short, opening lengthwise by slits ; ovary 1-celled with 1 or more *parietal* placentas or rarely the placentas meeting in the middle ; ovules 2 or more on each placenta ; styles or stigmas as many as the placentas ; fruit indehiscent, mostly a berry or drupe, very rarely a capsule, sometimes large ; seeds with fleshy endosperm and medium-sized embryo ; cotyledons often broad. B.H. 1 : 122 (under *Bixaceae*). E.P. 3, 6a : 1. Mainly Tropics. — ONCOBA, AZARA, SCOLOPIA, FLACOURTIA, XYLOSMA, HYDNOCARPUS, KIGGELARIA, etc.

USEFUL PRODUCTS : *Kei Apple* (Aberia Caffra), S. Africa ; *Chaulmugra Oil* (seeds of Taraktogenos Kurzii *King*), E. India ; *Lukrabo* or *Ta-Fung-Tsze* seeds (Hydnocarpus anthelminticus *Pierre*), Indo-China.

94. SAMYDACEAE

Trees or shrubs ; leaves simple, alternate, often pellucid-dotted or lined ; stipules small and deciduous or absent ; flowers ♀, actinomorphic, *perigynous* ; sepals united in the lower part, imbricate or valvate, persistent ; petals the

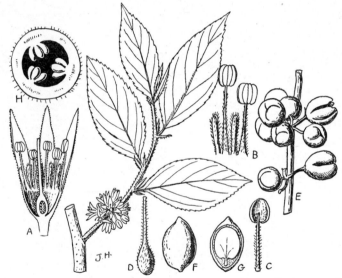

FIG. 94.—Casearia lasiophylla *Eichl.* (Samydaceae). A, section of flower. B, stamens and staminodes. C, stamen. D, ovary. E, fruits. F, seed. G, section of same. H, cross section of ovary.—After Martius.

same number as or more than the sepals or absent, often persistent ; *disk-glands* alternate with the stamens ; stamens definite or indefinite in number, in one or more rows, sometimes in *bundles* opposite the petals ; *staminodes* often present ; filaments free or connate at the base ; anthers 2-celled, short, opening lengthwise ; ovary free or *adnate* to the calyx-tube, sessile, 1-celled with 3-5 *parietal* placentas often towards the top of the cell ; style simple or 3-5 distinct styles ; ovules few or numerous ; fruit capsular or indehiscent ; seeds with fleshy copious endosperm and axile fairly large embryo. B.H. 1 : 794. E.P. 3, 6a : 1 (under *Flacourtiaceae*). Mostly Tropics, rare in the Subtropics.— CASEARIA, SAMYDA, RYANIA, BANARA, HOMALIUM, etc.

95. CANELLACEAE

(Winteranaceae)

Glabrous *aromatic* trees; leaves simple, alternate, *gland-dotted*; stipules absent; flowers ⚥, actinomorphic, cymose; bracts 3, imbricate, persistent; sepals 4-5, free, thick, imbricate; petals thin, imbricate or absent; stamens

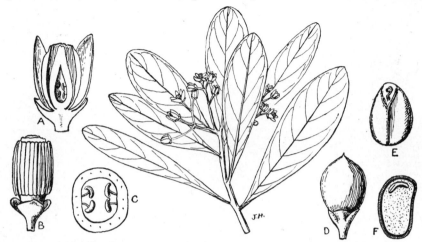

FIG. 95.—Canella alba *Murr.* (Canellaceae). A, section of flower. B, staminal tube. C, cross section of ovary. D, fruit. E, seed. F, section of same.—Orig.

hypogynous, up to 20; filaments *connate into a tube* with the anthers adnate to its outer side, opening lengthwise by valves; ovary superior, 1-celled; placentas 2-5, *parietal*; ovules several; style thick; stigmas 2-5; ovules subanatropous;

fruit a berry; seeds 2 or more, shining; endosperm oily and fleshy; embryo straight. B.H. 1 : 121. E.P. 3, 6 : 314. Tropical America. — CANELLA, CINNAMODENDRON.

USEFUL PRODUCTS : *Canella Bark* (Canella alba *Murr.*), West Indies and S. Florida.

96. CISTACEAE

Herbs or shrubs, often with *stellate* indumentum; leaves *opposite* or rarely alternate, simple; stipules present or adnate to the petiole; flowers ⚥,

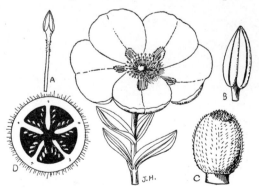

FIG. 96.—Cistus Loretii *Rany & Fouc.* (Cistaceae). A, stamen. B, anther. C, ovary. D, cross section of same.—After Bot. Mag.

actinomorphic, solitary to cymose, showy; sepals 3-5, *contorted*; petals 5 to 0, *contorted*, very soon falling off; stamens *numerous*, hypogynous; filaments free; anthers 2-celled, introrse, opening lengthwise; ovary superior, 1-celled with *parietal* placentas or incompletely septate towards the base; ovules 2 or more to each placenta ; style simple with 3-5 free or united stigmas ; fruit a capsule opening by valves from the top downwards ; seeds with endosperm and bent, coiled or folded embryo. B.H. 1 : 112. E.P. 3, 6 : 299. Mainly Mediterranean.—CISTUS, HELIANTHEMUM, HUDSONIA, LECHEA.

USEFUL PRODUCTS : *Labdanum* (Cistus polymorphus *Willk.*), S.W. Europe. Many handsome garden shrubs.

97. FRANKENIACEAE

Herbs or shrublets ; leaves *opposite*, exstipulate, often small and ericoid ;

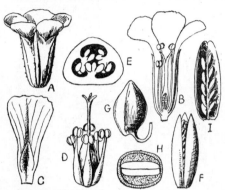

flowers actinomorphic, hermaphrodite, solitary or cymose, small ; sepals 4-6, persistent, connate, induplicate-valvate ; petals as many as the sepals, clawed, with a *scale-like appendage* on the inside, imbricate ; stamens usually 6, hypogynous, free or shortly connate at the base ; anthers 2-celled, didymous, dehiscing longitudinally ; ovary superior, sessile, 1-celled, with 2-4 *parietal* placentas ; ovules numerous ; style simple, filiform ; capsule enclosed in the persistent calyx, opening by valves ; seeds with endosperm ; embryo straight, axile. B.H. 1 : 140. E.P. 3, 6 : 283.

FIG. 97.—Frankenia pulverulenta *L.* (Frankeniaceae). A, flower. B, section of same. C, petal. D, stamens and ovary. E, cross section of ovary. F, fruit. G, seed. H, section of same.—After Le Maout & Decne.

Mostly maritime shores.—FRANKENIA.

Order 28. TAMARICALES

Trees or shrubs ; flowers hypogynous, ⚥, actinomorphic; sepals imbricate or valvate ; petals free to connate ; stamens mostly definite; syncarpous with parietal placentation; seeds with or without endosperm, often hairy. Leaves alternate or opposite, often very small ; no stipules.

98. TAMARICACEAE

Shrubs or trees with slender branches, and small *scale-like* alternate leaves; stipules absent; flowers very small, actinomorphic, usually hermaphrodite, in slender catkin-like spikes or

FIG. 98.—Tamarix articulata *L.* (Tamaricaceae). A, ovary and stamens. B, flower. C, fruit. D, seed. E, portion of inflorescence.—Orig.

racemes; sepals 4-6, imbricate, free; petals as many, free; disk present; stamens hypogynous, 5-10, free or connate at the base; anthers 2-celled, opening by longitudinal slits; ovary superior, 1-celled, with *parietal* or *basal* placentas; styles 3-4, free or united at the base; ovules numerous, ascending; fruit a capsule; seeds with or without endosperm, with a tuft of *hairs* at the apex or all round; embryo straight. B.H. 1 : 159. E.P. 3, 6 : 289. Mainly N. Hemisphere.—TAMARIX, MYRICARIA, HOLOLACHNE, REAUMURIA.

99. FOUQUIERACEAE

Spiny trees or shrubs with soft wood; leaves fasciculate or solitary, small, fleshy; flowers showy, paniculate, ⚥, actinomorphic; sepals 5, free, *much imbricate*; petals 5, hypogynous, *connate into a tube*, imbricate; stamens 10 or more, 1-2-seriate, *hypogynous*, the filaments free or slightly coherent; disk

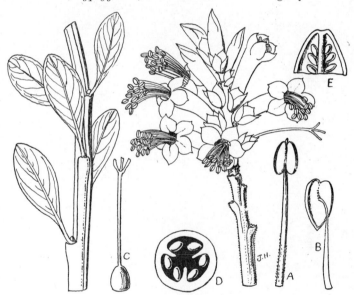

FIG. 99.—Fouquiera formosa *H. B. & K.* (Fouquieraceae). A, B, stamens. C, ovary. D, cross section of same. E, vertical section of same.—Orig.

annular, small; ovary 1-celled, with 3 *parietal* septiform placentas reaching to the top of the ovary, each about 6-ovulate; seeds oblong, compressed, with long *hyaline hairs* or *winged*; endosperm thin; embryo straight; cotyledons flat, rather thick. B.H. 1 : 161 (under *Tamaricaceae*). E.P. 3, 6 : 298. Mexico.—FOUQUIERA.

100. MALESHERBIACEAE

Herbs or undershrubs; leaves alternate, simple; stipules absent; flowers ⚥, actinomorphic; *calyx-tube long*, straight or curved; lobes 5, *valvate*; petals 5, *valvate*; corona membranous, denticulate; stamens 5, inserted on the villous lobed *gynophore*; anthers 2-celled, opening lengthwise; ovary *stipitate*, 1-celled, with 3-4 *parietal* placentas; styles 3-4, *separated at the base*, filiform; ovules numerous ; fruit a capsule enclosed by the persistent calyx, stipitate ; seeds pitted, with fleshy endosperm and straight medium-sized embryo with

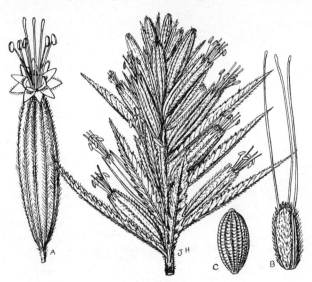

Fig. 100.—Malesherbia thyrsiflora *Ruiz & Pav.* (Malesherbiaceae). A, flower. B, ovary.
C, seed.—Orig.

orbicular cotyledons. B.H. 1 : 809 (under *Passifloraceae*). E.P. 3, 6a : 65. W.S. America.—MALESHERBIA, GYNOPLEURA.

Order 29. PASSIFLORALES

More or less as in *Bixales* (p. 159), but seeds without endosperm, and corona often present ; fruits often stipitate ; habit often more herbaceous and frequently climbing by tendrils ; stipules present or absent.

101. PASSIFLORACEAE

Herbaceous climbers with tendrils, or erect trees or shrubs ; leaves alternate, entire or lobed, often with *glands on the petiole* ; stipules usually small and deciduous ; flowers ⚥ or ♂ ♀ ; sepals 5, imbricate, persistent, free or partially united ; petals 5, rarely absent, free or shortly united, imbricate ; *corona* of one or more rows of thread-like filaments or scales or annular ; stamens 5 or more, hypogynous to perigynous, shortly united or in bundles, sometimes springing from the gynophore ; anthers 2-celled, opening lengthwise ; ovary superior, sometimes on a *gynophore*, 1-*celled*, with 3 or rarely 4-5 *parietal placentas* ; ovules numerous ; styles free or united stigmas often capitate ; fruit a capsule or berry, indehiscent or loculicidally 3-valved ; seeds with pitted testa surrounded by a pulpy aril ; endosperm fleshy ; embryo large, straight. B.H. 1 : 807. E.P. 3, 6a : 69. Tropics and Subtropics. — PASSIFLORA, TACSONIA, TRYPHOSTEMMA, PAROPSIA, SMEATHMANNIA, MODECCA, etc.

USEFUL PRODUCTS : *Granadillas fruits* (Passiflora quadrangularis *L.*, and

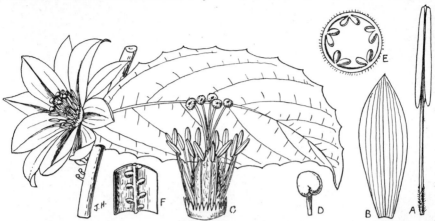

FIG. 101.—Smeathmannia pubescens *R. Br.* (Passifloraceae). A, stamen. B, sepal. C, stamens and ovary. D, stigma. E, cross section of ovary. F, placenta with ovules.—Orig.

P. macrocarpa *Mast.*) ; *Sweet Cup* or *Pomme d'Or* (P. maliformis *L.*) ; *Belle Apple* (P. laurifolia *L.*), Tropical America and W. Indies.

102. ACHARIACEAE

Slender herbs or shrublets ; leaves alternate, palmately lobed ; stipules absent ; flowers ♂ ♀, *monoecious*, solitary or racemose, actinomorphic ; male

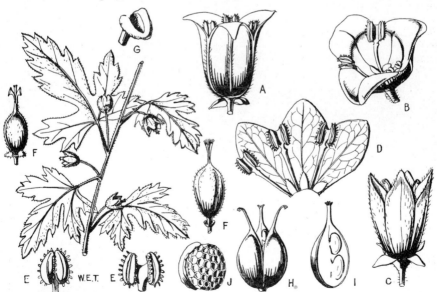

FIG. 102.—Acharia *tragodes* Thunb. (Achariaceae). A, male flower, side view. B, same from above. C, female flower. D, male flower showing stamens. E, anther before and after dehiscence. F, pistil. G, stigma. H, fruit. I, section of pistil.

flower : sepals free to the base ; *petals united into a campanulate tube* ; stamens 3-5 inserted at the base of or the filaments adnate to the corolla ; anthers 2-celled, opening lengthwise ; no rudimentary ovary ; female flower : calyx and corolla more or less as in the ♂ ; no staminodes ; ovary subsessile or stipitate, 1-celled with 3-5 *parietal* placentas ; stigmas 2-lobed ; ovules few or many ; fruit a stipitate capsule, 3-5-valved ; seeds with copious endosperm and small straight embryo. B.H. 1 : 814 (under *Passifloraceae*). E.P. Nachtr. : 256. S. Africa.—ACHARIA, CERATIOSICYOS.

Order 30. CUCURBITALES

Mostly herbaceous, often climbing by tendrils ; flowers epigynous ; ♂ ♀ ; calyx-lobes imbricate or valvate ; petals free or united, rarely absent ; stamens numerous to few, free or united ; anther-cells straight or often flexuous ; ovary inferior with parietal or axile placentation ; seeds with scanty or no endosperm.

103. CUCURBITACEAE

Herbs or rarely undershrubs with watery juice, often scabrid ; stems scandent or prostrate ; *tendrils mostly present*, spirally coiled ; flowers ♂ ♀, monoecious or dioecious, very rarely ☿, actinomorphic ; male flower : calyx tubular, lobes imbricate or open ; corolla polypetalous or gamopetalous, lobes imbricate or induplicate-valvate ; stamens free or variously united, mostly 3, rarely 1-5, *one anther always 1-celled*, the others 2-celled, cells straight or often curved, flexuous or conduplicate ; connective often produced ; female flower : calyx-tube adnate to the ovary and often produced beyond ; staminodes usually not present ; *ovary inferior* or very rarely free ; placentas often 3, *parietal* but often meeting in the middle ; ovules numerous, rarely few, arranged towards the walls of the ovary ; style simple or rarely 3 free styles ; stigmas thick ; seeds various, often flattened, *without endosperm*. B.H. 1 : 816. E.P. 4, 5 : 1. Mainly Tropics and Subtropics.—TRICHOSANTHES, TROCHOMERIA, PEPONIA, LUFFA, MOMORDICA, CUCUMIS, CITRULLUS, CEPHALANDRA, CUCURBITA, BRYONIA, ZEHNERIA, MELOTHRIA, ANGURIA, TRIANOSPERMA, ECHINOCYSTIS, CYCLANTHERA, SICYOS, SECHIUM, etc.

USEFUL PRODUCTS : Many kinds of *Gourds* and *Calabashes*. *Cucumber* (Cucumis sativus *L.*) ; *Melon* (Cucumis Melo *L.*) ; *Water Melon* (Citrullus vulgaris *Schrad.*) ; *Naras* (Acanthosicyos horrida *Welw.*), S. Africa ; *Bryony* (Bryonia dioica *Jacq.*), Europe, etc. ; *Bitter Apple* or *Colocynth* (Citrullus Colocynthis *Schrad.*), N. Africa to India.

104. BEGONIACEAE

Herbs or undershrubs, mostly succulent ; stems jointed, leaves alternate, simple, often *unequal - sided* or oblique ; stipules free, deciduous ; flowers *monoecious*, actinomorphic, or zygomorphic, mostly in axillary cymes, showy ; male flower : sepals 2, rarely 5, opposite, *valvate* ; petals 2-5, imbricate, or absent ; stamens numerous ; filaments free or connate ; anthers 2-celled, continuous with the filament, opening lengthwise ; female flower : perianth

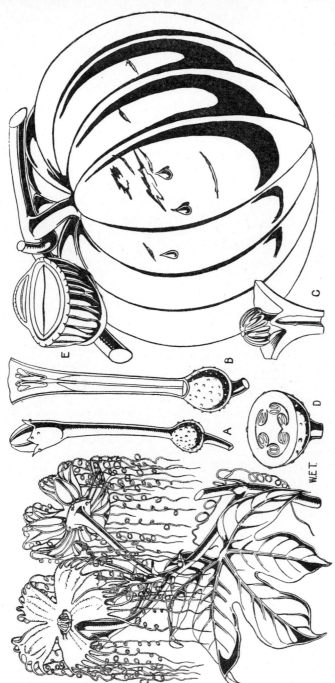

FIG. 103.—*Hodgsonia heteroclita H. f. & Thoms.* (Cucurbitaceae) and fruit. A, flower. B, longitudinal section of same. C, stamens. D, cross section of ovary. E, ditto of seed.—After Hook. f.

more or less as in the male ; staminodes absent or very small ; ovary *inferior*, or free at the apex (*Hillebrandia*), 2-4- (rarely 1-) celled, mostly *angled* or *winged* ; styles 2-5, free or connate, stigmas often *twisted*, papillose nearly all over ; ovules very *numerous*, on axile projecting simple or lobed placentas ; fruit a

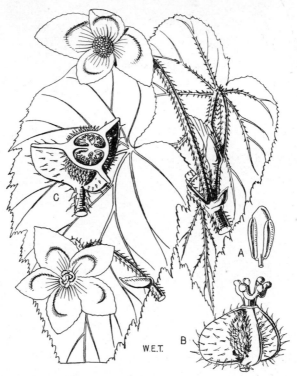

FIG. 104.—Begonia Cathcartii *Hook. f. & Thoms.* (Begoniaceae).　A, anther.　B, ovary.
C, cross section of same.—After Hook. f.

capsule or berry ; seeds minute and very numerous, with reticulate testa and scanty or no endosperm and straight embryo.　B.H. 1 : 841.　E.P. 3, 6a : 121. Tropics mainly.—BEGONIA, HILLEBRANDIA.

USEFUL PRODUCTS : Valuable ornamental garden plants.

105. DATISCACEAE

Herbs or trees, sometimes lepidote ; leaves alternate, simple or pinnate ; stipules absent ; flowers ♂ ♀, dioecious or rarely ⚥, actinomorphic, spicate or racemose ; male flower : calyx-lobes 3-9, short ; petals 8 or absent, small ; stamens 4-25, opposite the calyx-lobes ; anthers 2-celled, opening lengthwise ; rudimentary ovary small or absent ; female and hermaphrodite flowers : calyx-tube *adnate to the ovary* ; stamens similar to the ♂ or reduced to staminodes ; ovary 1-celled, open or closed at the apex ; placentas *parietal* ; styles free, simple or branched ; ovules very numerous, anatropous ; capsule opening amongst the styles, many-seeded ; seeds very numerous, minute, with scanty endosperm and cylindric straight embryo. B.H. 1 : 844. E.P. 3, 6a : 150. Northern Tropics and Subtropics.—DATISCA, TETRAMELES, OCTOMELES.

FIG. 105.—Datisca cannabina *L.* (Datiscaceae). A, male flower. B, C, fruit.

106. CARICACEAE

Small trees or shrubs with a terminal cluster of leaves and *milky juice* ; leaves alternate, often variously digitately lobed or foliolate ; stipules absent ; flowers ♀ and ♂ ♀, racemose ; male flower : calyx 5-lobed, small ; *petals united*

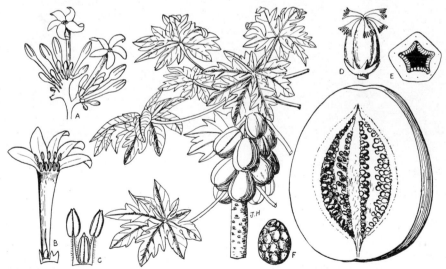

FIG. 106.—Carica Papaya *L.* (Caricaceae) and fruit in section. A, inflorescence. B, longitudinal section of flower. C, stamens. D, ovary. E, cross section of same. F, seed.—Orig.

into a slender tube ; lobes contorted or valvate ; *stamens* 10, inserted *on the corolla* ; filaments free or connate at the base ; anthers 2-celled, opening lengthwise ; rudimentary ovary present or absent ; female flower : calyx of the male ;

petals at first connivent, at length free ; no staminodes ; ovary superior, sessile, 1-celled or spuriously 5-celled, with *parietal placentas* ; ovules numerous ; style short or absent ; fruit a pulpy berry ; seeds with *fleshy endosperm* and straight embryo. B.H. 1 : 815 (under *Passifloraceae*). E.P. 3, 6a : 94. Tropical America.—CARICA, JACARATIA.

USEFUL PRODUCTS : *Papaw* (fruit of Carica Papaya *L.*), Tropics.

Order 31. CACTALES

Succulent or woody, often very spiny ; sepals, petals and stamens mostly numerous and in several series on a tubular axis ; ovary inferior, 1-celled, with parietal placentas ; fruit a berry ; seeds usually without endosperm and with straight or semicircular embryo.—Mostly desert regions of America.

107. CACTACEAE

Succulent herbs and shrubs of diverse habit, often very spiny, and usually with much *reduced leaves* ; flowers ⚥, solitary, actinomorphic ; calyx generally *petaloid*, superior ; petals epigynous, in *several series*, the innermost largest, sometimes coherent at the base ; stamens ∞, inserted at and free or adnate to

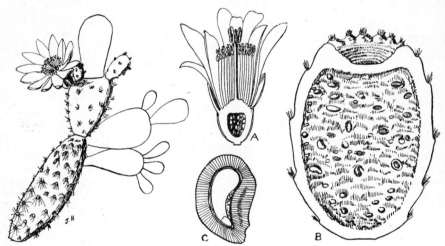

FIG. 107.—Opuntia vulgaris *L.* (Cactaceae). A, longitudinal section of flower. B, ditto of fruit. C, section of seed.

the base of the petals ; anthers 2-celled, opening lengthwise ; *ovary inferior*, 1-celled, with 3 or more many-ovuled *parietal placentas* ; stigmas spreading or close ; fruit a berry, often spiny or bristly, many-seeded ; seeds numerous, immersed in the pulp, testa often black ; endosperm usually absent ; embryo straight to semicircular. B.H. 1 : 845. E.P. 3, 6a : 156. America, naturalised in other warm countries.—PERESKIA, OPUNTIA, CEREUS, MAMILLARIA, EPIPHYLLUM, ECHINOCACTUS, RHIPSALIS, etc.

USEFUL PRODUCTS : *Cochineal dye* (derived from small insects living upon spp. of *Cactaceae* : *Opuntia* and *Nopalea*).

Order 32. THEALES

Trees, shrubs or rarely woody climbers ; leaves simple, alternate, with or without stipules ; flowers hypogynous to rarely subperigynous, mostly ♀ ; sepals imbricate, rarely contorted ; petals contorted or imbricate ; stamens numerous, free or shortly connate ; ovary superior, with axile placentation ; seeds with scanty or no endosperm ; calyx-lobes often accrescent and wing-like in fruit.

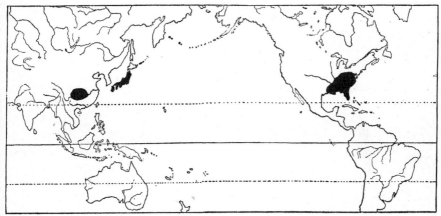

Distribution of Stuartia (Theaceae).

108. THEACEAE

(Ternstroemiaceae)

Trees or shrubs ; leaves alternate, simple, mostly evergreen ; *stipules* 0 ; flowers mostly solitary, rarely paniculate or racemose, often showy, actinomorphic, ♀ rarely ♂ ♀ ; bracts often paired below the calyx ; sepals 5, free or shortly connate, *much imbricate* ; petals 5, hypogynous, free or slightly connate, imbricate or contorted ; stamens *numerous* in several series, rarely definite, hypogynous, free or shortly connate, sometimes adnate to the base of the petals; anthers 2-celled, opening lengthwise, very rarely by *terminal pores* ; ovary superior, sessile, 3-5-celled ; styles free or connate ; ovules 2 or more in each cell, rarely 1, axile ; fruit dehiscent or not, loculicidal or septicidal, often leaving a central column ; seeds with usually scanty endosperm and straight or curved

FIG. 108.—Camellia chinensis *L.* (Theaceae). A, flower. B, ovary. C, longitudinal section of same. D, fruit. E, seed.—After Baill.

embryo variously *folded* or *spirally twisted*; incl. *Strasburgeriaceae*. B.H. 1 : 177, partly. E.P. 3, 6 : 175. Mainly Tropics and Temperate E. Asia.—VISNEA, TERNSTROEMIA, CLEYERA, EURYA, STUARTIA, GORDONIA, LAPLACEA, CAMELLIA (Thea), KIELMEYERA, PENTAPHYLAX, etc.

USEFUL PRODUCTS : *Tea Plant* (Camellia Thea *Link*), E. Asia ; *Mura Piranga* wood (Haploclathra paniculata *Benth.*), Brazil. Many beautiful garden plants.

109. MEDUSAGYNACEAE

Shrubs ; leaves *opposite*, simple ; stipules absent ; flowers in terminal panicles, red, actinomorphic, hermaphrodite ; sepals 5, *imbricate*, deciduous ; petals 5, *imbricate*, free ; stamens *very numerous*, hypogynous, shorter than the ovary ; filaments free, very slender ; anthers 2-celled, basifixed, opening lengthwise ; ovary superior, 20-25-celled, the carpels nearly free to the central axis ; styles stout, *in a ring on the shoulders* of the carpels ; stigmas capitate ; ovules 2 in each cell, and attached about the middle of the inner angle, one *ascending*, the other *descending* ; fruit capsular, the carpels septicidally dehiscent from the base and diverging like an umbrella ; seeds winged. (Hemsl. in Hook. Ic. Pl. t. 2790.)   Seychelles Islands.—MEDUSAGYNE.

110. MARCGRAVIACEAE

Climbing and mostly *epiphytic* shrubs, rarely arborescent ; leaves simple, alternate, sometimes *dimorphic* ; stipules 0 ; flowers ⚥, hypogynous, in terminal racemes or racemose umbels, the *bracts* of the *sterile* flowers variously modified into *pitcher-like, saccate* or *spurred bodies* adnate to or free from the pedicel ; sepals 5, much imbricate or joined into a calyptrate deciduous mass ; stamens 3 to numerous, free or slightly connate ; anthers 2-celled, opening lengthwise ; ovary 3- or more-celled ; stigmas sessile, radiate ; ovules numerous in several rows on thick placentas ; fruit thick and fleshy, globose, indehiscent or slightly dehiscent into the cells at the base ; seeds numerous, small, without endosperm ; embryo slightly curved, with large radicle and two small cotyledons. B.H. 1 : 178 (under *Ternstroemiaceae*). E.P. 3, 6 : 157.   Tropical America.— MARCGRAVIA, NORANTEA, RUYSCHIA.

111. CARYOCARACEAE

Erect trees or shrubs : leaves opposite or alternate, *digitately* 3-5-*foliolate* ; flowers ⚥, in terminal ebracteate racemes ; calyx 5-6-lobed, imbricate or truncate ; petals 5-6, free or cohering above, imbricate ; stamens subperigynous, numerous, in 5-6 series or shortly connate at the base ; filaments variously bent in bud, sometimes the inner ones *without anthers* ; anthers small, 2-celled, opening lengthwise ; ovary 4-20-celled ; styles the same number, filiform ; ovule solitary in each cell, ascending ; fruit rather drupaceous with a woody muricate endocarp breaking up into 1-seeded parts ; seeds kidney-shaped, with scanty thin endosperm ; embryo with a large spirally twisted radicle ; cotyledons small, hooked-inflexed. B.H. 1 : 178 (under *Ternstroemiaceae*). E.P. 3, 6 : 153.   Tropical America.—CARYOCAR, ANTHODISCUS.

USEFUL PRODUCTS : *Souari Nuts* (Caryocar nuciferum *L.*, and C. tomentosum *Willd.*), S. America.

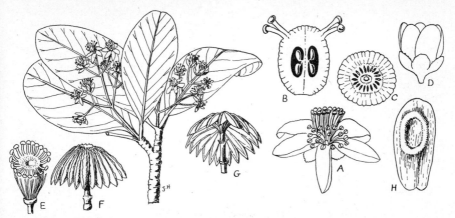

FIG. 109.—Medusagyne oppositifolia *Baker* (Medusagynaceae). A, flower, open. B, longitudinal section of ovary. C, cross section of same. D, flower, side view. E, styles and stigmas from above. F, fruit, side view. G, same from below. H, seed.—After Hook. Ic. Pl.

FIG. 110.—Marcgravia umbellata *L.* (Marcgraviaceae). A, flower. B, stamen. C, cross section of ovary. D, young shoot.

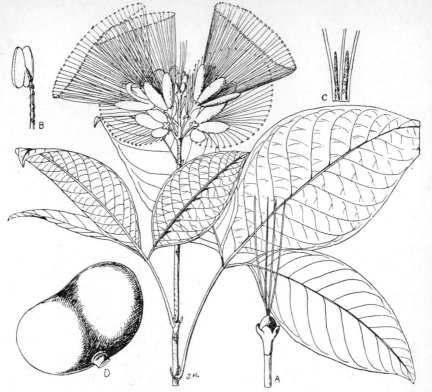

Fig. 111.—Caryocar glabrum *Pers.* (Caryocaraceae).   A, female flower.   B, stamen.   C, base of filaments.
D, fruit.—After Martius.

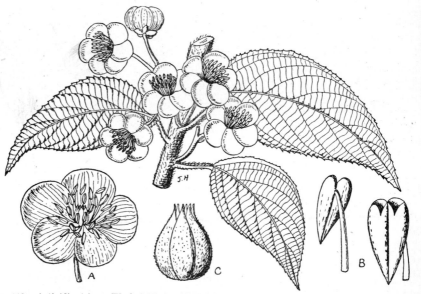

Fig. 112.—Actinidia strigosa *Hk. f. & Thoms.* (Actinidiaceae).   A, flower.   B, stamens.   C, ovary.—Orig.

112. Actinidiaceae

Trailing or climbing shrubs; leaves alternate, *simple*, rounded, glabrous, or with strigose, simple or *stellate* hairs; stipules 0; flowers small, in axillary cymes or fascicles, rarely subsolitary, ♀, polygamous or dioecious; sepals 5, *imbricate*; petals 5, imbricate or subcontorted, deciduous; stamens hypogynous, 10 or more; anthers versatile, *inflexed in bud*, opening lengthwise by slits; ovary 5- or more-celled, sometimes the carpellary walls scarcely reaching the central axis; cells 10- or more-ovuled; ovules spreading from the central axis, anatropous; styles 5 and united to the apex, or many and spreading, usually persistent; fruit a berry or dry capsule; seeds small, with copious endosperm and straight embryo with short cotyledons. B.H. 1 : 184 (under *Ternstroemiaceae*). Eastern Asia.—ACTINIDIA.

113. Saurauiaceae

Trees or shrubs; leaves alternate, simple, mostly serrate with *strong parallel nerves* diverging from the midrib as in *Dilleniaceae*, often roughly hairy or scaly; stipules 0; flowers hypogynous, mostly ♀, small to medium-sized, in small axillary or lateral panicles; bracts small, remote from the calyx; sepals 5,

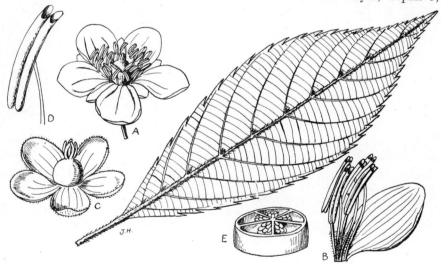

FIG. 113.—Saurauia barbigera *Hook.* (Saurauiaceae).   A, flower.   B, stamens and petal.   C, flower, to show ovary.   D, stamen.   E, cross section of ovary.—After Hook. Ic. Pl.

much imbricated; petals 5, imbricate, free or connate into a *short tube* at the base; stamens numerous, adnate to the base of the petals; anthers small, versatile, opening by an *apical pore or short slit*; ovary superior, 3-5-celled; styles 3-5, free or variously united, sometimes completely so; ovules numerous in each cell, on axile placentas, anatropous; fruit a berry, 3-5-celled, rarely somewhat dry and slightly dehiscent; seeds small, immersed in pulp; endosperm rather plentiful; embryo straight or slightly curved; cotyledons short. B.H. 1 : 184 (under *Ternstroemiaceae*). E.P. 3, 6 : 126 (under *Dilleniaceae*). Tropical and Subtropical America and Asia.—SAURAUIA.

N

114. Ochnaceae

Trees or shrubs with watery juice, rarely herbs ; leaves alternate, simple, very rarely pinnate, often with *numerous pinnate nerves* ; stipules present, sometimes *laciniate* ; flowers ☿, actinomorphic, mostly racemose or paniculate ; sepals 4-5, rarely 10, free, imbricate or rarely contorted ; petals free, 4-10,

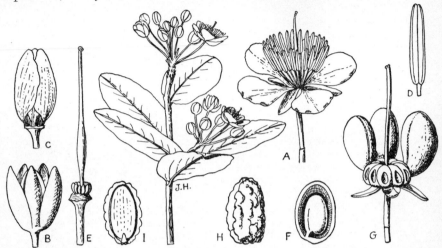

FIG. 114.—Ochna andravinensis *Baill.* (Ochnaceae). A, flower. B, sepals. C, petals. D, anther. E, ovary. F, seed, end open. G, fruit. H, seed. I, longitudinal section of seed.—After Baill.

subsessile, contorted or imbricate ; stamens few to many, free ; *staminodes* sometimes present, subulate or petaloid, sometimes connate into a tube; filaments persistent ; anthers linear, basifixed, opening lengthwise or by a *terminal pore* ; ovary entire to *deeply lobed*, 1-10-celled ; ovules 1 to many, axile or parietal or attached to the intrusive placentas ; style simple or fid at the apex ; fruiting carpels often becoming *quite separate* on the *enlarged torus* and drupaceous, or elongated, capsular and septicidal ; seeds 1 to many, with or without endosperm ; embryo usually straight (*incl.* Sauvagesieae). B.H. 1 : 316.   E.P. 3, 6 : 131. Tropics. — Ochna, Ouratea (Gomphia), Euthemis, Luxemburgia, Godoya, Sauvagesia, Lavradia, Neckia, etc.

Useful Products : *Meni Oil* (from kernels of Lophira alata *Banks*); wood known as *African Oak.*

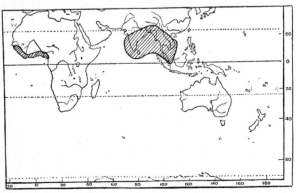

Distribution of Ancistrocladus.

115.

Ancistrocladaceae

Scandent shrubs ; *branches hooked* ; leaves alternate, simple ; stipules small, caducous ; flowers ☿, actinomorphic, small, paniculate with recurved branches ; calyx-tube short, at length *adnate to the base of the ovary* ; lobes imbricate, becoming unequally *enlarged and wing-like* in fruit ; petals 5, *contorted*, slightly connate ; stamens 5 or 10 ; anthers 2-celled, opening lengthwise ; ovary 1-celled ; ovule solitary, ascending ; style thick, with 3 stigmas ; fruit a nut, surrounded by the wing-like calyx-lobes ; seeds with the *testa intruding* between the folds of the embryo ; cotyledons remarkably *folded* and enclosing the radicle. B.H. 1:191 (under *Dipterocarpaceae*). E.P. 3, 6 : 274. Tropical Asia, West Tropical Africa (see map). — ANCISTROCLADUS.

FIG. 115.—Ancistrocladus Heyneanus *Wall.* (Ancistroclaceae). A, flower. B, stamen. C, fruit.—Orig.

116. DIPTEROCARPACEAE

Trees with *resinous wood* ; leaves alternate, simple ; indumentum of *stellate hairs* or of *peltate scales* ; stipules small or large, deciduous ; flowers ☿, actinomorphic, fragrant, in axillary panicles ; bracts usually absent ; calyx-tube short or long, free or adnate to the ovary ; lobes 5, imbricate or valvate, usually *enlarged and wing-like* in fruit ; petals 5, much

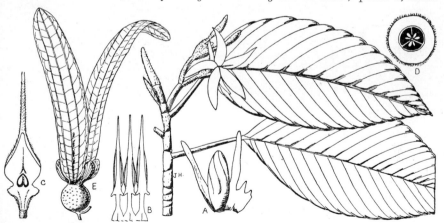

FIG. 116.—Dipterocarpus trinervis *Roxb.* (Dipterocarpaceae).   A, calyx and corolla.   B, stamens. C, longitudinal section of ovary.   D, cross section of same.   E, fruit.—After Blume.

twisted, free or slightly connate, often hairy ; stamens usually numerous, hypogynous or subperigynous ; anthers 2-celled, opening lengthwise, with *produced connective* ; ovary 3-celled ; style entire or 3-lobed ; ovules 2 in each cell, pendulous or lateral, anatropous ; fruit indehiscent, mostly 1-seeded ; seeds *without endosperm* ; cotyledons often twisted, enclosing the radicle. B.H. 1 : 189.   E.P. 3, 6 : 243.   Tropical Old World, rare in Africa.—DIP- TEROCARPUS, VATICA, SHOREA, HOPEA, DOONA, VATERIA, etc.

USEFUL PRODUCTS : Numerous valuable timbers from SHOREA, HOPEA, etc. ; *Sál or Saul Tree* (Shorea robusta *Gaertn.*), India ; *Piney Resin, Indian Copal* or *White Dammar* (from Vateria indica *L.*), S. India ; *Sumatra Camphor Tree* (Dryobalanops aromatica *Gaertn.*) ; *Garjan* or *Kanyin Oil* (Dipterocarpus turbinatus *Gaertn.*), E. India and Malay Peninsula ; *In* or *Eng Oil* (D. tuber- culatus *Roxb.*), E. India.

117. CHLAENACEAE

Shrubs or trees ; leaves alternate, entire ; stipules caducous ; flowers ♀, actinomorphic, cymose or paniculate ; *sepals 3, imbricate*, involucrate or bracteolate ; petals 5-6, *contorted*, free ; stamens 10 or more, inserted inside

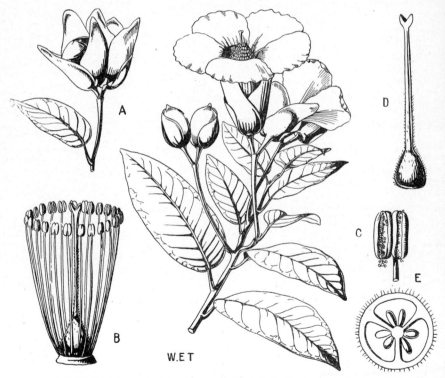

FIG. 117.—Rhodolaena altivola *Baill.* (Chlaenaceae). A, bud. B, stamens and ovary. C, anther. D, ovary. E, cross section of ovary.—After Baill.

an entire or toothed cupular ring of staminodes ; anthers 2-celled, opening lengthwise ; ovary 3-celled ; style simple, elongated ; stigma 3-lobed ; ovules 2 or more in each cell, mostly pendulous, anatropous ; capsule opening loculicid- ally, 3-valved or by suppression 1-celled and 1-seeded ; seeds with fleshy

or horny endosperm and straight embryo ; cotyledons flat or plaited. B.H.
1 : 194. E.P. 3, 6 : 168. Mascarene Islands.—Sarcolaena, Leptolaena,
Schizolaena, Rhodolaena.

An interesting family of beautiful trees and shrubs, remarkable in being confined
to the Mascarene Islands, where numerous other remarkable types of plants are
found.

Order 33. MYRTALES

More or less as in *Theales* (No. 32), but leaves mostly opposite and often
gland-dotted ; ovary inferior ; calyx becoming valvate, and ovules reduced
in number in the higher types ; stamens show tendency to grouping in
bundles as in *Hypericaceae*, becoming dimorphous and then opening by
terminal pores.

118. Myrtaceae

Trees or shrubs ; leaves simple, mostly entire, opposite or rarely alternate,
glandular-punctate ; stipules 0 or rarely very small ; flowers mostly actinomorphic, ⚥ or polygamous by abortion ; calyx-tube more or less adnate to the
ovary ; lobes 3 or more, imbricate or valvate or irregularly split ; petals 4-5,

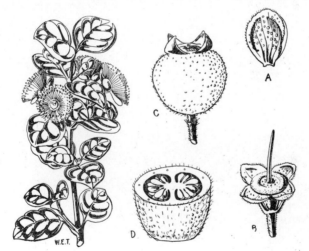

FIG. 118.—Myrtus bullata *Banks* (Myrtaceae). A, petal. B, pistil. C, fruit.
D, section of ovary.—After Bot. Mag.

rarely 6 or 0, inserted on the margin of the disk lining the calyx-tube, imbricate
or connivent in a mass ; stamens *numerous*, rarely few, inserted on the margin
of the disk, 1- or more-seriate, inflexed in bud or twice folded or straight ; filaments free or connate at the base into a short tube or in bundles opposite the
petals ; anthers small, 2-celled, opening lengthwise by slits or rarely by apical
pores, the connective often tipped by a *gland* ; *ovary inferior*, syncarpous, 1-
to many-celled, with mostly axile, rarely parietal, placentation ; ovules rarely
solitary or few ; fruit inferior, loculicidally dehiscent or indehiscent ; seeds
with no (or very little) endosperm ; embryo straight, incurved, circular or

spiral. B.H. 1 : 690, partly. E.P. 3, 7 : 57. Mainly Tropics and Australia.—
DARWINIA, VERTICORDIA, CALYTHRIX, BAECKEA, LEPTOSPERMUM, CALLI-
STEMON, MELALEUCA, CALOTHAMNUS, EUCALYPTUS, METROSIDEROS, FEIJOA,
CAMPOMANESIA, PSIDIUM, MYRTUS, MYRCIA, CALYPTRANTHES, PIMENTA, EUGENIA,
SYZYGIUM, etc.

USEFUL PRODUCTS : *Eucalyptus Oil* (Eucalyptus globulus *Labill.*), Australia ;
Cajaput Oil (Melaleuca Leucadendron *L.*), Tropical Asia ; *Citron Gum* (Eu-
calyptus maculata *Hook.*), Queensland ; *Red Gum* (E. rostrata *Schlechtend.*),
Australia ; *Blue Gum* (E. globulus *Labill.*), S.E. Australia ; *Iron Bark Tree*
(E. leucoxylon *F. Muell.*), West Australia ; *Karri Timber* (E. diversicolor *F.
Muell.*), and *Jarrah* (E. marginata *Sm.*), Australia ; *Guava Fruit* (Psidium
Guajava *L.*), Tropics (cultivated) ; *Pimenta* or *Allspice* (Pimenta officinalis
Lindl.), Jamaica ; *Cloves* (flower buds of Eugenia caryophyllata *Thunb.*),
cultivated Tropics ; *Rose Apple* (Eugenia Jambos *L.*), India, etc. ; *Jambolana
Fruit* (E. Jambolana *Lam.*), E. Tropics.

119. LECYTHIDACEAE

Trees or shrubs ; leaves simple, *alternate, not gland-dotted*, but sometimes
with *large glands* on the *margin* ; stipules absent ; flowers usually rather large
and showy, actinomorphic or zygomorphic, hermaphrodite ; calyx 4-6-lobed,
lobes *valvate* or slightly imbricate ; petals 4-6, free or united into a *campanulate*

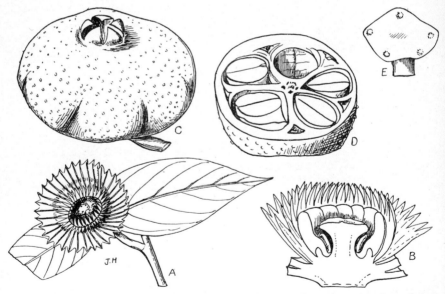

FIG. 119.—Napoleona Vogelii *Hk. f.* (Lecythidaceae). A, flower. B, same, vertical section. C, fruit.
D, same, cross section. E, stigma.—After Hook. Ic. Pl.

tube and then with many ribs ; stamens *numerous*, in several series, sometimes
the outer ones modified into staminodes and *resembling a corona* ; filaments
mostly united and often *arranged to one side* of the flower ; anthers basifixed
or rarely adnate, opening at the side by a slit ; staminal disk sometimes lobed ;

ovary inferior or semi-inferior, 2- or more-celled ; ovules 1 to many on axile placentas, sometimes towards the apex of the cells ; style mostly simple ; fruit woody, fibrous or fleshy, indehiscent or operculate at the apex ; seeds without endosperm ; embryo divided or entire.   B.H. 1 : 720 (under *Myrtaceae*). E.P. 3, 7 : 26.   Tropics.—BARRINGTONIA, PETERSIA, CAREYA, PLANCHONIA, GRIAS, GUSTAVIA, COURATARI, COUROUPITA, LECYTHOPSIS, LECYTHIS, NAPOLEONA, ASTERANTHOS, BERTHOLLETIA.

USEFUL PRODUCTS : *Couratari Fibre* (Couratari sp.) ;   *Wadadura Wood* (Lecythis grandiflora *Aubl.*), British Guiana ;   *Kakaralli Wood* (L. Ollaria *L.*), British Guiana ;   *Sapucaia Nuts* (L. usitata *Miers* and L. Ollaria *L.*) ;   *Brazil Nuts* (Bertholletia excelsa *H. B. & K.*), Brazil ;   *Anchovy Pear* (Grias cauliflora *L.*), W. Indies.

120. MELASTOMACEAE

Herbs, shrubs or trees, rarely scandent ; branches opposite ; leaves simple, *opposite* or *verticillate*, mostly with 3 to 9 *longitudinally parallel nerves,* rarely pinnately nerved ; stipules absent ; flowers ⚥, mostly very showy, actinomorphic ; calyx tubular, free or adnate to the ovary, sometimes by septa-like connections ; lobes imbricate or rarely valvate ; petals *imbricate*, free, rarely united at the base ; corona usually present between the petals and stamens ; stamens the same to double the number of the petals : filaments free, often

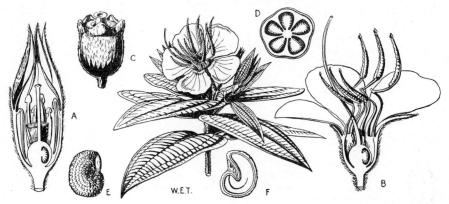

FIG. 120.—Melastoma malabathricum *L.* (Melastomaceae).   A, flower, vertical section, closed.   B, the same, open.   C, fruit.   D, ovary, cross section.   E, seed.   F, ditto, vertical section.—After Baill.

geniculate and inflexed ; anthers 2-celled, basifixed, opening by a single (rarely 2) *pore*, rarely by 2 slits ; *connective often thickened at the base and produced, often appendaged* ; ovary mostly *inferior*, 2- to many-celled, rarely 1-celled ; style simple ; ovules numerous, axile, rarely basal or parietal ; fruit capsular or baccate ; seeds often minute ; without endosperm ; embryo straight or conforming to the shape of the seed when large.   B.H. 1 : 725.   E.P. 3, 7 : 130. Mainly Tropics, rare in Subtropics. — MICROLICIA, PTEROLEPIS, PLEROMA, OSBECKIA, TRISTEMMA, MELASTOMA, DISSOTIS, MONOCHAETUM, RHEXIA, OXYSPORA, BLASTUS, SONERILA, AMPHIBLEMMA, MEDINILLA, OXYMERIS, MICONIA, CLIDEMIA, OSSAEA, ASTRONIA, MOURIRA, MEMECYLON, etc.

USEFUL PRODUCTS : Many beautiful flowering plants, a few cultivated.

121. COMBRETACEAE

Trees or shrubs, often scandent ; leaves *opposite*, alternate or rarely verticillate, simple ; *stipules 0* ; flowers spicate or racemose, mostly small, ⚥, rarely ♂♀ ; calyx-tube *adnate to the ovary* ; limb 4-8-fid or lobed, *lobes valvate* ; petals 4-5 or 0, rarely many, small, imbricate or valvate ; stamens 4-10, rarely more ; filaments *inflexed in bud* ; anthers versatile, didymous, opening lengthwise by slits ; disk epigynous ; ovary inferior, rarely half inferior, 1-celled ; style simple ; ovules 2-6, *suspended from the apex of the ovary* by slender funicles ;

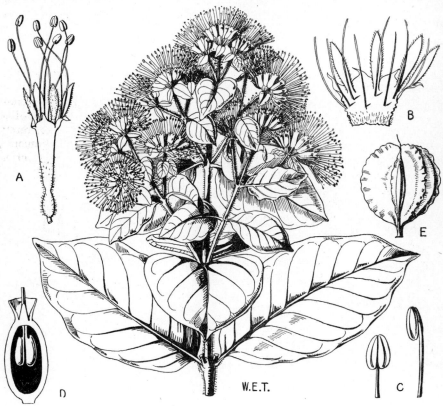

FIG. 121.—Combretum racemosum *Guill. & Perr.* (Combretaceae). A, flower. B, to show insertion of stamens. C, stamens. D, carpel. E, fruit.—After Guill. & Perr.

fruit often *winged*, rarely dehiscent ; seed pendulous, without endosperm ; embryo with convolute, plicate or contorted cotyledons and small radicle. B.H. 1 : 683. E.P. 3, 7 : 106. Tropics, rare in Subtropics.—COMBRETUM, PTELEOPSIS, TERMINALIA, ANOGEISSUS, GUIERA, LUMNITZERA, LAGUNCULARIA, QUISQUALIS, etc.

USEFUL PRODUCTS : *Bahera Tree* (Terminalia belerica *Roxb.*) ; *Asan* Wood (T. tomentosa *W. & A.*), India ; *Myrobalans* or *Hirda* fruits (T. Chebula *Retz.*), India ; *Bois Benzoin* (T. angustifolia *Jacq.*), Mauritius ; *Indian Almond* (T. Catappa *L.*), India. Some beautiful climbers.

122. Rhizophoraceae

Trees or shrubs, frequently on maritime shores; branches swollen at the nodes; leaves opposite and stipulate, rarely alternate and exstipulate, leathery, simple; stipules inter-petiolar, caducous; flowers ⚥, in axillary inflorescences; *calyx-tube adnate to the ovary* or free; lobes 3-14, per-sistent, *valvate*; petals usually small, often notched, bifid or lacerate, *convolute or inflexed in bud*; stamens equal or usually more than the petals, often in *pairs opposite the petals* on the edge or at the base of a perigynous disk; anthers

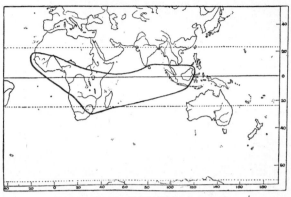

Range of Anisophyllea (Rhizophoraceae).

2- or many-celled; ovary mostly inferior, 2-6-celled or 1-celled by the suppression of the septa; style simple or rarely styles several; ovules 2, rarely

Fig. 122.—Anisophyllea laurina *R. Br.* (Rhizophoraceae).   A, male flower.   B, female flower.
C, petal.   D, stamen.—After Baill.

more, inserted towards the apex on the inner angle of the cells; fruit mostly indehiscent, usually 1-seeded or cells 1-seeded; seeds with or without fleshy endosperm ; cotyledons terete or connate. B.H. 1 : 677. E.P. 3, 7 : 42. Mainly mangrove trees of the Tropics.—RHIZOPHORA, BRUGUIERA, CARALLIA, CASSIPOUREA (Weihea), ANISOPHYLLEA, ANOPYXIS, POGA.

USEFUL PRODUCTS : *Poga Nuts* (Poga oleosa *Pierre*).

Besides the position assigned to this family here there is also strong affinity with the *Tiliales*.

Order 34. GUTTIFERALES

Advanced and continued hypogynous types of the *Theales* (p. 173), with opposite leaves as in *Myrtales* and frequently gland-dotted or resinous-lined ; some herbs ; stamens uniting into separate bundles (phalanges) ; no endosperm ; sepals always imbricate ; flowers tending to become unisexual.

123. HYPERICACEAE

Herbs to trees, rarely climbers ; *juice resinous* ; leaves *opposite* or *verticillate*, simple, often *gland-dotted* ; stipules absent ; indumentum when present often *stellate* ; flowers showy, mostly terminal, solitary to cymose-paniculate, yellow

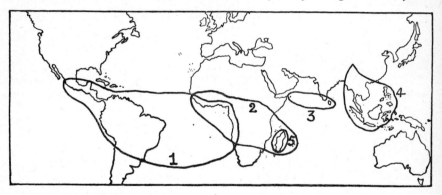

1, Distribution of Vismia ; 2, Haronga ; 3, Hypericum mysorense ; 4, Cratoxylon ; 5, Eliaea.

or white, ☿, actinomorphic ; sepals *imbricate* ; petals imbricate or contorted ; stamens *numerous*, hypogynous, often *united into bundles* ; anthers 2-celled, opening lengthwise ; ovary 1-celled or variously 3-5-celled ; styles mostly free ; ovules numerous, axile or pendulous, anatropous ; fruit a capsule or berry ; rarely a drupe ; seeds with straight or arcuate embryo, but no endosperm. B.H. 1 : 163. E.P. 3, 6 : 205 (under *Guttiferae*).—HYPERICUM, CRATOXYLON, ENDODESMIA, VISMIA, PSOROSPERMUM, HARONGA, etc.

USEFUL PRODUCTS : A few ornamental garden plants.

124. EUCRYPHIACEAE

Resinous, glabrous or tomentose trees ; leaves *opposite, simple* or *pinnate*, evergreen ; stipules small, *intrapetiolar* ; flowers axillary, solitary, actinomorphic, large, white ; sepals 4, rigid, imbricate, cohering at the apex and somewhat calyptrately deciduous ; petals 4, large, imbricate ; stamens numerous, in many series on a thin disk ; filaments filiform ; anthers small, *orbicular* ; ovary 5-12-celled, sulcate, narrowed into 5-12 slender styles ; ovules few in

FIG. 123.—Hypericum Hookerianum *Wight & Arn.* (Hypericaceae).   A, bundle of stamens.   B, ovary. C, cross section of same.   D, fruit.   E, seed.—After Bot. Mag.

each cell, pendulous from the inner angle of the cells ; fruit a leathery or woody capsule, oblong, *septicidally* 5-12-*valved*, valves boat-shaped, beaked by the persistent styles and separating from the axis ; seeds pendulous, oblong, compressed, imbricate, *winged* ; embryo in the middle of the endosperm ; cotyledons

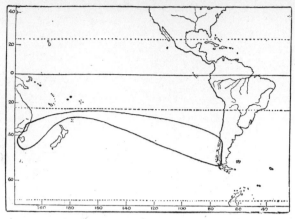

Distribution of Eucryphia (Eucryphiaceae).

FIG. 124.—Eucryphia glutinosa *Focke* (Eucryphiaceae). A, stamen. B, ovary. C, vertical section of same. D, fruit. E, segment of fruit. F, seed. G, cross section of same.—After Gay.

leafy ; radicle short. B.H. 1 : 616 (under *Rosaceae*). E.P. 3, 6 : 129.
Australia, Tasmania, Chile.—EUCRYPHIA.
Ornamental trees with showy flowers.

125. QUIINACEAE

Trees, shrubs or climbers ; leaves *opposite* or *whorled*, simple or pinnately
lobed ; *lateral nerves numerous*, tertiary nerves *feather-veined* ; stipules paired,
interpetiolar, rigid or foliaceous ; flowers ♀ or ♂ ♀, paniculate or racemose ;
sepals 4-5, imbricate in pairs, small, unequal ; petals 4-8, imbricate ; stamens

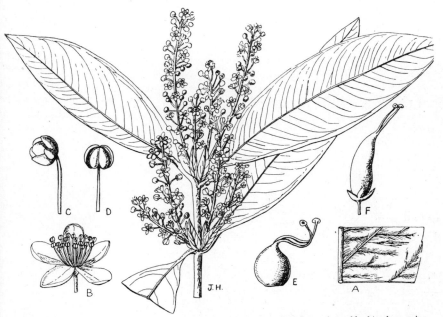

FIG. 125.—Quiina longifolia *Spruce* (Quiinaceae).   A, portion of under surface of leaf to show veins.
B, flower.   C, bud.   D, stamen.   E, ovary.   F, young fruit.—Orig.

15-30 or more, free or nearly so ; anthers 2-celled, opening lengthwise ; ovary
2-11-celled ; styles 2-3, free, with disk-like stigmas ; ovules paired, ascending ;
fruit a 1-4-seeded berry ; *seed tomentose* ; embryo straight ; endosperm 0.
B.H. 1 : 176 (under *Guttiferae*). E.P. 3, 6 : 165. Tropical America.—QUIINA.

126. GUTTIFERAE

Trees or shrubs with *resinous juice* ; leaves *opposite*, simple ; stipules absent ;
flowers actinomorphic, ♂ ♀ and polygamous or dioecious, rarely ♀ ; sepals 2-6,
rarely more, imbricate ; petals the same number, hypogynous, contorted or
imbricate, very rarely subvalvate ; stamens mostly numerous, hypogynous,
free or *variously connate* in the lower part or into bundles opposite the petals ;
anthers 2-celled, opening lengthwise ; rudimentary ovary sometimes present in
the ♀ flower ; staminodes often present in the ♀ flower ; ovary sessile, superior,

1- to many-celled ; ovules 1 to many, on the inner angle or erect from the base of the cells, rarely parietal ; stigmas various, sometimes radiating ; fruit

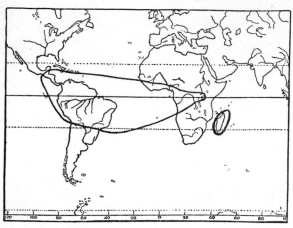

dehiscent or not, sometimes large and globose; seeds often arillate, without endosperm ; embryo large ; cotyledons often minute. B.H. 1 : 167, partly. E.P. 3, 6 : 194 (excl. *Hypericaceae*). Tropics. —CLUSIA, TOVOMITA, SYMPHONIA (see map), PENTADESMA, GARCINIA, XANTHOCHYMUS, RHEEDIA, CALOPHYLLUM, MAMMEA, etc.

Range of Symphonia (Guttiferae).

USEFUL PRODUCTS: *Mangosteen* fruits (Garcinia Mangostana *L.*), cultivated, Tropics ; *Butter* or *Tallow Tree* (Pentadesma butyracea *Sabine*), W. Africa ; *Gamboge Tree* (Garcinia Hanburyi *Hk. f.*), Siam ; *Bitter Kola*

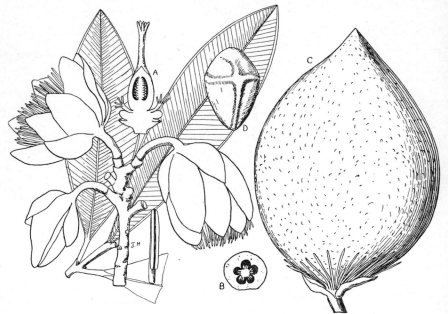

FIG. 126.—Pentadesma butyracea *Sabine* (Guttiferae).   A, vertical section of ovary.   B, cross section of same.   C, fruit.   D, seed.—After Hook. Ic. Pl.

(Garcinia· Kola *Heckel*), W. Africa ; *Alexandrian Laurel* (Calophyllum Inophyllum *L.*), India, etc., giving *Pinnay* or *Domba Oil* ; *Mammee Apple* (Mammea americana *L.*), Tropical America.

Order 35. TILIALES

Trees or shrubs ; indumentum mostly stellate ; leaves simple to compound, mostly alternate, stipulate ; flowers hypogynous, actinomorphic, ♀ or ♂♀ ; calyx valvate ; stamens free to monadelphous ; anthers 2-celled ; ovary superior, with axile placentation ; seeds with copious endosperm.—Mostly Tropics (except some *Tiliaceae*).

127. SCYTOPETALACEAE

Trees ; leaves alternate, simple ; stipules absent ; flowers ♀, actinomorphic, in terminal panicles or axillary racemes, or fasciculate on the old wood ; calyx cupular, entire or toothed ; petals 3-10, free, *valvate* ; stamens *numerous*, in

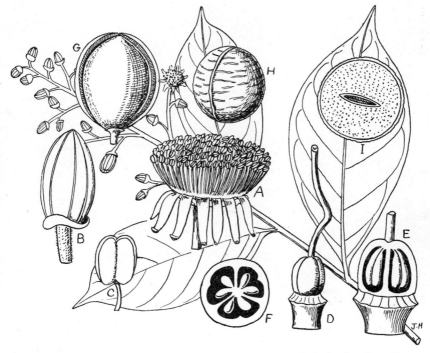

FIG. 127.—Oubanguia laurifolia *Pierre* (Scytopetalaceae). A, flower. B, bud. C, anther. D, ovary. E, vertical section of same. F, cross section of same. G, fruit. H, seed. I, cross section of same. —Orig. partly.

several series on the margin of or on the disk, free or united towards the base ; anthers 2-celled, opening by a *pore* or slit at the side or towards the top ; ovary superior, 3-6-celled ; ovules 2-several in each cell, axile ; fruit woody ; seed with ruminate or uniform copious endosperm and linear embryo. B.H. 1 : 995. E.P. N. 242. Tropical W. Africa. — SCYTOPETALUM, BRAZZEIA, RHAPTOPETALUM, OUBANGUIA.

128. Tiliaceae

Trees or shrubs, rarely herbs; leaves alternate, rarely opposite, simple; stipules paired or absent; flowers cymose, actinomorphic, ⚥, rarely ♂ ♀; sepals mostly 5 and *valvate*; petals free, present or absent, sometimes like the sepals, contorted, imbricate or valvate; stamens mostly numerous, *free* or *shortly connate* at the base or in 5-10 bundles; *anthers* 2-*celled,* opening by a slit lengthwise or by an apical pore; ovary superior, sessile, 2-10-celled; style usually simple and divided at the apex, rarely the stigmas sessile; ovules on axile placentas; fruit 2-10-celled, rarely 1-celled by abortion, sometimes more-

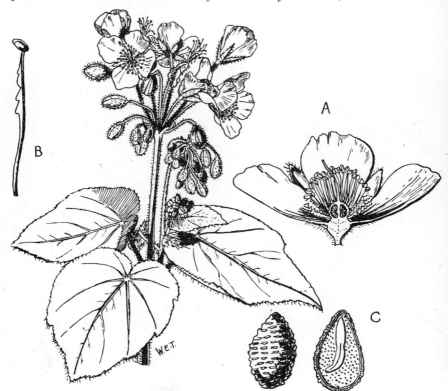

FIG. 128.—Sparmannia africana *L. f.* (Tiliaceae).   A vertical section of flower.   B, stamen.
C, seed and vertical section of same.—After Baill.

celled by transverse dissepiments, baccate or drupaceous or variously dehiscent; seeds solitary to many in each cell, not arillate, sometimes pilose, mostly with copious or thin endosperm; embryo usually straight; incl. *Elaeocarpaceae.* B.H. 1 : 228.   E.P. 3, 6 : 8.   Throughout the world.—Brownlowia, Grewia, Triumfetta, Sparmannia, Corchorus, Luhea, Tilia, Glyphaea, Prockia, Sloanea, Aristotelia, Elaeocarpus, Tricuspidaria, etc.

Useful Products : Several valuable fibres from *Corchorus, Grewia* and *Triumfetta. Common Lime* (Tilia vulgaris *Heyne*); *Basswood* (Tilia americana *L.*), N. America ; *Macqui Berries* (Aristotelia Maqui *L'Hérit.*), Chile.

129. GONYSTYLACEAE

Trees ; leaves alternate, leathery, penninerved, nerves numerous ; stipules absent ; flowers ♀, paniculate, actinomorphic ; calyx 5-lobed, imbricate ; *petals numerous*, linear, sometimes *divided nearly to the base* ; stamens *numerous* ;

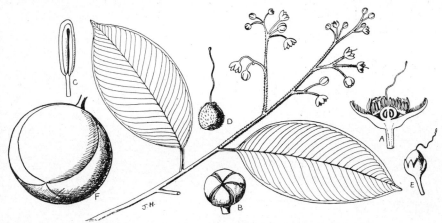

FIG. 129.—Gonystylus Miquelianus *T. & B.* (Gonystylaceae). A, vertical section of flower. B, bud. C, anther. D, ovary. E, young fruit. F, fruit.—Orig.

filaments free ; anthers basifixed, 2-celled, opening by longitudinal slits ; ovary 3-5-celled ; *style thread-like, bent* ; stigma small ; ovule solitary in each cell, pendulous from near the top ; fruit woody, at length opening into the cells ; seeds large, without endosperm. B.H. 3 : 201. E.P. N. 231 (under *Thymelaeaceae*). Malaya.—GONYSTYLUS.

130. STERCULIACEAE

Trees or shrubs with mostly soft wood, or rarely herbs ; indumentum often *stellate* ; leaves alternate or very rarely subopposite, simple or digitately compound ; stipules usually present ; flowers variously arranged, but inflorescence rarely terminal, ♀ or ♂ ♀, actinomorphic ; sepals 3-5, more or less partially united, *valvate* ; petals 5 or absent, hypogynous, free or adnate at the base to the staminal-tube, *contorted-imbricate* ; stamens often *connate into a tube* with as many staminodes, sometimes in more than one series, or the stamens quite free ; *anthers 2-celled*, very rarely the cells subconfluent at the apex ; ovary free, of 2-5 or rarely 10-12 more or less united carpels or reduced to one carpel ; ovules 2 or more in each cell, rarely 1, inserted on the inner angle, ascending or horizontal ; style simple or divided into lobes or rarely the styles free from the base ; fruit dry or rarely baccate, indehiscent or variously dehiscent; seed with fleshy or thin or no endosperm ; embryo straight or curved. B.H. 1 : 214. E.P. 3, 6 : 69. Mainly Tropics and Subtropics.—STERCULIA, COLA, HELICTERES, PTEROSPERMUM, DOMBEYA, MELHANIA, HERMANNIA, MAHERNIA, MELOCHIA, WALTHERIA, ABROMA, THEOBROMA, GUAZUMA, BUETTNERIA, RULINGIA, COMMERSONIA, THOMASIA, LASIOPETALUM, etc.

USEFUL PRODUCTS : Various fibrous barks. *Cola* or *Kola Nuts* (Cola vera

O

K. Schum.), W. Tropical Africa ; *Cocoa* and *Chocolate* (Theobroma cacao *L.*), Tropical America, now chief industry in Gold Coast.

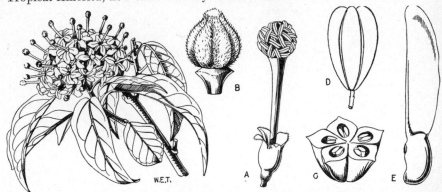

FIG. 130.—Reevesia thyrsoidea *Lindl.* (Sterculiaceae).   A, androgynoecium.   B, ovary.   C, cross section of same.   D, fruit.   E, seed.—Orig.

131. BOMBACACEAE

Trees with sometimes bulging stems through excess of water storage ; leaves simple or digitate, alternate, often lepidote ; stipules deciduous ; flowers ♂,

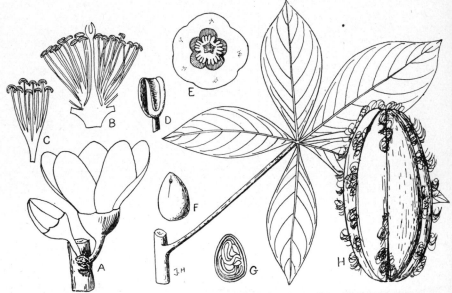

FIG. 131.—Bombax buonopozense *P. Beauv.* (Bombacaceae).   A, flowers.   B, stamens and ovary. C, single bundle of stamens.   D, anther.   E, cross section of ovary.   F, seed.   G, vertical section of same.   H, fruit.—After Engler, partly.

large and showy ; calyx closed and *valvate* in bud or rarely deeply 5-lobed with slightly imbricate lobes, often subtended by an epicalyx ; petals often elongated, sometimes absent ; stamens free or *united into a tube* ; anthers reniform to linear, 1-*celled* ; pollen smooth ; ovary superior, 2-5-celled ; style simple, capitate, or lobed ; ovules 2 or more on the inner angle of each cell ; capsule loculicidally dehiscent or not dehiscent, the valves rarely falling away ; seeds often embedded in hairs from the wall of the fruit, with little or no endosperm and flat or contorted or plicate cotyledons. B.H. 1 : 209 (under *Malvaceae*). E.P. 3, 6 : 53. Tropics. — ADANSONIA, PACHIRA, BOMBAX, ERIODENDRON, FREMONTIA, DURIO.

USEFUL PRODUCTS : *Baobab, Monkey Bread* or *Monkey Tamarind* (Adansonia digitata *L.*), Tropical Africa ; *Silk Cotton* or *Semul* (Bombax malabaricum *D.C.*), Tropical Asia, yields also *Mucherus Gum* ; *Kapok Tree* (Eriodendron anfractuosum *D.C.*), Tropics ; *Durian Fruits* (Durio Zibethinus *Murr.*), Malaya.

Order 36. MALVALES

More or less as in *Tiliales*, but herbaceous to softly woody, often fibrous ; stamens more perfectly monadelphous and anthers 1-celled.—Temperate Regions and Tropics.

FIG. 132.—Gaya Lyallii *Hook.*(Malvaceae). A and B, flowers. C, anther. C₁, ovary. D, fruit. E, vertical section of carpel. F, seed. G, section of fruiting carpel. H, stellate hair.—After Bot. Mag.

132. MALVACEAE

Herbs or shrubs, often with fibrous stems ; indumentum usually stellate or lepidote ; leaves alternate, entire or variously lobed, mostly palmately nerved ; stipules present ; flowers actinomorphic, ♀, or rarely dioecious or polygamous ; sepals 3-5, more or less united, *valvate*, sometimes subtended by an *involucre* of *bracteoles* (epicalyx) ; petals 5, free from each other, but often adnate at the base to the staminal-column, contorted or imbricate ; stamens numerous, hypogynous, *monadelphous*, the staminal-column divided at the apex and bearing 1-*celled anthers* (by the division of the filaments), opening lengthwise ; pollen muricate ; ovary 2- or more-celled, often 5-celled, rarely of 1 carpel, or rarely the carpels in vertical rows ; style branched above, rarely clavate ; ovules 1 or more from the inner angle at each cell ; fruit dry, rarely baccate, breaking into cocci, or capsular ; seed with usually some endosperm and straight or curved embryo ; cotyledons often plicate or contortuplicate. B.H. 1 : 200, partly. E.P. 3, 6 : 30. Throughout the world except very cold regions.— MALOPE, ALTHAEA, LAVATERA, MALVA, SIDALCEA, MALVASTRUM, PLAGIANTHUS, CRISTARIA, SIDA, WISSADULA, ABUTILON, SPHAERALCEA, URENA, PAVONIA, HIBISCUS, THESPESIA, GOSSYPIUM, etc.

USEFUL PRODUCTS : *Cotton* (Gossypium barbadense *L.*, etc.) ; *Oil-cake* from seeds. Many fibre plants.

Order 37. MALPIGHIALES

Mostly climbers with opposite leaves ; flowers hypogynous, actinomorphic to subzygomorphic ; calyx often bearing a pair of large glands ; stamens usually definite, often connate at the base ; anthers 2-celled ; ovary superior, syncarpous with subapical placentation ; ovules few ; seeds usually without endosperm.—Tropics.

133. MALPIGHIACEAE

Trees, shrubs or climbers, with often *appressed medifixed hairs* ; leaves mostly opposite, simple ; *glands* often present either on the petiole or on the lower surface of the leaves ; stipules present or absent, sometimes large and connate ; flowers ⚥, rarely polygamous, mostly symmetric ; sepals 5, imbricate or very rarely valvate, often *biglandular* outside ; petals 5, clawed, convolute ; disk small ; stamens mostly 10, hypogynous or nearly so, sometimes some without anthers ; filaments often connate at the base ; anthers short, 2-celled, sometimes winged, opening lengthwise ; carpels 3, rarely 2 or 4, free or more or less connate into a 3-celled ovary ; cells 1-ovuled ; styles usually distinct ; ovule ascending from a broad pendulous funicle ; fruiting carpels often winged, or carpels connate into a fleshy or woody drupe ; seeds without endosperm and with straight, curved or uncinate, rarely circinate, embryo. B.H. 1 : 247. E.P. 3, 4 : 41. Mainly Tropics, rare in Subtropics.—BYRSONIMA, MALPIGHIA, HETEROPTERYS, ACRIDOCARPUS, STIGMAPHYLLON, BANISTERIA, TRISTELLATEIA, ASPIDOPTERYS, TETRAPTERYS, HIRAEA, GAUDICHAUDIA, etc.

USEFUL PRODUCTS : *Shoemakers' Bark* (Byrsonima spicata *Rich.*), West Indies.

134. HUMIRIACEAE

Trees or shrubs ; leaves alternate, simple ; *stipules absent* ; flowers ⚥, actinomorphic ; sepals 5, imbricate, shortly or wholly connate ; petals 5, free, soon falling away, slightly imbricate-contorted ; stamens 10 or more, hypogynous, more or less *connate* in the lower part ; anthers versatile, 2-4-celled, opening lengthwise ; disk *annular* and often toothed or of separate glands, surrounding the base of the ovary ; ovary free, sessile, 5-7-celled ; style simple ; ovules 1-3, pendulous from the apex, anatropous ; fruit a drupe with rather thin fleshy

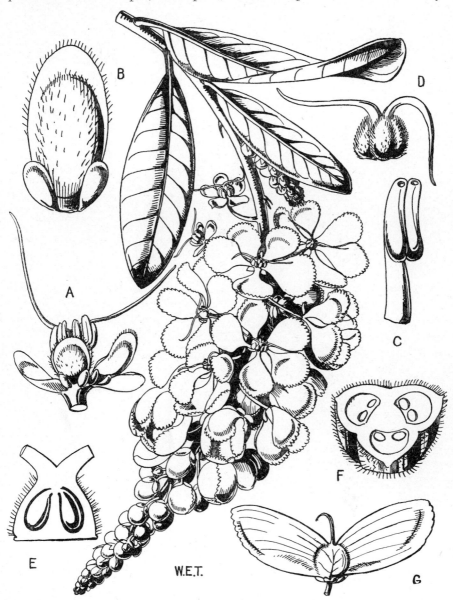

FIG. 133.—Acridocarpus natalitius *A. Juss.* (Malpighiaceae).   A, flower.   B, sepal with glands.   C, anther.
D, ovary.   E, vertical section of same.   F, cross section of same.   G, fruit.—After Bot. Mag.

pericarp and hard endocarp, sometimes with numerous resin-filled cavities ; seeds 1-2 in each cell ; embryo straight in the middle of copious endosperm ;

cotyledons short. B.H. 1 : 246.   E.P. 3, 4 : 35.   Tropical America and Africa.—HUMIRIA, SACOGLOTTIS, VANTANEA.

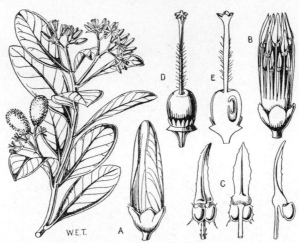

FIG. 134.—Humiria arenaria *Guill.* (Humiriaceae). A, flower-bud. B, stamens. C, views of anther. D, ovary. E, vertical section of same.—After Baill.

135. ERYTHROXYLACEAE

Trees, shrubs or undershrubs ; leaves alternate, rarely opposite, simple, entire ; *stipules intrapetiolar*, rarely extrapetiolar, often caducous ; flowers

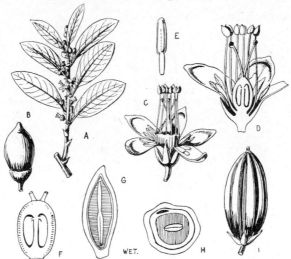

FIG. 135.—Erythroxylon Coca *L.* (Erythroxylaceae). A, shoot with flowers. B, flower-bud. C, flower. D, vertical section of same. E, anther. F, vertical section of ovary. G, vertical section of seed. H, cross section of same. I, fruit.—After Le Maout & Decne.

fasciculate, ⚥, rarely subdioecious, hypogynous, actinomorphic ; calyx persistent, campanulate, lobes 5, imbricate ; petals 5, free, deciduous, imbricate, mostly ligulate on the inside ; stamens 10, 2-seriate, more or less connate at the base ;

anthers ellipsoid, 2-celled, opening lengthwise ; ovary tricarpellary, 3-celled, mostly two of the cells sterile, fertile cells 1-2-ovuled ; ovules pendulous, anatropous ; styles 3, free or more or less connate ; stigmas oblique, depressed-capitate or clavate ; fruit drupaceous ; seeds with or without endosperm ; embryo straight. B.H. 1 : 244 (under *Linaceae*). E.P. 3, 4 : 37. Tropics and Subtropics.—ERYTHROXYLON, OCHTHOCOSMUS, PHYLLOCOSMUS, IXONANTHES, etc.

USEFUL PRODUCTS : *Cocaine* (Erythroxylon Coca *Lamk.*), S. America.

Order 38. EUPHORBIALES

Trees, shrubs or rarely annual herbs ; indumentum simple, stellate or lepidote ; leaves simple or rarely compound ; stipules mostly present ; flowers hypogynous, ♂ ♀, actinomorphic ; calyx rarely absent, imbricate or valvate ; petals rarely present ; stamens very numerous to solitary, free or monadelphous ; ovary superior, with axile placentation ; seeds with copious endosperm.

136. EUPHORBIACEAE

Herbs, shrubs or trees, occasionally with milky juice ; leaves alternate or rarely opposite, simple or compound, sometimes reduced, mostly stipulate ; flowers ♂ ♀, mostly monoecious ; sepals valvate or imbricate or in very specialised inflorescences sometimes much reduced or absent (*Euphorbia*) ; petals absent

FIG. 136.—A-G, Ricinus communis *L.* (Euphorbiaceae).   H-J, Euphorbia Lathyris *L.*—After Baill.

or rarely present and sometimes united (*Jatropha*) ; stamens from 1 to 1000, free or connate ; anthers 2- (3-4-) celled, erect or inflexed in bud, opening lengthwise, rarely by pores ; rudimentary ovary often present in the male flowers ; ovary mostly 3-celled ; styles free or united at the base ; ovules solitary or paired, pendulous ; funicle often thickened ; disk often present in both sexes, annular or of separate glands ; fruit a capsule or drupe ; seeds often with a conspicuous *caruncle* ; endosperm mostly copious, fleshy ; embryo straight. B.H. 3 : 239 (excl. *Buxaceae*). E.P. 3, 5 : 1. Tropics and Temperate Regions.— EUPHORBIA, BRIDELIA, PHYLLANTHUS, APOROSA, ANTIDESMA, BACCAUREA, HYMENOCARDIA, HEVEA, JATROPHA, ALEURITES, CROTON, CODIAEUM, CLUYTIA,

Argithamnia, Manihot, Acalypha, Alchornea, Macaranga, Mallotus, Ricinus, Tragia, Dalechampia, Sapium, Hura, Pera, etc.

Useful Products : This family furnishes very many valuable commodities, amongst which the most important are *Hevea Rubber* (Hevea brasiliensis *Müll. Arg.*), native of Brazil, much cultivated in Eastern Tropics ; *Ceara Rubber* (Manihot Glaziovii *Müll. Arg.*), S. America ; *Castor Oil* (Ricinus communis *L.*), widely cultivated ; *Tapioca* (Manihot) ; *Kamala* (Mallotus philippinensis *Müll. Arg.*), India to Austral. ; *Cascarilla Bark* (Croton Eluteria *Benn.*) ; *Physic Nut* (Jatropha Curcas *L.*), Tropical America ; *Garden Croton* (*Codiaeum* spp. and vars.).

Order 39. CUNONIALES

Trees or shrubs ; leaves alternate, opposite or whorled, simple or compound ; stipules mostly present ; flowers mostly ⚥, perigynous to epigynous ; petals usually present, free ; stamens numerous to few ; carpels free or united, with parietal or axile placentation ; seeds with mostly copious endosperm and small embryo.—Temperate and Subtropical Regions.

137. Cunoniaceae

Trees or shrubs ; leaves *trifoliolate* or *pinnate*, rarely simple, mostly *opposite* or rarely verticillate ; leaflets often *glandular-serrate* ; stipules sometimes large and *united in pairs* within the petioles ; flowers ⚥ or dioecious, from solitary to paniculate or capitate ; sepals imbricate or valvate, sometimes accrescent ; petals present or absent, entire or toothed, or 2-3-lobed, the lobes sometimes gland-tipped ; stamens numerous to few and then alternate with the petals ; filaments free ; anthers 2-celled, opening lengthwise ; disk often annular ; carpels superior, free or united into a 2-5-celled ovary with axile or apical placentas ; styles free, straight or circinate

FIG. 137.—Cunonia capensis *L.* (Cunoniaceae). A, flower. B, stamens. C, ovary.—After Bot. Mag.

in bud ; ovules numerous or few ; fruit dehiscent or not ; seeds glabrous or long-pilose ; endosperm usually copious with rather small straight embryo. B.H. 1 : 649 (under *Saxifragaceae*). E.P. 3, 2a : 94. Mainly Australasia ; a

few in S. Africa and S. America.—CODIA, PANCHERIA, CALLICOMA, SPIRAE-
ANTHEMUM, WEINMANNIA, CUNONIA, CERATOPETALUM.

USEFUL PRODUCTS : *Lightwood* (Ceratopetalum apetalum *D. Don*), New
South Wales.

138. BRUNELLIACEAE

Trees, sometimes spiny, often tomentose ; leaves *opposite* or verticillate,
simple, *trifoliolate or imparipinnate* ; stipules present ; flowers small, in axillary
or terminal panicles, *dioecious*, actinomorphic ; calyx 4-5-partite, *valvate* ;
petals absent ; disk hirsute, adnate to the calyx, 8-10-lobed ; stamens 8-10,

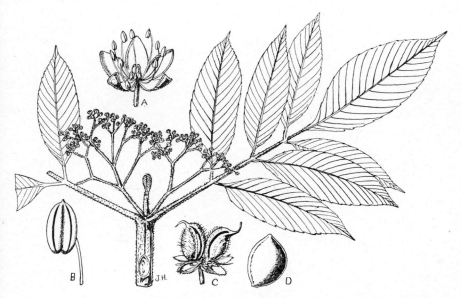

FIG. 138.—Brunellia comocladifolia *H.B. & K.* (Brunelliaceae). A, flower. B, stamen. C, fruit.
D, seed.—Orig.

inserted at the base of the disk ; ovary rudimentary, sessile ; rudiments of
stamens in the ♀ flowers ; carpels 4-5, *free*, sessile, 1-celled ; styles subulate,
recurved, with simple stigmas ; ovules paired, collateral ; fruits 4-5 or
fewer, spreading, 2-valved, 1-2-seeded ; seeds with fleshy endosperm and flat
cotyledons. B.H. 1 : 313 (under *Simarubaceae*). E.P. Nachtr. 182. Tropical
America.—BRUNELLIA.

139. ESCALLONIACEAE

Trees or shrubs ; leaves simple, alternate, rarely subopposite or subverticillate, mostly with *gland-tipped teeth* ; flowers ☿, rarely dioecious or polygamous, mostly racemose ; sepals mostly united in the lower part, rarely free ;
imbricate or valvate, often persistent ; petals free or rarely connate into a
short tube, imbricate or valvate ; stamens 5, rarely 4 or 6, sometimes alternating
with staminodes, perigynous, free ; anthers 2-celled, opening lengthwise ; disk-

lobes alternating with the stamens ; ovary *superior* to *quite inferior*, syncarpous
or rarely apocarpous, 1-6-celled ; ovules numerous, *parietal* in the 1-celled
ovaries, otherwise on central placentas ; fruit a capsule or berry ; seeds with

FIG. 139.—Escallonia macrantha *Lindl.* (Escalloniaceae).   A, sepals and ovary.   B, ovary.
C, cross section of same.—After Bot. Mag.

small embryo and copious endosperm.   B.H. 1 : 644.   E.P. 3, 2a : 79 (under
Saxifragaceae).   Mainly S. Hemisphere, rare in Africa.—ESCALLONIA, BREXIA,
ARGOPHYLLUM, CARPODETUS, CHORISTYLIS, ITEA, POLYOSMA, PHYLLONOMA,
ANOPTERUS, etc.—Some useful garden shrubs.

140. GREYIACEAE (Hutchinson, fam. nov.)

Small trees with soft wood ; leaves alternate, simple, currant-like ; petiole
clasping the branchlets ; stipules absent ; flowers actinomorphic, racemose, ⚥ ;
sepals 5, free, imbricate, persistent ; petals 5, perigynous, imbricate ; disk cupular,
crowned by 10 gland-like processes ; stamens within the disk, free ; anthers
2-celled, didymous ; ovary deeply 5-grooved, 1-celled but nearly 5-celled by
the intrusive margins of the carpels ; style 1 ; ovules numerous, parietal ; fruit
a capsule opening between the carpels ; seeds minute, with endosperm and very
small embryo.   B.H. 1 : 1000 (under *Sapindaceae*).   E.P. 3, 5 : 382 (under
Melianthaceae).   S. Africa.—GREYIA.

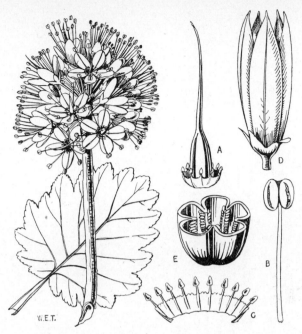

FIG. 140.—Greyia Sutherlandii *Harv.* (Greyiaceae). A, ovary. B, stamen. C, disc with staminodes. D, fruit. E, cross section of ovary.—Partly after Harv.

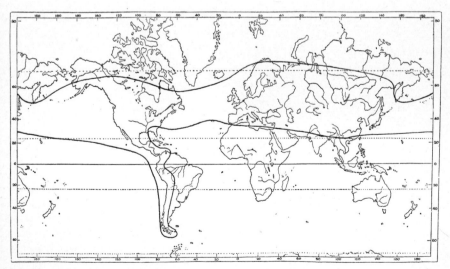

Range of genus Ribes (Grossulariaceae).

141. GROSSULARIACEAE

Shrubs, often armed with spines ; leaves often fasciculate, simple, *plicate*, or *convolute* in bud ; stipules absent or adnate to the petiole ; flowers often unisexual by abortion, racemose or subsolitary ; calyx-tube adnate to the ovary, lobes imbricate or subvalvate ; petals 4-5, mostly small or scale-like ; stamens 4-5, alternate with the petals ; anthers 2-celled, didymous or subglobose, opening lengthwise ; ovary *inferior*, 1-celled, with 2 *parietal* placentas ; styles

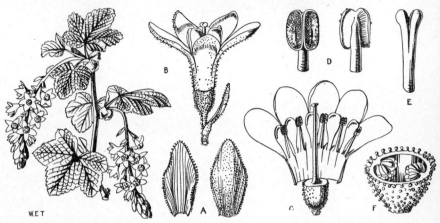

FIG. 141.—Ribes sanguineum *L.* (Grossulariaceae). A, sepals. B, flower. C, same opened. D, front and back views of anther. E, stigma. F, cross section of ovary.—Orig.

2, free or connate, with undivided stigmas ; ovules few or numerous, 2- or more-seriate ; fruit a pulpy berry, crowned by the persistent calyx ; seed with endosperm and rather small embryo. B.H. 1 : 654. E.P. 3, 2a : 88 (under *Saxifragaceae*). Temperate N. Hemisphere, Andes of S. America.—RIBES.

USEFUL PRODUCTS : *Gooseberries* (Ribes Grossularia *L.*) ; *Black currants*, *Red currants*, *White currants* (forms of R. rubrum *L.*). Some beautiful early-flowering shrubs.

142. HYDRANGEACEAE

Shrubs or trees ; leaves *opposite*, simple, without stipules, glabrous or hairy, the hairs either simple, *stellate*, or *lepidote-glandular* ; flowers small, hermaphrodite or some sterile, in corymbose or paniculate cymes, sometimes the marginal flowers sterile and with conspicuously enlarged sepals ; calyx of 4-10 perigynous sepals ; petals 4-10, valvate, imbricate or contorted in bud ; stamens *perigynous*, 5 to many ; filaments free or slightly connate at the base ; ovary partly or wholly *inferior*, of 2-5 or rarely 10 united carpels with short separate or connate styles and rather thick stigmas ; ovules few or numerous, anatropous ; fruit a *capsule opening at the top* or sometimes strongly ribbed and the seeds escaping between the ribs, rarely baccate ; seeds usually numerous and small, rarely solitary. B.H. 1 : 640. E.P. 3, 2a : 73 (under *Saxifragaceae*). N. Temperate and Subtropical Zone.—HYDRANGEA, DEUTZIA, PHILADELPHUS, JAMESIA, FENDLERA, CARPENTERIA, etc.

USEFUL PRODUCTS : Many beautiful flowering shrubs.

FIG. 142.—Carpenteria californica *Torr.* (Hydrangeaceae). A, stamen. B, ovary. C, cross section of same. D, seed. E, vertical section of same.—After Bot. Mag. partly.

Order 40. ROSALES

Trees, shrubs or herbs; leaves alternate or rarely opposite, simple or compound; stipules rarely absent; flowers mostly ♀, actinomorphic; petals free; stamens perigynous to epigynous, mostly free; carpels free or variously united and then ovary often inferior ; seeds without endosperm.—Mainly Temperate Regions.

143. Rosaceae

Trees, shrubs or herbs ; leaves various, simple or compound, alternate or rarely opposite, sometimes with glandular teeth ; stipules mostly present and paired, sometimes adnate to the petiole ; flowers mostly actinomorphic and ♀ ; calyx free or adnate to the ovary ; lobes mostly 5, imbricate, the fifth lobe adaxial ; disk lining the tube of the calyx ; petals the same number as the calyx - lobes, rarely absent, equal or rarely unequal, imbricate ; stamens numerous, rarely definite or reduced to 1 or 2 ; filaments free, rarely connate ; anthers small , 2-celled, opening lengthwise ; carpels 1 or more, free or variously connate, often more or less adnate to the calyx-tube; styles free or rarely connate ; ovules in each carpel 2 or more, superposed ; fruit superior or inferior, drupaceous, pomaceous, follicular or achenial, sometimes on an enlarged fleshy torus; seeds without (very rarely with a little) endosperm. B.H. 1 : 600. E.P. 3, 3 : 1. Distribution cosmopolitan, but mainly N. Temperate Regions. — Licania, Parinarium, Hirtella, Prunus, Pygeum, Nut-

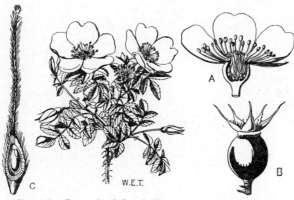

FIG. 143.—Rosa spinosissima L. (Rosaceae). A, vertical section of flower. B, fruit. C, single carpel.—After Baill.

tallia, Spiraea, Exochorda, Kerria, Lindleya, Rubus, Dryas, Geum, Fragaria, Potentilla, Alchemilla, Agrimonia, Acaena, Poterium, Cliffortia, Rosa, Neurada, Pyrus, Crataegus, Cotoneaster, Amelanchier, etc.

Useful Products : Many important foods and some of the most ornamental of garden plants. Amongst the former are the *Apple* (Pyrus Malus *L.*) ; *Pear* (P. communis *L.*) ; *Plum* (Prunus domestica *L.*) ; *Prunes* (P. domestica var. Juliana *D.C.*), France ; *Peach* (P. persica *Stokes*) ; *Apricot* (P. armeniaca *L.*) ; *Sweet Almonds* (Prunus Amygdalus, var. dulcis *Baill.*), Mediterranean ; *Bitter Almonds* (P.A. var. amara *Baill.*) ; *Strawberry* (Fragaria vesca *L.*) ; *Blackberry* (Rubus spp.) ; *Loquat* (Eriobotrya japonica *Lindl.*) ; and the *Coco Plum* (Chrysobalanus Icaco *L.*), etc. *Cherry Laurel* (Prunus Laurocerasus *L.*), widely cultivated ; *Cusso* (Brayera anthelmintica *Kunth*), N.E. Tropical Africa.

144. Chailletiaceae

(Dichapetalaceae)

Small trees or shrubs, sometimes climbing ; leaves alternate, simple ; stipules present ; flowers small, ♀, rarely ♂ ♀, actinomorphic or slightly zygo-

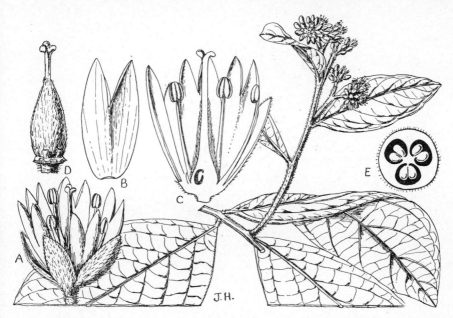

FIG. 144.—Dichapetalum Thonneri *De Wild.* (Dichapetalaceae). A, flower. B, petal. C, vertical section of flower. D, ovary. E, cross section of same.—After De Wild.

morphic ; sepals 5, free or partially connate, imbricate ; petals mostly *2-lobed* or 2-parted, free or united with the stamens into a tube ; stamens 5, alternate with the petals, free or united ; anthers 3-5, 2-celled, opening lengthwise, the connective often *dorsally thickened* ; hypogynous glands *opposite* to the petals, free or connate ; ovary superior to quite inferior, 2-3-celled ; style mostly simple, 2-3-fid at the apex ; ovules 2 in each cell, pendulous from the apex ; fruit a drupe, dry or rarely fleshy, sometimes the epicarp splitting ; seeds without endosperm ; embryo large, straight. B.H. 1 : 340. E.P. 3, 4 : 345. Tropics.—DICHAPETALUM (*Chailletia*), STEPHANOPODIUM, TAPURA.

PRODUCTS : Some poisonous plants.

145. CALYCANTHACEAE

Shrubs ; leaves *opposite*, simple ; stipules absent ; flowers axillary, solitary, fragrant, ☿ ; sepals and petals in *several series*, imbricate, inserted on the outside of the *thick urceolate receptacle* ; stamens numerous, inserted at the top of the receptacle, the inner ones *sterile* ; anthers 2-celled, dehiscing lengthwise ; carpels numerous, free, inserted on the inside of the receptacle ; styles filiform ; ovules solitary, or 2 superposed in each carpel, anatropous, ascending ; fruit an *achene*, 1-seeded, enclosed in the fleshy enlarged receptacle ; seed erect, without endosperm ; cotyledons leafy, convolute. B.H. 1 : 16. E.P. 3, 2 : 94. E. Asia, N. America.—CALYCANTHUS, CHIMONANTHUS.

USEFUL PRODUCTS : Aromatic early-flowering garden shrubs.

FIG. 145.—Calycanthus occidentalis *Hook. & Arn.* (Calycanthaceae). A, flower with perianth removed.
B, vertical section of same. C, stamen. D, carpel.—After Bot. Mag.

Order 41. LEGUMINOSAE [1]

Trees, shrubs or herbs ; leaves simple to bipinnate ; stipules present
or absent ; flowers actinomorphic to zygomorphic ; petals free or some
partially united ; stamens numerous to few, free or variously connate,
often diadelphous ; carpels solitary, superior ; fruit mostly a *legume* ;
seeds without endosperm.   World-wide distribution.

146. CAESALPINIACEAE

Trees, shrubs or rarely herbs ; leaves pinnate or bipinnate, rarely simple
or 1-foliolate ; stipels mostly absent ; flowers mostly showy, racemose, spicate,

[1] I adopt here the old family name for this order, which is perhaps best split up into
three distinct families.

or rarely cymose, *zygomorphic*, rarely subactinomorphic ; sepals 5 or the 2 upper ones connate, mostly free, imbricate or rarely valvate ; petals 5 or fewer or absent, the adaxial (upper) one *inside*, the others variously imbricate ; stamens mostly 10, very rarely numerous, often free or variously connate ; anthers various, sometimes opening by terminal pores ; ovary superior, 1-celled ; seeds with copious, thin or no endosperm and large embryo.   B.H. 1 : 562.   E.P. 3, 3 : 125 (under *Leguminosae*).   Mainly Tropics.—PELTOPHORUM, MEZONEURUM, CAESALPINIA, PTEROLOBIUM, GLEDITSCHIA, POINCIANA, PARKINSONIA, CASSIA, DIALIUM, CERATONIA, BAUHINIA, CERCIS, BROWNEA, AMHERSTIA, MACRO-LOBIUM, BERLINIA, AFZELIA, TAMARINDUS, BAIKIAEA, BRACHYSTEGIA, HY-

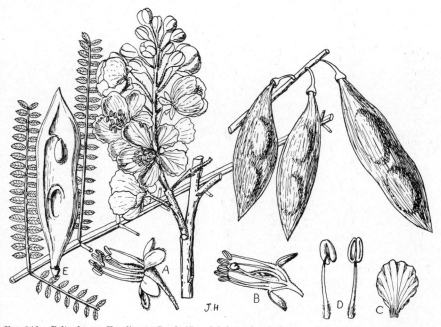

FIG. 146.—Peltophorum Vogelianum *Benth.* (Caesalpiniaceae).   A, flower.   B, longitudinal section of same. C, petal.   D, stamens.   E, pod showing seed.—After Martius.

MENAEA, SARACA, CRUDIA, DETARIUM, COPAIFERA, CYNOMETRA, DIMORPHANDRA, ERYTHROPHLOEUM, etc.

USEFUL PRODUCTS : *Sassy Bark* (Erythrophloeum guineense *G. Don*), W. Africa ;   *Cassia Pods* (Cassia Fistula *L.*), India, etc. ;   *Senna* (Alexandrian) (Cassia acutifolia *Del.*), E. Tropical Africa ; *Indian Senna* (Cassia angustifolia *Vahl*), Arabia to India ;   *Tamarind* (Tamarindus indica *L.*), Tropics ; *Locust* (West Indian) (Hymenaea Courbaril *L.*) ;   *Purple Heart Wood* (Copaifera pubi-flora *Benth.*), British Guiana, and many other timber trees.

147. MIMOSACEAE

Trees or shrubs, very rarely herbs ; leaves mostly *bipinnate*, rarely simply pinnate ; flowers ♂, small, spicate, racemose or capitate, actinomorphic, 3-6-usually 5-merous ; calyx tubular, *valvate* or very rarely (*Parkieae*) imbricate,

5-lobed or toothed; petals *valvate*, free or connate into a short tube, mostly hypogynous; stamens equal in number to the sepals or more numerous or indefinite, free or monadelphous; anthers small, 2-celled, opening lengthwise, often with a *deciduous gland* at the apex; ovary superior; fruit a *legume*; seeds with scanty or no endosperm. B.H. 1 : 588. E.P. 3, 3 : 99 (under *Leguminosae*). Tropics and Subtropics, many in dry regions.—Pentaclethra,

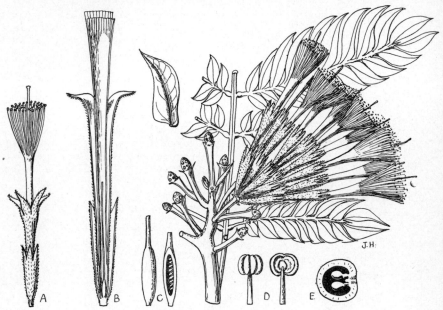

FIG. 147.—Pithecolobium Spruceanum *Benth.* (Mimosaceae). A, flower. B, vertical section of same. C, ovary. D, anthers. E, cross section of ovary.—After Martius.

Parkia, Entada, Piptadenia, Prosopis, Mimosa, Acacia, Calliandra, Albizzia, Pithecolobium, Inga, etc.

Useful Products : *Cacoon, Mackay* or *Sea Bean* (Entada scandens *Benth.*), Tropics; *Mesquit Tree* (Prosopis juliflora *D.C.*), West Indies, Central America; *Ironwood* (Xylia dolabriformis *Benth.*), India; *Gum Arabic* (Acacia Senegal *Willd.*, etc.), Tropical Africa; *Cutch* (Acacia Catechu *Willd.* and A. Suma *Kurz*), India and Burma; *Australian Blackwood* (Acacia melanoxylon *R. Br.*); *Wattle Barks* (various Austral. spp. of *Acacia*); *Sabicu* (Lysiloma Sabicu *Benth.*); *Rain Tree* (Pithecolobium Saman *Benth.*), etc. Many other valuable timbers.

148. Papilionaceae

(Fabaceae)

Herbs, shrubs or trees; leaves simple or compound; flowers zygomorphic, mostly ♂; sepals usually 5, more or less connate into a tube; petals 5, imbricate, free, the upper (adaxial) exterior and forming the standard, the two lateral (*wings*) more or less parallel with each other, the lower two interior and connate by their lower margins into a *keel*; stamens inserted with the petals, often 10, monadelphous or diadelphous, mostly all perfect ; anthers mostly opening lengthwise ; fruit usually dehiscent ; seeds without or with very scanty endosperm. B.H. 1 : 465. E.P. 3, 3 : 184 (under *Leguminosae*). General distribution.—PODALYRIA, OXYLOBIUM, CHORIZEMA, GASTROLOBIUM, PULTENAEA, BOSSIAEA, RAFNIA, LOTONONIS, LEBECKIA, ASPALATHUS, CROTALARIA, LUPINUS, ARGYROLOBIUM, ADENOCARPUS, LABURNUM, GENISTA, SPARTIUM, ULEX, CYTISUS, ONONIS, PAROCHETUS, TRIGONELLA, MEDICAGO, MELILOTUS, TRIFOLIUM, ANTHYLLIS, LOTUS, HOSACKIA, PSORALEA, AMORPHA, INDIGOFERA, GALEGA, TEPHROSIA, MILLETTIA, WISTARIA, ROBINIA, SESBANIA, CARMICHAELIA, CLIANTHUS, LESSERTIA, SWAINSONA, COLUTEA, CARAGANA, ASTRAGALUS, OXYTROPIS, GLYCYRRHIZA, CORONILLA, HEDYSARUM, ONOBRYCHIS, AESCHYNOMENE,

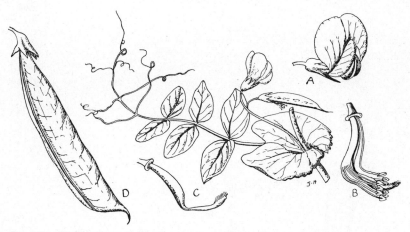

FIG. 148.—Pisum sativum *L.* (Papilionaceae). A, flower. B, same with perianth removed. C, ovary. D, fruit.—After Baill.

STYLOSANTHES, ARACHIS, DESMODIUM, LESPEDEZA, VICIA, LATHYRUS, ABRUS, CENTROSEMA, CLITORIA, KENNEDYA, HARDENBERGIA, etc.

USEFUL PRODUCTS : Very many valuable commodities, the most important being : *Peas* (Pisum sativum *L.*) ; *Broad Bean* (Vicia Faba *L.*) ; *Ground Nuts* (Arachis hypogaea *L.*) ; *Soy Beans* (Glycine hispida *Maxim.*), Orient ; *Lentils* (Lens esculentus *Moench*) ; *Clover* (Trifolium pratense *L.* and T. repens *L.*) ; *Tagasaste* (Cytisus palmensis *Christ*), Canaries ; *Calabar Beans* (Physostigma venenosum *Balf.*), W. Africa ; *Common Broom* (Cytisus scoparius *Link*), Europe ; *Liquorice Root* (Glycyrrhiza glabra *L.*), Europe, Asia ; *Indigo Dyes* (Indigofera tinctoria *L.*, etc.) ; *Gum Tragacanth* (Astragalus gummifer *Lab.*, etc.), Orient ; *Tolu Balsam* (Myroxylon toluifera *H.B. & K.*), S. America ; *Kino* (Pterocarpus Marsupium *Roxb.*), S. India, Ceylon. Many valuable timbers, including *American Rosewood* (Dalbergia spp.) ; *Indian Rosewood* (D. latifolia *Roxb.*) ; *Bastard Teak* (Pterocarpus Marsupium *Roxb.*), India ; *Camwood* (Baphia nitida *Lodd.*), W. Africa ; *Moreton Bay Chestnuts* (Castanospermum australe *A. Cunn.*), Austral., and many others.

Order 42. HAMAMELIDALES

Trees or shrubs ; leaves simple, alternate, rarely opposite, mostly
stipulate ; flowers usually ⚥, actinomorphic, often collected into heads or
pendulous catkins ; petals present or absent ; stamens perigynous or sub-
epigynous ; ovary semi-inferior to inferior, often bicarpellary ; ovules
pendulous from axile placentas ; seeds with rather thin endosperm and
straight embryo.

149. BRUNIACEAE

Shrubs or undershrubs, often *heath-like* ; leaves small, entire, usually imbricate ; stipules absent ; flowers ⚥, small, actinomorphic, generally in a *spike*

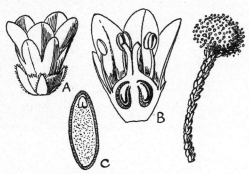

or *head*, sessile, 5-bracteate; calyx
4-5-partite, persistent or deciduous, imbricate ; petals 4 - 5,
usually free, sometimes connate
with the stamens into a tube at
the base, imbricate ; stamens
equal in number to and alternate
with the petals ; filaments free,
or sometimes adnate to the
claws of the petals ; anthers
introrse, 2-celled, cells parallel
or diverging at their base, opening lengthwise ; ovary *semi-
inferior* or *inferior*, very rarely
free, 1-3-celled ; styles 2-3,
terminal, more or less cohering ;

FIG. 149.—Brunia pinifolia *Brongn.* (Bruniaceae). A, flower.
B, vertical section of same. C, vertical section of seed.
—After Le Maout & Decne.

stigmas minute, papillose ; ovules 1-2, pendulous from near the top ; fruit
crowned by the calyx, and sometimes by the persistent corolla and androecium,
dry, indehiscent or capsular, often with two 1-2-seeded cocci, dehiscence internal,
lengthwise ; seeds minute, with straight embryo at the top of a copious fleshy
endosperm ; cotyledons short ; radicle conical, superior. B.H. 1 : 670. E.P.
3, 2a : 131. S. Africa.—BERZELIA, BRUNIA, RASPALIA, STAAVIA, etc.

150. STACHYURACEAE

Shrubs or small trees ; leaves alternate ; *stipules 0* ; flowers small, in axillary
racemes or spikes ; bracteoles 2, connate at the base ; sepals 4, much imbricate ;
petals 4, free, imbricate ; stamens 8, free ; anthers 2-celled, opening lengthwise ;
ovary 4-celled ; style simple, with a *capitate-peltate* stigma ; ovules numerous,
on axile placentas ; fruit a 4-celled berry ; seeds small ; endosperm fleshy ;
embryo straight ; cotyledons elliptic. B.H. 1 : 184 (under *Ternstroemiaceae*).
E.P. 3, 6 : 192. E. Asia.—STACHYURUS.

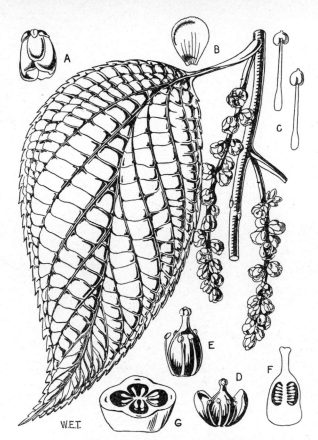

FIG. 150.—Stachyurus praecox *Sieb. & Zucc.* (Stachyuraceae). A, flower. B, petal. C, stamens. D, ovary and stamens. E, another view of same. F, vertical section of ovary. G, cross section of same.—After Bot. Mag.

151. HAMAMELIDACEAE

Trees or shrubs, often with *stellate indumentum*; leaves alternate, rarely opposite, deciduous or evergreen, simple, teeth sometimes glandular; *stipules mostly paired*, often persistent, sometimes large; flowers small, sometimes precocious, ☿ or ♂ ♀, often capitate, actinomorphic or zygomorphic; calyx-tube more or less *adnate to the ovary*; lobes imbricate or valvate; petals 4 or more, rarely 0, perigynous or epigynous, imbricate or valvate, rarely circinate; stamens 4 or more, perigynous, 1-seriate; filaments free; anthers oblong, 2-celled, opening lengthwise or by valves, the connective often produced; disk absent or annular or of separate glands between the stamens and ovary; ovary inferior or nearly so, rarely superior, composed of 2 carpels often *free at the apex*, 2-celled; styles subulate, free, often *recurved*; ovules 1 or more in each cell, pendulous from axile placentas; fruit a capsule, woody; seeds various, with thin fleshy endosperm and straight embryo. B.H. 1 : 664. E.P. 3, 2a : 115. Asia, Africa, N. America.—PARROTIA, FOTHERGILLA, DISTYLIUM, SYCOPSIS, CORY-

LOPSIS, DICORYPHE, HAMAMELIS, TRICHOCLADUS, LOROPETALUM, RHODOLEIA, BUCKLANDIA, LIQUIDAMBAR, etc.

USEFUL PRODUCTS : Timber trees : Altingia exceisa *Noronha*, E. India, etc. ;

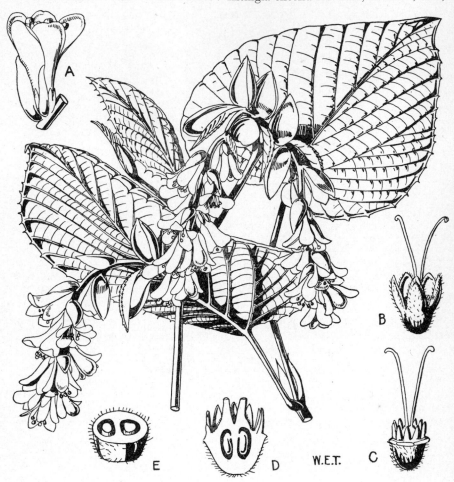

FIG. 151.—Corylopsis spicata *Maxim*. (Hamamelidaceae). A, flower. B, same, corolla removed. C, ovary. D, vertical section of same. E, cross section of same.—After Bot. Mag.

Liquidambar formosana *Hance*, Formosa. *Satin Walnut* (L. styraciflua *L.*). N. America. Ornamental shrubs, some flowering in winter (*Hamamelis* spp.— Witch Hazels).

152. EUCOMMIACEAE

Trees ; leaves deciduous, alternate, simple, *exstipulate*, petiolate, serrate, penninerved ; flowers *dioecious, without a perianth*, appearing with the leaves from *perulate buds* ; male flowers in loose bracteate clusters, shortly stalked, composed only of about 10 linear apiculate stamens dehiscing longitudinally ;

female flowers solitary in the axil of each bract or bract-like leaf on the lower part of each shoot, shortly stalked ; ovary syncarpous, flattened, stigmatose within the V-shaped apex ; ovules 2, collateral, pendulous, anatropous ; fruit samaroid, indehiscent, 1-seeded, thinly coriaceous, stipitate, oblong-oblanceolate, bifid at the apex ; seed solitary, pendulous from the apex of the cell, elongate-

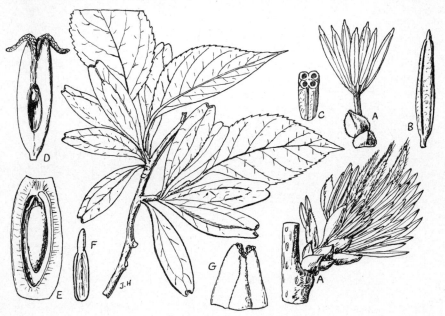

FIG. 152.—Eucommia ulmoides *Oliv.* (Eucommiaceae). A, inflorescence. A, male flower. B, anther.
C, cross section of same. D, vertical section of ovary. E, same enlarged. F, embryo. G, apex
of fruit.—After Hook. Ic. Pl.

oblong ; endosperm copious ; testa membranous ; raphe dorsal ; embryo central, straight, as long as the endosperm, with a superior more or less compressed radicle ; cotyledons flat, fleshy, oblong-linear, longer than the radicle. Hook. Ic. Pl. t. 1950 China.—EUCOMMIA.

USEFUL PRODUCTS : Bark of Eucommia ulmoides *Oliv.* contains caoutchouc, and is a valued medicine of the Chinese.

153. MYROTHAMNACEAE

Undershrub, resinous, rigid, with opposite branches, subspinulose with the persistent stipules and petioles ; leaves opposite, *flabellate-cuneate, plicate-nerved*, articulate with the subvaginate petiole ; stipules small, subulate on the sheathing base of the petiole ; flowers *dioecious*, spicate ; spikes catkin-like, erect, terminal ; bracts 1-flowered ; *no calyx or corolla* ; stamens 4-8, often 5 ; filaments connate, free at the apex ; anthers large, subquadrate, cells opening laterally lengthwise, connective produced into a beak ; no rudimentary ovary ; ovary in the ♀ sessile, 3-celled : 3-lobed, styles free, recurved, subspathulate ; ovules numerous, inserted on the inner angle of the cells, 2-seriate ; capsule small, leathery, the carpels divaricate, dehiscing on the inside, many - seeded ; seeds minute,

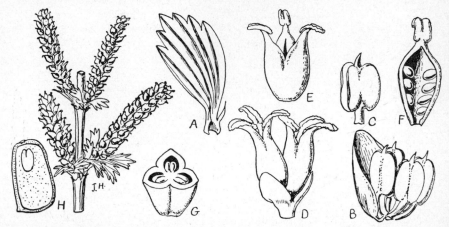

FIG. 153.—Myrothamnus flabellifolia *Welw.* (Myrothamnaceae). A, leaf showing stipules. B, male flower. C, stamen. D, female flower. E, ovary. F, vertical section of same. G, cross section of same. H, section of seed.—After Welw.

pendulous, with copious endosperm and minute embryo. B.H. 1 : 1005 (under *Hamamelidaceae*). E.P. 3, 2a : 103. Tropics and S. Africa.—MYROTHAMNUS.

154. BUXACEAE

Trees, shrubs or rarely herbs ; leaves evergreen, alternate or opposite, simple, coriaceous ; *stipules absent* ; flowers ♂ ♀ or rarely a few ☿, monoecious or dioecious, spicate or densely racemose, bracteate ; sepals imbricate or absent, usually 4 ; *petals 0* ; stamens 4 or 6, rarely more, when 4 then opposite the sepals, when 6 two pairs opposite the inner sepals ; anthers large, sessile or borne on fairly long filaments ; cells 2-valved or opening lengthwise ; rudimentary ovary present or absent in the ♂ flowers ; female flowers often larger than the males and fewer or solitary, often pedicellate ; sepals as in the ♂ ; ovary superior, 3-celled ; styles contiguous or widely separated, undivided ; ovules 1-2, pendulous, anatropous ; fruit capsular or drupaceous ; seeds *black* and shining, with fleshy endosperm and straight embryo with flat or thick cotyledons. B.H. 3:265 (under *Euphorbiaceae*). E.P. 3, 5 : 130. Distribution rather scattered, rare in S. America.—BUXUS, NOTOBUXUS, SIMMONDSIA, STYLOCERAS, SARCOCOCCA, PACHYSANDRA.

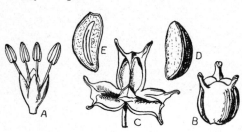

FIG. 154.—Buxus sempervirens *L.* (Buxaceae). A, male flower. B, ovary. C, dehisced fruit. D, seed. E, section of same.

USEFUL PRODUCTS : *Boxwood* (Buxus sempervirens *L.*), Europe, etc. ; *Cape Boxwood* (B. Macowanii *Oliv.*), S. Africa.

155. PLATANACEAE

Trees often with deciduous bark ; leaves alternate, *palmately nerved and lobed, the dilated petiole enclosing the young bud* ; stipules membranous, caducous ; flowers monoecious, densely arranged in *unisexual capitula* ; bracts absent from the ♂ capitulum, present in the female ; calyx 0 ; male capitula : anthers numerous, subsessile, each subtended by a minute scale, oblong or linear, 2-celled, opening lengthwise, the connective peltate at the apex ; female capitula : carpels numerous, distinct, subsessile, here and there with linear bracts intermixed ; ovary linear, 1-celled, with a unilateral stigma ; ovule 1 or rarely 2, pendulous, orthotropous ; carpels in fruit surrounded at the base by long hairs, indehiscent ; seed one in each carpel, linear ; endosperm thin ; embryo linear, straight. B.H. 3 : 396. E.P. 3, 2a : 137. N. Temperate and Subtropical Zone.—PLATANUS.

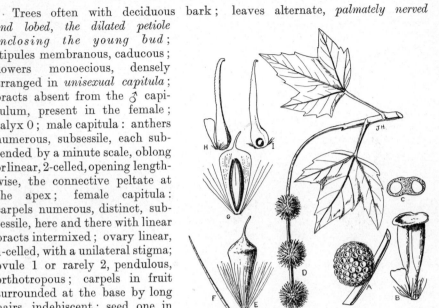

FIG. 155.—Platanus orientalis *L.* (Platanaceae).   A, male inflorescence. B, male flower. C, cross section of anther. D, female inflorescence. E, fruit. F, pappusseta. G, vertical section of same. H, female flower. I, vertical section of same.—Orig.

USEFUL PRODUCTS : *American Plane* (Platanus occidentalis *L.*), N. America ; *Lacewood* or *Oriental Plane* (P. orientalis *L.*), Near East.

Order 43. SALICALES

Trees or shrubs ; leaves alternate, stipulate ; flowers dioecious, in erect or pendulous catkins ; calyx absent or much reduced ; petals absent ; stamens 2 or more ; ovary 1-celled, with parietal placentas ; ovules numerous, ascending ; seeds covered with fine hairs ; no endosperm ; embryo straight.

156. SALICACEAE

Trees or shrubs ; leaves alternate, simple, deciduous ; stipules free, small or sometimes foliaceous and persistent ; flowers ♂ ♀, dioecious, densely arranged in erect or pendulous catkins often produced before the leaves ; bracts membranous, fugacious or persistent, each subtending a flower ; calyx absent or represented by a small cupular disk or 2 glandular scales ; male flowers : stamens 2 or more, filaments slender, free or more or less united ; anthers 2-celled, opening lengthwise ; female flowers : ovary sessile or shortly stipitate, 1-celled, with 2-4 *parietal placentas*; style short or long, 2-4-fid; ovules numerous, ascending, anatropous; capsule 2-4-valved; seeds numerous, small or minute, with numerous *fine hairs arising from the funicle and enveloping the seed*; endo-

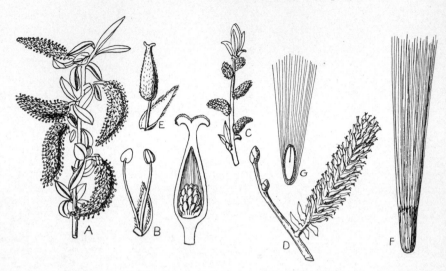

FIG. 156.—Salix alba *L.* (Salicaceae). A, shoot with male inflorescences. B, male flower. C, female shoot. D, female inflorescence. E, female flower. F, seed. G, vertical section of same.—After Baill.

sperm none; embryo straight. B.H. 3 : 411. E.P. 3, 1 : 29. Wide distribution, but absent from Australasia and Malay Archipelago.—SALIX, POPULUS.

USEFUL PRODUCTS : *Osiers* for basket-making (Salix spp.); *Cricket Bat Willow* (Salix coerulea *Sm.*).

Order 44. GARRYALES

Trees or shrubs; leaves opposite, exstipulate; flowers dioecious, in catkins; male sepals valvate, female 0; stamens 4, alternate with the sepals; ovary superior, bicarpellary, 1-celled, with apical placentation.

157. GARRYACEAE

Trees or shrubs; leaves *opposite*, simple, evergreen, with petioles *connate at the base*; stipules absent; flowers dioecious; arranged in silky catkin-like racemes; ♂ sepals 4, *valvate*; stamens 4, *alternate* with the sepals, free; anthers 2-celled; rudimentary ovary present; female sepals 0; ovary 1-celled, superior; styles 2, free, subulate; ovules 2, pendulous from the apex of the ovary, with a single integument; fruit a berry crowned by the styles, 1-2-seeded; seed ovoid or subglobose, with minute embryo at the apex of the *copious fleshy endosperm*. B.H. 1 : 951. E.P. 3, 8 : 255 (under *Cornaceae*). N. America and West Indies.—GARRYA. Garden shrubs.

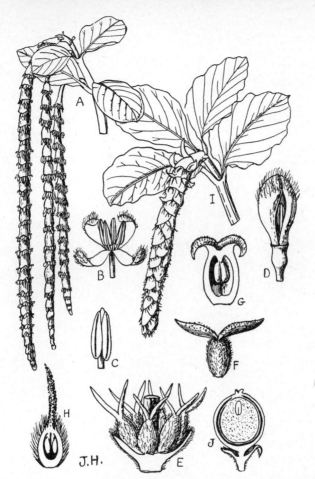

FIG. 157.—Garrya elliptica *L.* (Garryaceae). A, male inflorescences. B, male flower. C, stamen.
D, unopened male flower. E, whorl of female flower. F, ovary. G, vertical section of same.
H, another view of same. I, female inflorescence. J, vertical section of fruit.

Order 45. LEITNERIALES

Shrubs ; leaves alternate ; no stipules ; flowers dioecious, in erect
catkin-like spikes ; no calyx in the ♂ flowers, small in the ♀ ; stamens
few ; ovary superior, with 1 parietal ovule ; seeds with thin endosperm
and straight embryo.

158. LEITNERIACEAE

Shrubs with silky young parts ; leaves alternate, simple ; stipules 0 ; flowers
dioecious, in catkin-like erect spikes, solitary in each bract, the lower bracts
often sterile ; flower ♀ : calyx 0 ; stamens 3-12 ; filaments free ; anthers
erect, basifixed, 2-celled, cells opening lengthwise ; rudimentary ovary 0 ;

♀ flower : calyx small, of unequal scales connate at the base ; ovary sessile, 1-celled, narrowed into a long undivided style stigmatose on one side ; ovule 1, attached to the *wall* of the ovary, ascending ; drupe oblong, compressed, with

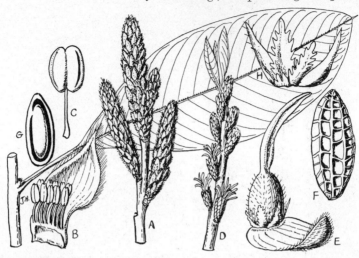

FIG. 158.—Leitneria floridana *Chapm.* (Leitneriaceae). A, male inflorescences. B, male flower. C, stamen. D, female inflorescences. E, female flower. F, seed. G, section of same. H, female perianth.—Orig.

a hard endocarp ; endosperm thin, fleshy ; embryo straight, slightly shorter than the seed ; cotyledons flat. B.H. 3 : 396. E.P. 3, 1 : 28. S.E. United States.—LEITNERIA.

Order 46. MYRICALES

Trees or shrubs, aromatic ; leaves alternate, exstipulate ; flowers unisexual, in axillary spikes; no sepals or petals ; stamens 2 or more ; ovary 1-celled, with 1 erect basal ovule ; seed without endosperm.

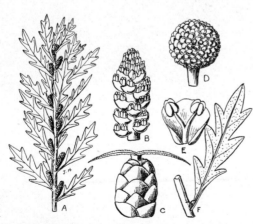

FIG. 159.—Myrica quercifolia *L.* (Myricaceae). A, twig with male inflorescences. B, male inflorescence. C, female flower. D, fruit. E, male flower. F, female flower in leaf-axil.—Orig.

159. MYRICACEAE

Trees or shrubs, often strongly *aromatic*; leaves alternate, simple, sometimes pinnately lobed ; stipules 0 ; flowers unisexual, monoecious or dioecious, sometimes the sexes alternating on the same individual year by year, in axillary spikes, dense-flowered, when the inflorescence bisexual then the ♂ flowers below the ♀ ; sepals and petals absent, or the ♀ with a few sepal-like whorled bracteoles ; ♂ flower subtended by a solitary bract ; stamens 2 to many, usually 4-8 ; filaments free or connate ; anthers 2-celled, opening lengthwise by slits ; rudimentary ovary rarely present ; ♀ flower : ovary sessile, 1-celled ; style short, 2-branched ; ovule 1, erect, basal, orthotropous ; drupe small, often warted, warts waxy ; endocarp hard ; seed erect ; endosperm 0 ; embryo straight. B.H. 3 : 400. E.P. 3, 1 : 26. Widely distributed, numerous and variable in S. Africa.—MYRICA.

USEFUL PRODUCTS : *Sweet Gale* (Myrica Gale *L.*), used in medicine ; *Sweet Fern* (M. asplenifolia *L.*), N. America.

Order 47. BALANOPSIDALES

Trees or shrubs ; leaves alternate ; no stipules ; flowers dioecious, male in catkins, female solitary in an involucre of bracts ; no sepals or petals ; stamens few ; ovary imperfectly 2-celled, with two parietal sub-basal placentas ; seeds with some endosperm and straight embryo.

160. BALANOPSIDACEAE

Trees or shrubs ; leaves alternate, simple ; stipules absent ; flowers dioecious, the male in catkins on the young branchlets or below the leaves, the female solitary in an involucre of bracts ; ♂ calyx represented by a single unilateral scale at the apex of the pedicel; stamens 2-12, often 5 or 6; anthers subsessile, ovoid, 2-celled, opening lengthwise ; rudimentary ovary absent or minute ; ♀ flowers without a perianth ; ovary sessile, imperfectly 2-celled, with 2 parietal placentas ; styles 2, 2-partite to near the base-branches, subulate ; ovules 2 on each placenta, collateral, erect from near the base ; drupe supported by the persistent involucre, ovoid, with 1 or 2 pyrenes ; pericarp shining ; seed solitary in each pyrene, erect, with fleshy endosperm and fairly large straight embryo. B.H. 3 : 341. E.P. Nachtr. 114. New Caledonia.—BALANOPS.

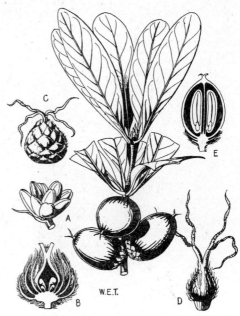

FIG. 160.—Balanops Vieillardii *Baill.* (Balanopsidaceae). A, male flower. B, vertical section of female flower. C, female flower. D, ovary. E, vertical section of fruit.—After Baill.

Order 48. FAGALES

Shrubs or trees with perulate buds ; leaves alternate, simple, stipulate ; flowers often precocious, ♂ ♀, monoecious, in erect or pendulous catkin-like spikes or the female like cones ; calyx much reduced or absent, the female flower often surrounded by an involucre of bracts ; stamens 2 to many ; ovary inferior or nude, 2-6-celled ; styles free or nearly so ; ovules 1-2 in each cell, pendulous ; seeds without endosperm.—Mainly North Temperate Zone.

161. BETULACEAE

Trees or shrubs with *perulate* buds ; leaves alternate, prominently *penni-nerved*, mostly *serrate* ; stipules free, often deciduous ; flowers monoecious ; male inflorescence a pendulous catkin, often *precocious*, terminal or lateral ; female flowers in cylindric cone-like *spikes* with imbricate bracts, 2-3 to each bract ; ♂ flower : bracteoles within each scale 2-5 ; calyx membranous, usually

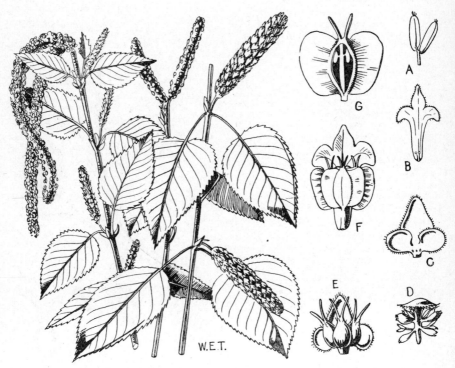

FIG. 161.—Betula papyrifera *Michx*. (Betulaceae). A, stamen. B, fruit bract. C, bract of female flower. D, group of male flowers. E, female flowers. F, fruits. G, section of single fruit.—After De Wild.

4-partite, slightly imbricate ; stamens 2 or 4 ; filaments very short ; anthers 2-celled, cells connate or separate, opening lengthwise ; no rudimentary ovary ; ♀ flower : perianth absent ; ovary nude, compressed, 2-celled ; styles 2, free, cylindric ; ovules solitary and attached near the apex of each cell ; fruiting spikes cylindric or ovoid, the bracts falling off or persisting ; nuts small, nude or winged, often crowned by the persistent styles ; seed solitary, pendulous, without endosperm, with straight embryo and flat cotyledons. B.H. 3 : 404

(under *Cupuliferae*).   E.P. 3, 1 : 38.   Mainly N. Temperate Zone, also in S. America.—BETULA, ALNUS.

USEFUL PRODUCTS : Good timbers from *Black Birch* (Betula lenta *L.*), N. America ; *B. utilis* D. Don, Himalaya ; *White Birch, B. alba* L., Europe.

162. CORYLACEAE

Shrubs or small trees with *perulate* buds ; leaves alternate, prominently *penninerved*, mostly *serrate* ; stipules present ; flowers monoecious ; spikes unisexual, the male in *catkins*, the female geminate in a short spike, bracteate ; male calyx absent ; stamens several, inserted on the bract ; filaments often divided ; anthers with separate cells often hairy at the apex ; no rudimentary

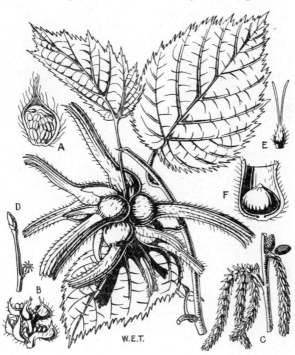

FIG. 162.—Corylus mandshurica *Maxim.* (Corylaceae).   A, male flower.   B, group of male flowers. C, male inflorescences.   D, female inflorescence.   E, ovary.   F, nut.—After Bot. Mag.

ovary ; female calyx present, adnate to the ovary, irregularly lobed at the top ; ovary inferior, rather imperfectly 2-celled ; ovules 2 or by abortion 1, pendulous from the apex ; styles 2, free or nearly so, linear ; nut enclosed in the foliaceous accrescent involucre ; seed solitary, without endosperm ; embryo straight, with large fleshy cotyledons much longer than the small radicle.   B.H. 3 : 405 (under *Cupuliferae*).   E.P. 3, 1 : 41 (under *Betulaceae*).   N. Temperate Zone. —OSTRYOPSIS, CARPINUS, OSTRYA, CORYLUS.

USEFUL PRODUCTS : *Hornbeam* (Carpinus Betulus *L.*) ; *Filberts* and *Barcelona Nuts* from varieties of the common *Hazel* (Corylus Avellana *L.*), Europe, etc. ; *Turkey Filberts* (C. Colurna *L.*).

163. Fagaceae

Trees ;   leaves alternate, evergreen or deciduous, simple, penninerved ; stipules present, often soon falling ; flowers unisexual, monoecious, the male in erect or catkin-like spikes ;   male calyx 4-6-lobed or rarely 7-lobed, lobes imbricate ;   stamens few to numerous, up to about 40 ;   filaments free, filiform ; anthers erect, 2-celled, cells contiguous, opening lengthwise ;   rudimentary ovary

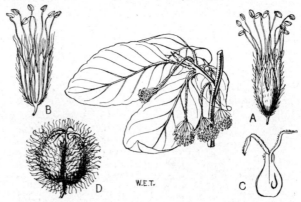

FIG. 163.—Fagus sylvatica *L.* (Fagaceae). A, male flower. B, vertical section of same.
C, female flower. D, female inflorescence.—After Baill.

present or obsolete ;   female flower *solitary* within an *involucre* of often numerous imbricate scales ;   staminodes present or absent ;   calyx adnate to the ovary, 4-6-lobed ;   ovary inferior, 3-6-celled ;   styles as many as the ovary-cells ;   ovules 2 in each cell ;   involucre in fruit often hardened, cupular or altogether closed, often tuberculate or echinate ;   fruit a nut, free or adnate to the involucre, sometimes completely enclosed by the latter, which opens like a pericarp ;   seed usually solitary by abortion, without endosperm.   B.H. 3 : 407 (under *Cupuliferae*).   E.P. 3, 1 : 47.   Temperate and Tropical Regions, absent from Tropical and S. Africa (except cultivated).—Quercus, Pasania, Castanopsis, Castanea, Fagus, Notofagus.

Useful Products : *Common Beech* (Fagus sylvatica *L.*), Europe, etc.

Order 49. CASUARINALES

Trees or shrubs with jointed branches and much reduced connate leaves ;   flowers ♂ ♀, male spicate, female in heads ;   calyx and petals absent ;   stamen solitary ;   ovary superior, 1-celled ;   ovules 2, inserted above the base of the ovary ;   fruits in cone-like heads ;   seeds without endosperm.

164. Casuarinaceae

Trees or shrubs with *jointed branches* ;   leaves *reduced* to many-toothed sheaths surrounding the nodes of the branches ;   flowers monoecious or dioecious, the ♂ spicate, ♀ in heads ;   ♂ flowers arranged in the *sheaths* towards the ends of the branchlets, each with 4 bracteoles ; calyx absent ; stamen *solitary*, central ; filament lengthening during flowering ; anther 2-celled, opening lengthwise ; ♀ flowers *capitate* at the tips of the branchlets or lateral ; calyx

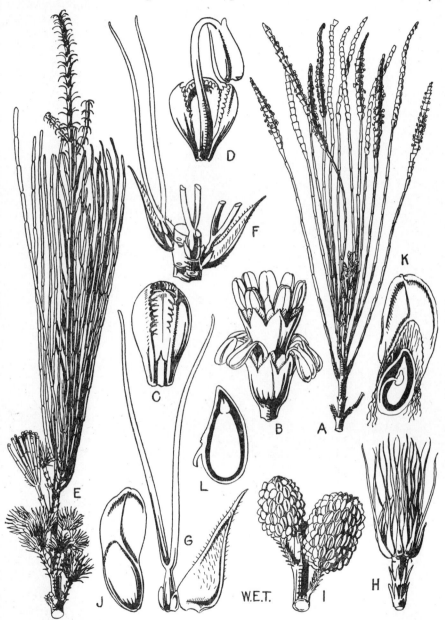

FIG. 164.—Casuarina suberosa *R. Br.* (Casuarinaceae). A, female inflorescences. B, portion of same, enlarged. C, male flower, unopened. D, same, opened. E, female inflorescences. F, female flowers. G, single one enlarged. H, female inflorescence. I, fruit. J, seed —After Hook. f.

absent ; ovary small, superior, 1-celled ; style short, terminal, with elongated linear branches ; ovules 2, collateral above the base of the ovary, ascending ; fruits crowded into a *cone* with persistent bracts, the bracts opening like a capsule and exposing the samaroid indehiscent nut ; seed solitary, without endosperm ; embryo straight, with short radicle and large flat cotyledons. B.H. 3 : 401.   E.P. 3, 1 : 16.   Mascarene Islands through Malaya to New Caledonia and Australia.—CASUARINA.

USEFUL PRODUCTS : *Beefwood* or *Forest Oak* (Casuarina equisetifolia *Forst.*), India to Malaya, Australia, etc. ; *She Oak* (C. stricta *Ait.*), Australia.

Order 50. URTICALES

Trees, shrubs or herbs, sometimes epiphytic ; leaves mostly alternate and usually stipulate ; flowers ⚥ or ♂ ♀ ; calyx small ; no petals ; stamens few, erect or inflexed in bud ; ovary superior, 1-2-celled ; ovule solitary, erect or pendulous ; seeds with or without endosperm.

165. ULMACEAE

Trees or shrubs ; leaves alternate, simple, often *unequal-sided* ; stipules *paired*, caducous ; flowers fasciculate, arising from the one-year-old branchlets,

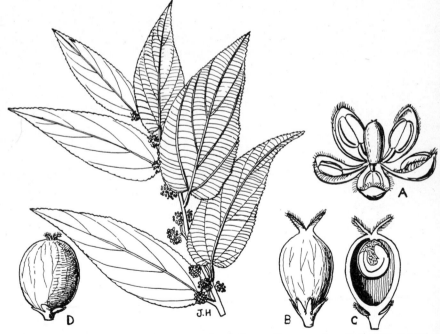

FIG. 165.—Trema Commersonii *Baill.* (Ulmaceae).   A, flower.   B, ovary.   C, vertical section of same. D, fruit.—After Baill.

⚥ or ♂ ♀ ; calyx herbaceous, subcampanulate, shortly 4-8-lobed, lobes imbricate, persistent ; stamens inserted at the bottom of the calyx, *erect* in bud, the same number as the calyx-lobes and *opposite* to them, or a few more ; filaments separate ; anthers 2-celled, opening lengthwise ; ovary composed of 2 *connate carpels*, 1-2-celled ; styles 2, divergent, stigmatose on their inner face ; ovules solitary, *pendulous* from near the top ; fruit compressed, membranous, dry or thinly fleshy, often winged or appendiculate ; seed without endosperm ; embryo straight ; cotyledons flat, sinuous or conduplicate. B.H. 3 : 351 (under *Urticaceae*). E.P. 3, 1 : 59. Mostly N. Temperate Zone.—ULMUS, HOLOPTELEA, PHYLLOSTYLON, PLANERA.

USEFUL PRODUCTS : Valuable timber trees are the common *Elm* (Ulmus campestris *L.*) ; *Keyaki* (Zelkova acuminata *Planch.*), Japan.

166. BARBEYACEAE

Trees ; leaves opposite, simple, entire, tomentose below with crooked hairs ; stipules absent ; flowers dioecious, shortly cymose, actinomorphic ; male calyx 3-4-fid, lobes *valvate* ; petals absent ; stamens 6-9 ; filaments very short ; anthers *erect* in bud, 2-celled, opening lengthwise, connective *apiculate* ; female

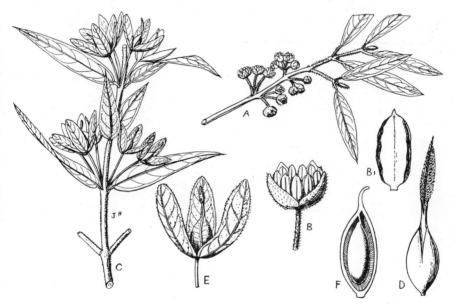

FIG. 166.—Barbeya oleoides *Schweinf.* (Barbeyaceae). A, male flowers. B, male flower. B₁, stamen. C, female flowers. D, ovary. E, female flower. F, vertical section of ovary.—Orig.

calyx divided to the base into 3 or 4 segments which *enlarge* and become sub-membranous and venose in fruit ; no staminodes ; ovary superior, subsessile, 1-celled ; style linear, *simple*, stigmatose all round ; ovule solitary from near the apex of the cell, anatropous ; fruit dry, indehiscent, ellipsoid, pericarp thin, nervose ; seed without endosperm ; embryo straight. Rendle in Fl. Tropical Africa, 6, 2 : 14. Arabia, and N.E. Tropical Africa.—BARBEYA.

167. MORACEAE

Trees or shrubs, rarely herbs, with *milky juice* ; leaves alternate, rarely opposite, simple, penninerved or palminerved ; stipules 2, often caducous and *leaving a scar* ; flowers much reduced, often in heads, disks or hollow receptacles ; ♂ ♀, monoecious or dioecious, actinomorphic ; calyx-lobes usually 4, sometimes reduced or absent, imbricate or valvate ; stamens usually equal in number and *opposite* to the sepals ; filaments *inflexed* or straight in bud ; anthers 2-celled, opening lengthwise ; rudimentary ovary present or not ; female flower : ovary superior to inferior, of 2 carpels, one often not developed, usually 1-celled ; ovule solitary, *pendulous* from the apex, rarely basal and erect ; styles mostly 2, filiform ; fruit a small achene, nut or drupe ; seed with or without endosperm, with often curved embryo. B.H. 3 : 357 (under *Urticaceae*). E.P. 3, 1 : 66.

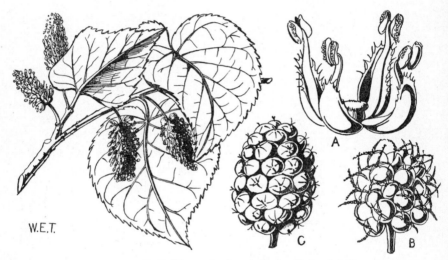

W.E.T.

FIG. 167.—Morus alba *L.* (Moraceae). A, male flower. B, female inflorescence. C, fruit.—After Baill.

Mainly Tropics.—PSEUDOSTREBLUS, MORUS, TROPHIS, MACLURA, CHLOROPHORA, BROUSSONETIA, STREBLUS, DORSTENIA, MESOGYNE, CUDRANIA, TRECULIA, ARTOCARPUS, PEREBEA, CASTILLOA, ANTIARIS, BROSIMUM, FICUS, CONOCEPHALUS, MUSANGA, MYRIANTHUS, COUSSAPOA, POUROUMA, CECROPIA.

USEFUL PRODUCTS : *Mulberry* (Morus nigra *L.*) ; *White Mulberry* (M. alba *L.*) ; *Paper Mulberry* (Broussonetia papyrifera *Vent.*), E. Tropics ; *Fustic* (Chlorophora tinctoria *Gaud.*), Tropical America ; *Iroko Tree* (Chlorophora excelsa *Benth.*), W. Africa ; *Osage Orange* (Maclura aurantiaca *Nutt.*), N. America ; *Contrayerva Root* (Dorstenia brasiliensis *Lamb.*), Brazil ; *Fig* (Ficus Carica *L.*) ; *Sycamore Fig* (F. Sycomorus *L.*), Tropical Africa, etc. ; *Indiarubber Fig* (F. elastica *Roxb.*), E. Tropics ; *Cow Tree* (Brosimum Galactodendron *Don*), S. America ; *Castilloa Rubber* (Castilloa elastica *Cerv.*), Central and S. America ; *Affon* or *African Bread-fruit* (Treculia africana *Decne.*) ; *Bread Fruit* (Artocarpus incisa *L.*), cultivated in Tropics ; *Jack-fruit* (A. integrifolia *L.*).

168. Scyphostegiaceae (Hutchinson fam. nov.)

Scandent shrub ; leaves alternate, simple ; stipules 0 ; flowers ♀, in lax racemes branched below ; ♂ flowers unknown ; ♀ flower : involucre 6-lobed nearly to the base, lobes biseriate, imbricate, persistent ; receptacle fleshy and resembling a thick corolla, thickened and nearly closed at the mouth ; female flowers several within the receptacle, each with 3 hyaline sepals variously united at the base ; stigma oblique, depressed ; ovule erect, anatropous ; fruits enclosed in the enlarged receptacle, stipitate, cylindric, slightly curved, erect, dry ; pericarp chartaceous ; seed erect, with thin testa, fleshy endosperm and embryo longer than half the seed. Borneo. —Scyphostegia.

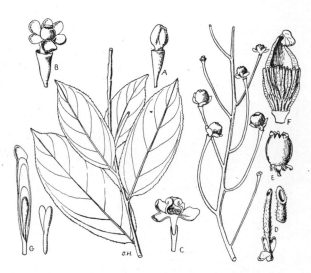

FIG. 168.—Scyphostegia borneensis *Stapf* (Scyphostegiaceae).   A, bud. B, the same, open.   C, vertical section of same.   D, female flower. E, receptacle.   F, vertical section of receptacle.   G, section of fruit with embryo.—After Hook. Ic. Pl.

A very remarkable plant of which only the female flowers and young fruit have been seen. When male flowers are known this genus may be found to belong to *Moraceae*. It is found on Mt. Kinabalu at about 2000 ft. altitude.

169. Urticaceae

Herbs, undershrubs, or rarely soft-wooded trees, very rarely climbing, often armed with *stinging hairs* ; epidermal cells mostly with prominent *cystoliths* ; stems often *fibrous* ; leaves alternate or opposite, simple ; stipules present, very rarely absent ; flowers very small, unisexual, usually cymose, sometimes crowded on a common enlarged receptacle ; male flowers : calyx mostly 4-5-lobed, lobes imbricate or valvate ; stamens the same number as and opposite to the calyx-lobes ; filaments *inflexed in bud* ; anthers 2-celled, opening lengthwise ; rudimentary ovary usually present ; female flowers : calyx as in the male, often enlarged in fruit, rarely absent ; staminodes scale-like, opposite the calyx-lobes, or absent ; ovary free or adnate to the calyx, sessile or shortly stipitate, 1-celled ; style simple ; ovule solitary, erect ; fruit a dry achene or fleshy drupe ; seed mostly with endosperm ; embryo straight. B.H. 3 : 341, partly. E.P. 3, 1 : 98. Generally distributed.—Urtica, Urera, Laportea,

FLEURYA, PILEA, ELATOSTEMA, PROCRIS, BOEHMERIA, POUZOLZIA, PIPTURUS, PARIETARIA, HELXINE, FORSKOHLEA, etc.

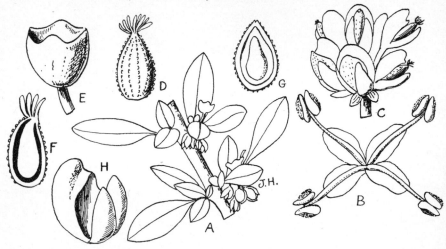

FIG. 169.—Pilea muscosa *L.* (Urticaceae). A, male flowers. B, single male flower. C, female flowers. D, ovary. E, calyx. F, vertical section of ovary. G, section of fruit. H, embryo.

USEFUL PRODUCTS : Stems fibrous in many. *Ramie fibre* (Boehmeria nivea *Gaud.*). Some noxious weeds.

170. CANNABINACEAE

Erect or scandent herbs ; leaves alternate or opposite, simple, undivided or palmately lobed ; stipules present ; flowers dioecious, axillary, male paniculate, female sessile, crowded or strobilate, the female with large conspicuous persistent bracts; male flower: calyx 5-partite, segments imbricate ; stamens 5 ; anthers erect in bud, 2-celled, opening lengthwise ; rudimentary ovary absent ; female flower: calyx closely enveloping the ovary, membranous, entire ; ovary sessile, 1-celled ; style central, 2-partite ; ovule solitary, pendulous ; fruit an achene, covered by the persistent perianth ; seed with fleshy endosperm ;

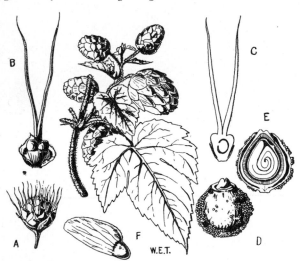

FIG. 170.—Humulus Lupulus *L.* (Cannabinaceae). A, female inflorescence. B, female flower. C, vertical section of same. D, fruit. E, vertical section of same. F, seed.—After Baill.

embryo curved or spirally involute.   B.H. 3 : 356 (under *Urticaceae*).   E.P.
3, 1 : 96 (under *Moraceae*).   N. Temperate Zone.—HUMULUS, CANNABIS.

USEFUL PRODUCTS : *Hops* and *Lupulin* (Humulus Lupulus *L.*), Europe, etc. ;
Hemp Fibre and drug (Cannabis sativa *L.*).

Order 51. CELASTRALES

Trees, shrubs or climbers ; leaves alternate or opposite, simple, not
glandular ; stipules absent or very small ; flowers actinomorphic, mostly
♀, often small ; calyx imbricate or valvate ; petals usually present,
imbricate, free to partially connate ; stamens definite, alternate with the
petals ; disk present ; ovary superior or partially immersed in the disk ;
ovules 1-2, erect or pendulous from the inner angle ; seeds with endosperm.
—Generally distributed, but mostly tropical.

171. AQUIFOLIACEAE
(Ilicaceae)

Trees or shrubs, mostly evergreen ; leaves alternate, simple ; *stipules
absent* ; flowers actinomorphic, ♀ or ♂ ♀, cymose, fasciculate or rarely solitary ;
calyx imbricate ; petals 4-5, free or connate at the base, hypogynous, imbricate ;
stamens hypogynous, 4-5, rarely more, free ; anthers 2-celled, opening length-

FIG. 171.—Ilex aquifolium *L.* (Aquifoliaceae).   A, flower.   B, vertical section of same.   C, seed.
D, vertical section of same.

wise ; *disk absent* ; ovary 3- or more-celled ; style terminal or absent ; ovules
1-2 in each cell, pendulous from the apex ; fruit drupaceous, of 3 or more 1-seeded
pyrenes ; seed with copious fleshy endosperm and small straight embryo.
B.H. 1 : 356.   E.P. 3, 5 : 183.   Generally distributed, but rare in Africa and
Australia.—ILEX, BYRONIA, NEMOPANTHES.

USEFUL PRODUCTS : *Common Holly* (Ilex Aquifolium *L.*), useful wood ; *Bird-lime* (from holly bark) ; *Yerba de Maté* or *Paraguay Tea* (Ilex paraguensis *St. Hil.*), S. America.

172. EMPETRACEAE

Shrubs with small *ericoid, crowded,* alternate leaves pulvinate at the base ; stipules 0 ; flowers small, axillary or crowded into terminal heads, ♀ or rarely

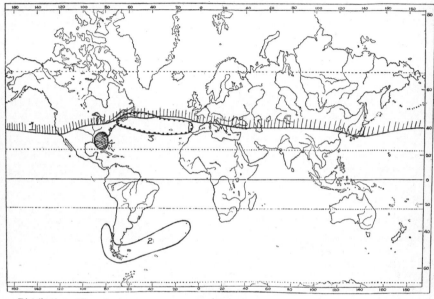

Distribution of Empetraceae.   1, Southern limit of Empetrum nigrum ;   2, E. rubrum ;   3, Corema ;
4, Ceratiola.

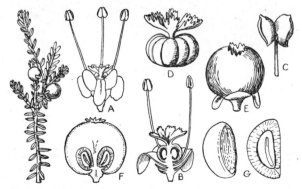

FIG. 172.—Empetrum nigrum *L.* (Empetraceae).   A, flower.   B, vertical section of same.   C, anther.
D, ovary.   E, fruit.   F, section of same.   G, seeds.—After Le Maout & Decne.

polygamous ; sepals 4-6, somewhat petaloid, much overlapping and sub-biseriate ; petals absent ; stamens 2-4, central or around the rudimentary ovary, hypogynous in the ♂ flower ; filaments free ; anthers 2-celled, small, opening longitudinally ; disk 0 ; ovary sessile, 2-9-celled, globose ; style short, variously divided ; ovules solitary in each cell, central, amphitropous ; fruit subglobose, drupaceous, succulent, with 2 or more pyrenes each with 1 seed ; seeds with copious fleshy endosperm and central straight embryo nearly as long as the endosperm ; cotyledons small. B.H. 3 : 413. E.P. 3, 5 : 123. N. Temperate and Arctic, southernmost S. America and Tristan da Cunha (see map).—EMPETRUM, COREMA, CERATIOLA.

173. CELASTRACEAE

Erect trees, shrubs or climbers ; leaves alternate or opposite, simple ; stipules small and caducous or absent ; flowers mostly *cymose* or *fasciculate*, often ♀, actinomorphic, small ; calyx 4-5-lobed, imbricate, very rarely valvate ; petals 5, rarely 0, imbricate or rarely valvate ; stamens 4-5, rarely more, alternate with the petals, inserted on or below the margin of the disk ; anthers 2-celled, opening lengthwise ; *disk usually present*, often fleshy and flat ; ovary

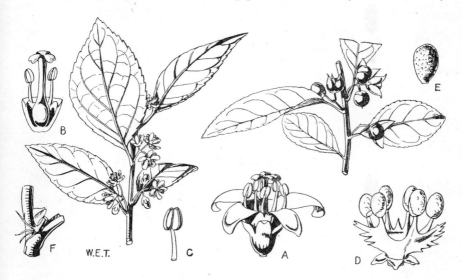

FIG. 173.—Celastrus articulatus *Loes.* (Celastraceae). A, flower. B, ovary. C, stamen. D, seeds.

superior, free or adherent to the disk, 1-5-celled ; style short, more or less 3-lobed ; ovules mostly 2, from the inner angle of the cells ; fruit various ; seeds mostly with copious fleshy endosperm and rather large straight embryo ; cotyledons flat, foliaceous. B.H. 1 : 357. E.P. 3, 5 : 189. Generally distributed.— EUONYMUS, CELASTRUS, MAYTENUS, GYMNOSPORIA, ELAEODENDRON, etc.

USEFUL PRODUCTS : *Arabian Tea* (Catha edulis *Forsk.*) ; *Spindle Tree* (Euonymus europaeus *L.*) ; *Paiche Wood* (Euonymus europaeus, var. Hamiltonianus), India, etc. ; *Kokoon Tree* (Kokoona zeylanica *Thw.*), Ceylon ; *Euonymus Bark* (Euonymus atropurpureus *Jacq.*), United States.

174. Corynocarpaceae

Trees ; leaves alternate, simple, entire ; stipules absent ; flowers ⚥, actinomorphic ; sepals 5, much imbricate, free ; petals 5, adnate to the base of the sepals, imbricate ; stamens perigynous, 5, inserted on the base of the petals and opposite to them, alternating with as many petaloid toothed bifid clawed *staminodes* ; anthers 2-celled, opening lengthwise ; disk-glands large, within the base and opposite to the staminodes ; ovary superior, 1-2-celled ; styles 1-2, *free* ; ovule solitary and pendulous ; fruit a drupe ; seed without endosperm ; cotyledons plano-convex ; radicle minute. E.P. Nachtr. 215. Polynesia, New Caledonia, N. Zealand. —Corynocarpus.

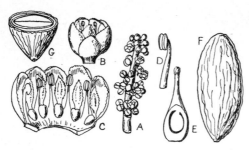

FIG. 174.—Corynocarpus laevigata *Forst.* (Corynocarpaceae). A, flowers. B, single flower. C, flower opened to show stamens. D, stamen. E, vertical section of ovary. F, seed. G, cross section of same.— After Bot. Mag.

175. Cyrillaceae

Shrubs ; leaves alternate, simple ; stipules absent ; flowers ⚥, actinomorphic, racemose; calyx 5-lobed, *valvate*; petals 5, *shortly connate* at the base, contorted or imbricate ; stamens 5 or 10, hypogynous, inserted on the receptacle ; filaments free ; anthers 2-celled, opening lengthwise ; ovary superior, 2-4-celled ; style short, with 2 acute stigmas or stigmas subsessile ; ovules 1 or more in each cell, pendulous ; fruit a capsule or drupe, sometimes winged ; seeds with fleshy endosperm and straight cylindric embryo. E.P. 3, 5 : 179. S.E. United States to Brazil.—Cliftonia, Costaea, Cyrilla.

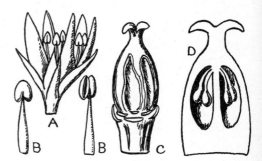

FIG. 175.—Cyrilla brevifolia *N.E.Br.* (Cyrillaceae). A, flower. B, stamens. C, ovary. D, vertical section of same.— After N.E.Br.

176. Cneoraceae

Small shrublets, glabrous or clothed with medifixed hairs ; flowers ⚥, axillary, cymose, the *peduncle adnate* to the petiole ; sepals 3-4, persistent ; petals 3-4, elongated, imbricate ; *torus elongated*, columnar, 3-4-grooved ; stamens 3-4, inserted on the middle of the torus ; filaments free ; anthers 2-celled, opening lengthwise ; ovary sessile on the gynophore, 3-4-celled, cells 1-2-ovuled ; style 3-4-lobed ; ovules pendulous ; fruit of 1-4 cocci, cocci

drupaceous, globose, sometimes spuriously septate; seeds uncinately conduplicate, with fleshy endosperm and uncinate embryo. B.H. 1 : 311 (under
Simarubaceae). E.P. 3, 4 : 93. Mediterranean and Canary Islands.—CNEORUM.

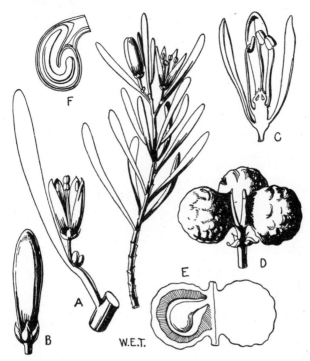

FIG. 176.—Cneorum pulverulentum *Vent.* (Cneoraceae). A, flower. B, bud. C, vertical section
of flower. D, fruit. E, vertical section of same. F, section of seed.—Orig.

177. PANDACEAE

Small trees ; leaves alternate, simple ; stipules present ; flowers ♂ ♀,
dioecious ; male flowers racemose ; racemes fasciculate from the older wood ;

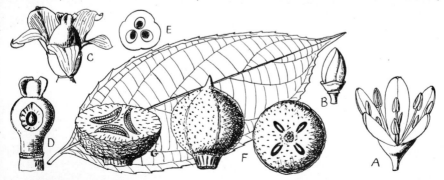

FIG. 177.—Panda oleosa *Pierre* (Pandaceae). A, male flower. B, flower-bud. C, female flower.
D, ovary showing ovule. E, cross section of same. F, fruit. G, cross section of same.—After Pierre.

calyx cupular, open in bud; petals 5, valvate; stamens 10, alternately long and short; anthers 2-celled, opening lengthwise; rudimentary ovary linear-subulate; female flowers racemose, fasciculate on the main trunk; calyx cupular, truncate or toothed; petals 5 [imbricate?]; staminodes and disk absent; ovary subsessile, 3-4-celled; style 3-4-branched, reflexed; ovule solitary, pendulous from near the apex of the axis; fruit drupaceous; seed with copious oily endosperm; cotyledons cordate. Pierre in *Soc. Linn. Bull., Paris*, 2 : 1255 (1896). West Tropical Africa.—PANDA.

178. HIPPOCRATEACEAE

Mostly glabrous, small erect trees or shrubs or scandent; leaves mostly *opposite*, simple; stipules small or absent; flowers fasciculate or cymose, hermaphrodite, actinomorphic, mostly quite small; calyx small, 5-partite, imbricate; petals 5, imbricate or valvate; *disk present*, conical, cupular or expanded; *stamens mostly* 3, rarely 2-5, inserted on the disk, alternate with

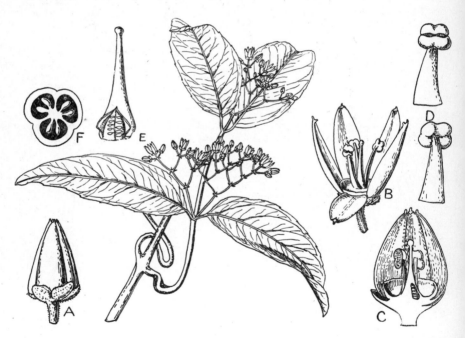

FIG. 178.—Hippocratea cymosa *De Wild. & Th. Durand* (Hippocrateaceae). A, flower-bud. B, flower. C, vertical section of same. D, stamens. E, ovary. F, cross section of same.—After De Wild.

the petals; anther-cells distinct or confluent; ovary superior or more or less confluent with the disk, 3-celled; style subulate or short, mostly 3-fid; ovules 2-10 in each cell, axile, 1-2-seriate; fruit capsular and compressed or baccate; seeds compressed and often *winged* or angular, without endosperm; cotyledons large, connate, thick. B.H. 1 : 369 (under *Celastraceae*). E.P. 3, 5 : 222. Tropics generally.—HIPPOCRATEA, SALACIA.

179. ICACINACEAE

Trees or shrubs ; leaves mostly *alternate*, simple ; *stipules absent* ; flowers ♀ or rarely unisexual by abortion, actinomorphic ; calyx small, inferior, 4-5-lobed ; lobes imbricate or rarely valvate ; petals 4-5, free or united, *valvate*, rarely absent ; stamens the same number as the petals and alternate with them ; anthers 2-celled (sometimes deeply 4-lobed) ; filaments often *hairy*

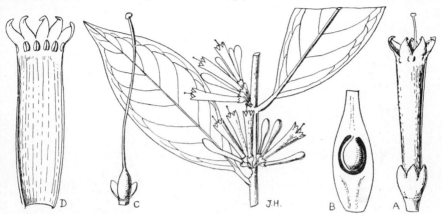

FIG. 179.—Leptaulus daphnoides *Benth.* (Icacinaceae). A, flower. B, vertical section of ovary.
C, ovary. D, corolla with stamens.—After Hook. Ic. Pl.

below the anthers, free ; disk rarely present ; ovary 1-celled, rarely 3-5-celled ; ovules pendulous from near the top of the ovary, usually 2 ; style usually short ; fruit drupaceous, 1-celled, 1-seeded, rarely winged ; seeds mostly with endosperm ; embryo usually small, more or less straight. B.H. 1 : 350 (under *Olacaceae*). E.P. 3, 5 : 233. Tropics.—LASIANTHERA, GOMPHANDRA, DESMOSTACHYS, APODYTES, PENNANTIA, MAPPIA, ICACINA, VILLARESIA, PHYTOCRENE, IODES, etc.

180. SALVADORACEAE

Trees or shrubs, unarmed or with axillary spines ; leaves opposite, simple ; rudimentary stipules often present ; flowers in dense axillary fascicles or panicles, ♀ or dioecious, actinomorphic ; calyx 3-4-toothed ; petals 4, free or partially connate, *imbricate* ; *stamens* 4, inserted on or near the base of the petals and alternate with them ; filaments free or connate at the base ; anthers 2-celled, *cells back to back*, opening lengthwise ; disk absent or of separate glands between the filaments ; ovary superior, 1-2-celled ; style short ;

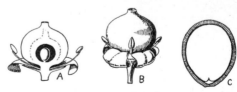

FIG. 180.—Salvadora persica *L.* (Salvadoraceae). A, vertical section of flower. B, flower. C, seed.—After Le Maout & Decne.

ovules 1-2, erect ; fruit a berry or drupe ; seed erect, without endosperm ; embryo with thick cordate cotyledons. B.H. 2 : 680. E.P. 4, 2 : 17. Tropical Africa and Mascarene Islands. —DOBERA, SALVADORA, AZIMA.

USEFUL PRODUCTS : *Tooth-brush tree* (Salvadora persica *L.*), E. Tropics.

181. Stackhousiaceae

Small herbs with a *woody branched rhizome*; leaves alternate, simple, fleshy or leathery; stipules absent; flowers ☿, racemose, spicate or fasciculate; *calyx tubular*, lobes imbricate; petals 5, perigynous, linear or spathulate, long-clawed, *claws connate into a tube but free at the base*, imbricate; disk thin, lining the calyx-tube; stamens 5, erect, alternate with the petals; anthers 2-celled, opening lengthwise; ovary superior, 2-5-celled; styles 2-5, free or connate; ovules basal, solitary, erect in each cell; fruit of 2-5 indehiscent 1-seeded cocci; seed with fleshy endosperm and equally large straight embryo. B.H. 1 : 371. E.P. 3, 5 : 231. Philippines to Australia and New Zealand.—Stackhousia.

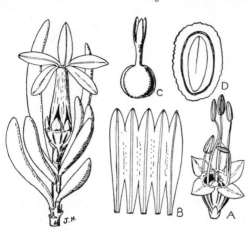

FIG. 181.—Stackhousia pulvinaris *F. Muell.* (Stackhousiaceae). A, flower. B, corolla. C, ovary. D, section of seed.—After F. Muell.

Order 52. OLACALES

More or less as in *Celastrales*, but petals mostly valvate, sometimes more or less connate; ovules pendulous.—Tropics mainly.

182. Olacaceae

Trees, shrubs or climbers; leaves alternate, simple; *stipules absent*; flowers actinomorphic, usually ☿ and small; calyx-lobes imbricate or open in bud; petals free or variously connate, *valvate*; disk various, often annular; stamens free or rarely united into a column, the same number as and *opposite* to or fewer or more numerous than the petals, some often without anthers; anthers 2-celled, opening lengthwise or by pore-like slits; ovary superior or slightly immersed in the disk, 1-3-celled, sometimes imperfectly so; style simple, with a 2-5-lobed stigma; ovules 1-5 from the apex of the central placenta of the 1-celled ovaries, or pendulous from the inner angle of the 2- or more-celled ovaries; fruit often drupaceous, sometimes enclosed by the enlarged calyx; seeds with copious endosperm and small or medium-sized straight embryo. B.H. 1 : 342, partly. E.P. 3, 1 : 231. Tropics and Subtropics.—Aptandra, Heisteria, Ximenia, Olax, Liriosma, Strombosia, Schoepfia, etc.

183. Opiliaceae

Trees, shrubs or woody climbers; leaves alternate, simple; stipules absent; flowers mostly ☿, actinomorphic; *calyx minute*; petals 4-5, free or more or less united; stamens as many as the petals and opposite to them, free or united

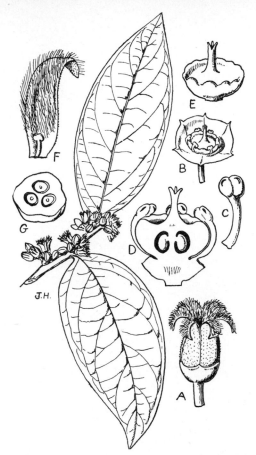

FIG. 182.—Anacolosa densiflora *Bedd.* (Olacaceae). A, flower. B, same, petals removed. C, stamen. D, vertical section of ovary. E, ovary. F, petal. G, cross section of ovary.

to the base of the petals ; anthers 2-celled, opening lengthwise by slits ; disk-glands alternating with the stamens ; ovary superior or semi-inferior, 1-*celled* ;

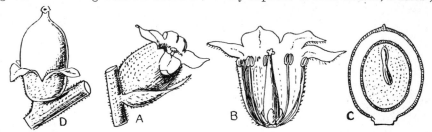

FIG. 183.—Cansjera timorensis *Decne.* (Opiliaceae). A, flower. B, vertical section of same. C, section of seed. D, fruit.

stigma sessile or style slender ; ovule solitary, pendulous or erect ; fruit *drupaceous*, often fleshy ; seed with copious endosperm and rather small embryo. B.H. 1 : 349. E.P. 3, 1 : 240 (under *Olacaceae*). Tropical Asia and Africa ; rare in Tropical America (Brazil).—OPILIA, RHOPALOPILIA, CANSJERA, CHAMPEREIA, MELIENTHA, LEPIONURUS, AGONANDRA.

Order 53. SANTALALES

Trees, shrubs or herbs, often parasitic ; leaves mostly opposite, some-times reduced to scales ; stipules absent ; flowers actinomorphic ; calyx valvate or open, often reduced ; petals present or absent ; stamens definite, opposite the calyx-lobes, or opposite the petals when latter present ; disk often present ; ovary inferior ; placentation axile ; ovules few ; seeds with abundant endosperm and straight embryo.—Mainly Tropics.

184. OCTOKNEMATACEAE

Trees or shrubs ; leaves alternate, simple, with stellate hairs ; stipules absent ; flowers unisexual, in axillary racemes ; male flower : sepals 5, valvate ; petals absent ; stamens 5, opposite the sepals, free ; rudimentary ovary present ; female flower : sepals 5, valvate ; no staminodes or disk ; ovary inferior,

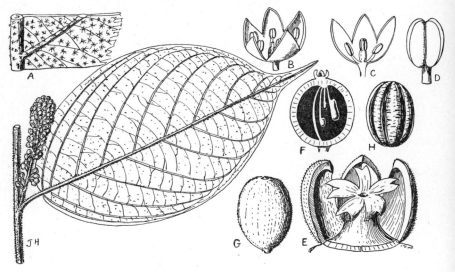

FIG. 184.—Octoknema gabonensis *Pierre* (Octoknemataceae). A, leaf showing stellate hairs. B, male flower. C, vertical section of same. D, anther. E, female flower. F, vertical section of ovary. G, fruit. H, seed.—After Pierre, partly.

1-celled ; style very short, 3-5-lobed, lobes bifid ; ovules 3, at the apex of a basal thread-like placenta which reaches and is adnate to the top of the ovary ; fruit drupaceous, with a single seed ; endosperm slightly ruminate, with small embryo, the radical much longer than the cotyledons. Engl. and Gilg, Syllab. eds. 9 and 10 : 187 (1924). West Africa.—OCTOKNEMA.

185. Loranthaceae

Shrubs *parasitic* on trees or very rarely erect terrestrial trees or shrubs ; leaves mostly *opposite* or whorled, simple, entire, sometimes reduced to scales ; stipules absent ; flowers actinomorphic, ☿ or ♂ ♀, often very brightly coloured ; perianth double or apparently single by suppression of calyx-rim ; calyx adnate to the ovary, annular or cupular or obscure ; petals free or united into a tube which is often *split down one side* ; stamens the *same number* as the petals and

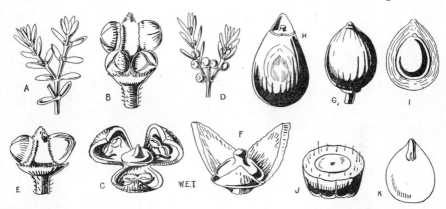

FIG. 185.—Viscum Bolleanum *Seem.* (Loranthaceae). A, shoot. B, male flowers. C, single male flower. D, fruits. E, female flowers. F, single female flowers. G and H, fruit. I, vertical section of fruit. J, cross section of same. K, embryo with one cotyledon removed.—After Seem.

inserted on them or at their base ; anthers normally 2-celled, sometimes 1-celled by the confluence of the cells, opening lengthwise or by terminal pores or transverse slits, sometimes transversely locellate ; disk present or absent ; rudimentary ovary often present in the male flowers, staminodes in the female ; ovary *inferior* ; ovules mostly not distinct ; style simple or absent ; fruit a berry or drupe ; seed solitary, devoid of testa ; endosperm mostly copious ; embryo large, sometimes up to 3 in one seed. B.H. 3 : 205. E.P. 3, 1 : 156. Mainly Tropics.—Loranthus, Viscum, Dendrophthora, Phoradendron, etc.

Useful Products : *Mistletoe* (Viscum album *L.*).

186. Santalaceae

Trees, shrubs or herbs, sometimes *parasitic* on trees or roots ; leaves alternate or opposite, entire, sometimes reduced to scales ; *stipules absent* ; flowers often greenish, ☿ or ♂ ♀, actinomorphic ; calyx green or petaloid, often fleshy, adnate to the ovary ; lobes 3-6, *valvate* or slightly imbricate ; stamens the same number as the calyx-lobes and opposite to them ; anthers 2-celled, opening lengthwise ; disk epigynous ; ovary *inferior* or half inferior, 1-celled ; style more or less simple ; ovules 1-3, pendulous from a *basal placenta* ; fruit indehiscent, nut-like or drupaceous ; seed without a testa ; endosperm copious, fleshy ; embryo often oblique, straight ; cotyledons mostly terete. B.H. 3 : 217. E.P. 3, 1 : 202. Widely distributed in Tropical and Temperate Regions.—Thesium,

R

Comandra, Santalum, Colpoon, Buckleya, Osyris, Henslowia, Leptomeria, Exocarpus, etc.

Useful Products : *Sandalwoods* : Sandwich Islands (Santalum Frey-

FIG. 186.—Santalum album *L.* (Santalaceae). A, section of flower. B, sepal and stamen. C, fruit. D, section of fruit.

cinetianum *Gaud.*) ; Fiji (S. Yasi *Seem.*) ; India and Malaya (S. album *L.*) ; Australia (Fusanus spicatus *R. Br.*, F. acuminatus *R. Br.*). *Bark Bosch* or *Cape Sumach* (Colpoon compressum *Berg.*).

187. Grubbiaceae

Shrubs ; leaves *opposite*, simple, linear ; stipules absent ; flowers ⚥, small, arranged in small axillary bracteate cones ; calyx adnate to the ovary ; segments 4, *valvate* ; stamens 8, 4 at the base of the lobes and 4 alternate and slightly shorter ; anthers small, opening laterally ; disk hairy ; ovary *inferior*, at first 2-celled ; style bifid at the apex ; ovules 2, pendulous on a *central placenta* or the latter sometimes adnate to the ovary wall ; fruit a drupe ; seed 1, with a thin testa and fleshy endosperm ; embryo linear, central, subterete, the radicle much longer than the cotyledons. B.H. 3 : 231 (under *Santalaceae*). E.P. 3, 1 : 228. S. Africa.—Grubbia.

188. Myzodendraceae

Undershrubs parasitic on trees ; leaves alternate, small or *reduced* ; flowers dioecious, minute, ebracteate, or arranged in small catkins ; male flower *without a calyx or corolla* ; stamens 2-4, around a small disk ; filaments slender ; anthers 1-*celled*, opening by 2 *valves* ; female flower : calyx adnate to the ovary and free at the top ; no staminodes ; ovary inferior, 1-celled, crowned by an obscure disk ; style thick, with 3 stigmas ; ovules 3, pendulous from the apex of a thick *central placenta* ; fruit small, nut-like ; seed with fleshy endosperm and fleshy central embryo. B.H. 3 : 229 (under *Santalaceae*). E.P. 3, 1 : 198. Temperate S. America.—Myzodendron.

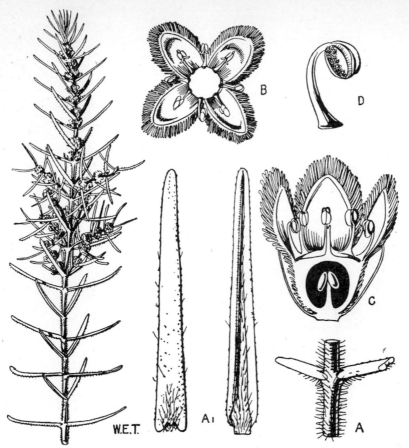

FIG. 187.—Grubbia rosmarinifolia *Thunb.* (Grubbiaceae). A, node. A1, leaves. B, flower.
C, vertical section of same. D, stamen.—Orig.

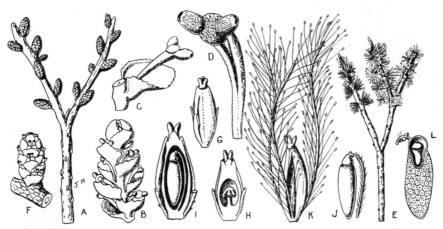

FIG. 188.—Myzodendron punctulatum *Banks & Soland* (Myzodendraceae). A, male shoot. B, male
inflorescence. C, male flower and bract. D, male flower. E, female shoot. F, female inflorescence.
G, ovary. H, vertical section of same. I, vertical section of fruit. J, seed with abortive ovules at
top. K, fruit with ciliate setae. L, section of seed.—After Hook.

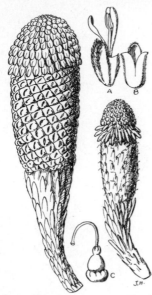

FIG. 189.—Mystropetalon Thomii *Harv.* (Balanophoraceae). A, male flower. B, calyx. C, female flower.

189. BALANOPHORACEAE

Fleshy herbs *parasitic* on roots, annual or perennial, *destitute of chlorophyll* and stomata; flowers ♂ ♀, very rarely ☿, densely crowded into unisexual or androgynous inflorescences; ♂ flowers without or with a valvate 3-8-lobed perianth; stamens 1-2 in the achlamydeous flowers, in those with a perianth often equal in number to and *opposite* the lobes; filaments free or connate; anthers 2-4-celled or with many cells, free or connate, opening by pores or slits; ovary 1-3-celled, adnate to the perianth when present; styles 1-2, terminal or rarely the stigma sessile and discoid; ovule solitary in each cell, mostly pendulous, nude or with a single integument; fruit small, nut-like, 1-celled, 1-seeded; seeds with abundant endosperm, and very small embryo, incl. *Cynomoriaceae.* B.H. 3 : 232. E.P. 3, 1 : 243. Mainly Tropics and Subtropics.—CYNOMORIUM, SARCOPHYTE, BALANOPHORA, THONNINGIA, SCYBALIUM, HELOSIS, CORYNAEA, etc.

Order 54. RHAMNALES

Trees, shrubs or climbers; leaves alternate or opposite, simple to compound, mostly stipulate; flowers more or less as in *Celastrales* (p. 231), but stamens opposite the petals or alternate with the sepals when petals absent; petals imbricate or valvate; seeds with copious or scanty endosperm, sometimes ruminate; embryo usually straight. Tropics and Temperate Regions.

190. RHAMNACEAE

Trees or shrubs, very rarely herbs, sometimes scandent; leaves simple, alternate or opposite; stipules mostly present; flowers mostly *cymose*, small, ☿, rarely polygamous-dioecious; calyx tubular, 4-5-lobed, lobes *valvate*; petals 4 or 5, or absent, small; stamens 4-5, *opposite* to and often *embraced by the petals*; anthers 2-celled, opening lengthwise; disk mostly present, *perigynous*, sometimes *lining the calyx-tube*; ovary sessile, free or sunk in the disk, 2-4-celled; style shortly lobed; ovules solitary, rarely paired, erect from the base, anatropous; fruit various, often *drupaceous*; seed mostly with copious endosperm and large straight embryo. B.H. 1 : 371. E.P. 3, 5 : 393. Mostly Tropics and Temperate Regions.—VENTILAGO, PALIURUS, ZIZYPHUS, BERCHEMIA, RHAMNUS, HOVENIA, CEANOTHUS, SCUTIA, SAGERETIA, COLUBRINA, PHYLICA, ALPHITONIA, POMADERRIS, SPYRIDIUM, CRYPTANDRA, COLLETIA, DISCARIA, GOUANIA, etc.

USEFUL PRODUCTS : *Popli-chekké root bark* (Ventilago maderaspatana *Gaertn.*), India ; *Lote fruit* (Zizyphus Lotus *Lam.*), Mediterranean ; *Indian Jujube* or *Chinese Date* (Z. Jujuba *Lam.*) ; *Cascara Sagrada* (Rhamnus Purshiana

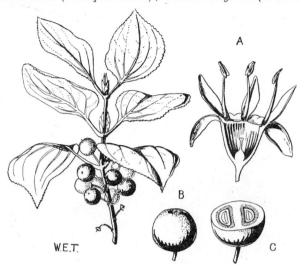

FIG. 190.—Rhamnus cathartica *L.* (Rhamnaceae). A, flower. B, fruit. C, section of same.—After Baill.

D.C.), Pacific N. America ; *Alder Buckthorn* (R. Frangula *L.*), Europe to Siberia ; *Sap Green* pigment from berries of *Buckthorn* (R. cathartica *L.*) ; *Coral Tree* (Hovenia dulcis *Thunb.*), East Asia ; *Mabee Bark* (Ceanothus reclinatus *L'Hérit.*), Tropical America ; *Chew Stick* (Gouania domingensis *L.*), West Indies.

191. ELAEAGNACEAE

Trees or shrubs with *lepidote* or *stellate indumentum* ; leaves alternate, rarely opposite, entire ; flowers ♀ or ♂ ♀, often dioecious, solitary, fasciculate, spicate or racemose ; calyx tubular, hypogynous, constricted and persistent around the ovary, 2-4-lobed or rarely truncate, *valvate* ; stamens inserted in the tube of the calyx or at the base in the ♂, 4 and *alternating* with the lobes or 8 alternate and opposite ; filaments free ; anthers 2-celled, opening lengthwise ; no staminodes in the ♀ flower ; ovary sessile at the base of the calyx, 1-celled ; style terminal, linear, stigmatose on one side ; ovule 1, basal, erect, anatropous ; fruit enclosed by the persistent berry-like thickened calyx ; seed erect, with scanty or no endosperm, straight embryo and thick fleshy cotyledons. B.H. 3 : 203. E.P. 3, 6a : 245. N. Temperate Zone, Tropical Asia to Australia.— ELAEAGNUS, HIPPOPHAE, SHEPHERDIA.

USEFUL PRODUCTS : *Trebizonde Dates* (Elaeagnus angustifolia *L.*), Europe to N. Asia ; *Buffalo Berries* (Shepherdia argentea *Nutt.*), N. America.

192. HETEROPYXIDACEAE

Trees ; leaves alternate, *pellucid-punctate* ; stipules absent ; flowers paniculate, ♀, actinomorphic ; calyx 5-lobed, lobes imbricate ; petals 5, shortly clawed, *gland-dotted* ; stamens 5, *opposite the petals* ; anthers oblong, 2-celled,

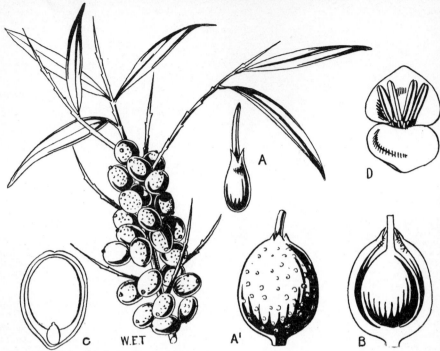

FIG. 191.—Hippophaë rhamnoides *L.* (Elaeagnaceae). A, female flower. A1, fruit. B, section of same. C, section of seed. D, male flower.—Orig.

opening lengthwise; ovary superior, 2-3-celled; style single, with capitate stigma; ovules numerous, on an axile placenta; fruit a small capsule, loculicidally 2-3-valved; seeds without endosperm; cotyledons flat, with stout straight radicle. B.H. 1 : 785 (under *Lythraceae*). E.P. N. 335. South-east and East Tropical Africa.—HETEROPYXIS.

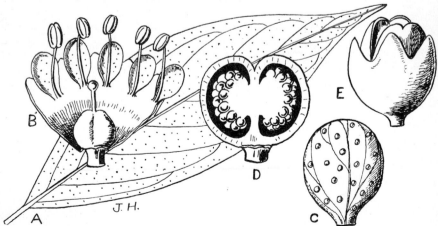

FIG. 192.—Heteropyxis canescens *Oliv.* (Heteropyxidaceae). A, leaf. B, flower. C, petal. D, vertical section of ovary. E, fruit.—After Hook. Ic. Pl.

193. AMPELIDACEAE
(Vitaceae)

Mostly climbing shrubs or small trees, *nodose* or *jointed*, often with watery juice ; leaves alternate or the lower sometimes opposite, simple or variously compound, often pellucid-punctate ; stipules petiolar or absent ; flowers ♀ or ♂ ♀, actinomorphic, small, in *leaf-opposed* spikes, racemes, panicles or cymes ; peduncles often *cirrhose* ; calyx small, entire or 4-5-toothed or lobed ; petals

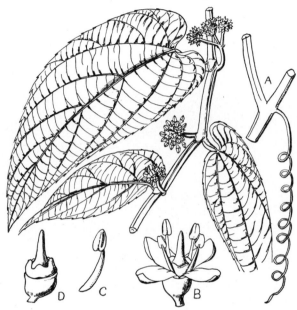

FIG. 193.—Cissus discolor *Planch.* (Ampelidaceae). A, branch showing tendril. B, flower. C, stamen. D, ovary.—After Bot. Mag.

4-5, free or united, caducous, *valvate* ; stamens 4-5, *opposite the petals*, inserted at the base of the disk ; anthers free or connate, 2-celled, opening lengthwise ; disk intra-staminal, mostly very distinct ; ovary 2-6-celled, cells 1-2-ovuled ; style short ; stigma capitate or discoid ; fruit baccate, often watery, 1-6-celled ; seed with copious sometimes ruminate endosperm and small embryo. B.H. 1 : 386. E.P. 3, 5 : 427. Tropics and warm Temperate Regions.—VITIS, CISSUS, AMPELOCISSUS, PARTHENOCISSUS, PTERISANTHES, LEEA.

USEFUL PRODUCTS : *Grape Vine* (Vitis vinifera *L.*) ; various forms producing *Muscatels, Sultanas, Raisins, Currants, Wines, Grape Sugar,* etc. Ornamental climbers : *Virginia Creeper* (Parthenocissus tricuspidata *Planch.*), etc.

Order 55. RUTALES

Trees, shrubs or climbers, rarely herbs ; leaves often gland-dotted, simple or compound ; stipules very rarely present ; flowers hypogynous to slightly perigynous, mostly ♀ ; sepals mostly imbricate ; petals contorted to valvate, free or connate near the base ; disk mostly conspicuous ; ovary superior, syncarpous or subapocarpous ; styles free or connate ; ovules 1-2 ; seeds with or without endosperm and straight or curved embryo.— Mainly Tropics.

194. RUTACEAE

Shrubs or trees, very rarely herbs ; leaves simple or compound, mostly gland-dotted ; stipules absent ; flowers ⚥, rarely ♂ ♀, rarely zygomorphic ; sepals 4-5, imbricate, free or connate ; petals imbricate, rarely valvate, mostly free ; stamens the same or double the number of the petals, rarely many, free or rarely united ; anthers 2-celled, introrse, opening lengthwise, the connective often glandular at the apex ; disk usually present within the stamens ; ovary superior, syncarpous and often 4-5-celled, or sometimes the carpels free towards

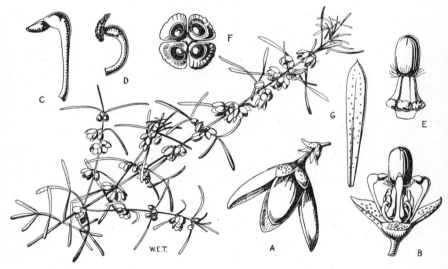

FIG. 194.—Boronia heterophylla *F. Muell.* (Rutaceae). A, flower. B, same opened. C, stamen before dehiscence. D, same after dehiscence. E, ovary. F, fruit. G, leaf.—Orig.

the base, or rarely altogether free ; styles free or connate ; ovules often 2, superposed ; fruit baccate, drupaceous or coriaceous, rarely capsular ; seeds with or without endosperm ; embryo straight or curved. B.H. 1 : 278. E.P. 3, 4 : 95. Temperate and warmer regions ; very numerous in S. Africa and Australia.—ALMEIDEA, GALIPEA, TICOREA, RUTA, PEGANUM, DICTAMNUS, CALODENDRUM, DIOSMA, ACMADENIA, ADENANDRA, BAROSMA, AGATHOSMA, BORONIA, ERIOSTEMON, PHEBALIUM, CORREA, MELICOPE, EVODIA, CHOISYA, ZANTHOXYLUM, ESENBECKIA, etc.

USEFUL PRODUCTS : *Lemons* (Citrus medica, var. Limonum, *Brand.*) ; *Oranges* (C. Aurantium *L.*) ; *Limes* (Citrus medica, var. Acida, *Brand.*), India ; *Cape Chestnut* (Calodendrum capensis *Thunb.*) ; *Buchu* (Barosma betulina *B. & W.*, etc.), S. Africa ; *Japan Pepper* (Zanthoxylum piperitum *D.C.*) ; *Jaborandi* (Pilocarpus Jaborandi *Holmes*), Brazil ; *Bael Fruit* (Aegle Marmelos *Corr.*), India ; *Cusparia Bark* (Galipea officinalis *Hancock*), Tropical S. America.

195. SIMARUBACEAE

Trees or shrubs, sometimes with a very *bitter bark*; leaves alternate or rarely opposite, *pinnate*, rarely simple or glandular; stipules absent or very rare; flowers small, unisexual or polygamous, rarely ⚥, actinomorphic; calyx-lobes 3-5; petals 3-5, imbricate or valvate, rarely absent, or united into a tube; *disk present*; stamens inserted at the base of the disk, equal or double the number of the petals, rarely numerous, free, sometimes with a scale at the base;

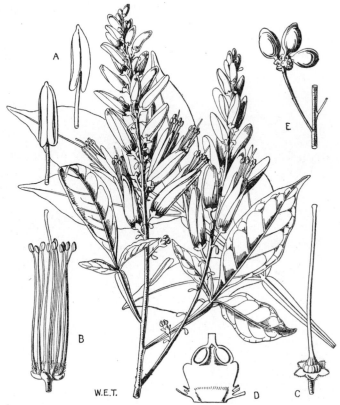

FIG. 195.—Quassia amara *L.* (Simarubaceae). A, stamens. B, stamens and ovary. C, ovary.
D, section of lower portion of same. E, fruits.—After Kohler.

anthers 2-celled, opening lengthwise; ovary mostly 2-5-*lobed*, 1-5-celled, or carpels quite separate; styles 2-5; ovules usually solitary, rarely 2 or more, axile; fruit usually indehiscent, sometimes samaroid; seeds with or without endosperm; embryo straight or curved. B.H. 1 : 306. E.P. 3, 4 : 202. Mainly Tropics. — QUASSIA, SIMABA, HANNOA, SIMARUBA, AILANTHUS, CASTELA, PICRASMA, SURIANA, etc.

USEFUL PRODUCTS: *Surinam Quassia Wood* (Quassia amara *L.*), Surinam; *Cedron* (Simaba Cedron *Planch.*), Central America; *Simaruba Bark* (Simaruba amara *Aubl.*), Tropical America; *Quassia Wood* (Picraena excelsa *Lindl.*), West Indies; *Dika Bread* (Irvingia Barteri *Hook. f.*), W. Africa; *Tree of Heaven* (Ailanthus glandulosa, *Desf.*), China.

196. Burseraceae

Trees or shrubs, secreting *resin* or *oil*; leaves alternate, rarely opposite, *compound*, rarely 1-foliolate, usually not punctate; *stipules absent*; flowers ♀ or ♂ ♀, small; sepals 3-5, imbricate or valvate; petals 3-5, rarely absent, free or variously connate, imbricate or valvate; *disk present*; stamens equal or generally double the number of the petals; filaments free; anthers 2-celled,

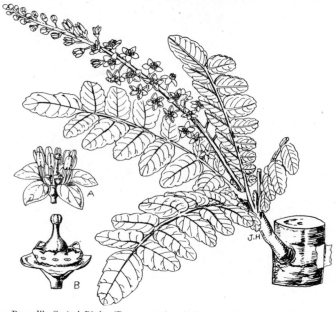

FIG. 196.—Boswellia Carteri *Birdw.* (Burseraceae). A, flower. B, ovary and disc.—After Birdw.

opening lengthwise; ovary superior, 2-5-celled; ovules 2 or rarely 1 in each cell, axile; fruit a drupe or tardily dehiscent; seeds without endosperm and often contortuplicate cotyledons. B.H. 1 : 321. E.P. 3, 4 : 231. Tropics.— Boswellia, Garuga, Balsamodendron, Bursera, Canarium, Amyris, etc.

Useful Products : Abounding in fragrant *balsams* and resins. *Gum Olibanum* or *Frankincense* (Boswellia Carteri *Birdw.*), Somaliland, Arabia; *Myrrh* (Balsamodendron, etc.), S. Arabia, etc.; *Carana gum resin* (Protium Carana *Marsh.*), S. America.

Order 56. MELIALES

Very similar to preceding group, but stamens often completely connate into a tube with the anthers inside; leaves not gland-dotted.

197. Meliaceae

Trees or shrubs, mostly with hard *scented* wood, very rarely subherbaceous; leaves alternate, *mostly pinnate*; stipules absent; flowers actinomorphic, mostly ♀; calyx often small, imbricate, rarely valvate; petals free or partially connate, contorted or imbricate, or adnate to the staminal-tube and valvate;

stamens mostly 8 or 10, rarely numerous, mostly with connate filaments and the anthers often sessile in the tube; anthers 2-celled, opening lengthwise; disk various; ovary superior, often 3-5-celled; stigma often *disciform* or *capitate*; ovules mostly 2, rarely 1 or more; fruit baccate, capsular or rarely a drupe, often with a large central axis; seeds with or without endosperm, sometimes winged. B.H. 1 : 327. E.P. 3, 4 : 258. Warm regions.—Turraea, Melia, Dysoxylum, Aglaia, Milnea, Amoora, Guarea, Ekebergia, Trichilia, Carapa, Swietenia, Khaya, Cedrela, Flindersia, etc.

Fig. 197.—Pseudocedrela Kotschyi *Schweinf.* (Meliaceae). A, flower. B, same with corolla removed. C, portion of staminal ring. D, ovary. E, fruit. F, seed.

Useful Products : *Neem or Margosa* (Melia Azadirachta *L.*), India; *Persian Lilac* (Melia Azedarach *L.*), Tropics (generally cultivated); *Lansa or Langsat fruit* (Lansium domesticum *Jack*); *Mafureira Seeds* (Trichilia emetica *Vahl*), Tropical Africa; *Mahogany Wood* (Swietenia Mahogani *L.*, etc.), Tropical America, West Indies; *Guiana Crab Tree* (Carapa guianensis *Aubl.*); *African Cedar* (Khaya senegalensis *Juss.*, etc.), West Africa; *Rohan Tree or Indian Redwood* (Soymida febrifuga *A. Juss.*), India; *Chittagong Wood* (Chickrassia tabularis *A. Juss.*), India, Burma, etc.; *Toon Wood* (Cedrela Toona *Roxb.*), India, etc.; *Satin Wood* (Chloroxylum Swietenia *D.C.*), India, etc.; *Yellow Wood* (Flindersia Oxleyana *F. Muell.*), E. Australia.

Order 57. SAPINDALES

Trees or shrubs; leaves mostly compound, usually pinnate, not gland-dotted; stipules rare; flowers hypogynous or slightly perigynous, often polygamous or unisexual, sometimes zygomorphic; sepals imbricate; petals mostly present; disk present; ovary superior, with 1-2 ovules in each cell, axile ; seeds mostly without endosperm ; embryo curved or crumpled.—Mainly Tropics.

198. SAPINDACEAE

Trees, shrubs or climbers ; leaves alternate or very rarely opposite, simple or *compound* ; stipules rarely present ; flowers actinomorphic or zygomorphic, often much reduced and usually *polygamo-dioecious*, variously arranged ; sepals free or variously connate, imbricate or rarely valvate ; petals 3-5 or rarely more, often absent, equal or unequal, imbricate ; disk usually present, sometimes *unilateral* ; stamens hypogynous, often 8, inserted *within the disk* or unilateral filaments, free, often hairy ; anthers 2-celled ; ovary superior, entire, lobed, or divided nearly to the base, 1-4- (often 3-) celled ; style terminal or between the lobes, rarely styles 2-4, simple or divided ; ovules 1-2 or rarely

FIG. 198.—Koelreuteria paniculata *Laxm.* (Sapindaceae). A and B, flower. C, vertical section of same. D, bract. E, sepal. F, petal. G, stamens. H, cross section of ovary. I, carpel opened. J, bud —After De Wild.

many in each cell, inserted on the central axis and usually ascending ; fruit various ; seeds without endosperm, often arillate, with often plicate or twisted embryo ; incl. *Hippocastanaceae* and *Bretschneideraceae*. B.H. 1 : 388, partly. E.P. 3, 5 : 277. Mainly Tropical Regions. — URVILLEA, SERJANIA, CARDIO-SPERMUM, PAULLINIA, ERIOGLOSSUM, ALLOPHYLLUS (Schmidelia), KOELREUTERIA, AESCULUS, CUPANIA, RATONIA, ERIOCOELUM, THOUINIA, TALISIA, SAPINDUS, DEINBOLLIA, NEPHELIUM, HARPULLIA, etc.

199. AKANIACEAE

Trees ; leaves alternate, imparipinnate ; flowers paniculate, ☿, actinomorphic ; sepals 5, imbricate ; petals 5, contorted ; disk absent ; stamens usually 8, the 5 outer opposite the sepals, the others around the base of the

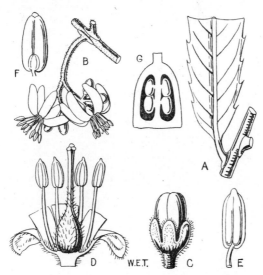

FIG. 199.—Akania Hillii *Hk. f.* (Akaniaceae).   A, twig with leaf.   B, flowers.   C, flower bud.   D, single flower enlarged.   E and F, anthers.   G, vertical section of ovary.—After Bot. Mag.

ovary ; filaments free ; anthers 2-celled, opening lengthwise ; ovary 3-celled ; style simple ; stigma minute, 3-lobed ; ovules 2 in each cell, superposed, pendulous ; fruit a capsule, loculicidally 3-valved ; seeds not arillate, with fleshy copious endosperm ; embryo straight.   B.H. 1 : 409 (under *Sapindaceae*). Stapf in *Kew Bull.* 19, 12 : 378.   Eastern Australia.—AKANIA.

200. ACERACEAE

Trees or shrubs with *perulate* buds ; leaves *opposite*, simple or palmately lobed or pinnately foliolate ; flowers in fascicles, racemes or corymbs, actinomorphic, andromonoecious or dioecious ; sepals and petals 4-5, rarely without petals ; disk annular or lobed, or reduced to teeth, rarely absent, either outside or within the stamens ; stamens 4-10, often 8, hypogynous or perigynous, or in the ♂ flowers central ; filaments free ; rudimentary ovary often present in the ♂ flowers ; ovary 2-celled, compressed contrary to the septum ; styles 2, free or connate at the base ; ovules 2 in each cell, attached to the central axis ; *fruit samaroid*, 2-winged, the carpels at length separating at the base, indehiscent ; seeds often solitary, compressed, without endosperm ; embryo with elongated radicle and flat or plicate cotyledons.   B.H. 1 : 409 (under *Sapindaceae*). E.P. 3, 5 : 263.   N. Temperate Hemisphere.—ACER, NEGUNDO, DOBINEA.

USEFUL PRODUCTS : *Sycamore* (Acer Pseudoplatanus *Linn.*) ; *Maple* (Acer campestre *L.*) ; *Sugar Maple* (A. saccharinum *Wang.*), N. America.

FIG. 200.—Acer campestre *L.* (Aceraceae). A, male flower. B, ovary. C, fruit.—Orig.

201. SABIACEAE

Trees or shrubs ; leaves alternate, simple or pinnate ; *stipules absent* ; flowers ♀ or polygamo-dioecious, small, often paniculate ; calyx 4-5-partite, imbricate ; petals 4-5, im-

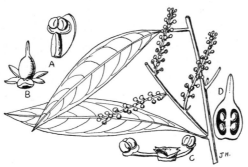

bricate, opposite or alternate with the sepals ; disk small, annular ; stamens 4-5, *opposite the petals*, free or adherent to the petals, sometimes only 2 with anthers ; anthers 2-celled, with a thick connective ; ovary sessile, 2-3-celled ; styles more or less united ; ovules 1-2 in each cell, horizontal or pendulous ; fruit dry or drupaceous ; seed without or with very thin endosperm adhering to the testa, and large embryo ; cotyledons contorted, with curved radicle.

FIG. 201.—Meliosma Henryi *Diels* (Sabiaceae). A, petal and stamen. B, pistil and calyx. C, stamens and disk. D, vertical section of ovary.—After Hook. Ic. Pl.

B.H. 1 : 413. E.P. 3, 5 : 367. Mainly Northern Tropics and Subtropics.— SABIA, MELIOSMA, PHOXANTHUS, OPHIOCARYON.

USEFUL PRODUCTS : Some ornamental shrubs (*Meliosma*).

202. Melianthaceae

Shrubs or small trees ; leaves alternate, *pinnate*, stipulate ; stipules intra-petiolar, often large ; flowers ♀, rarely ♂ ♀, racemose, zygomorphic ; calyx of 5 unequal segments, imbricate ; petals 5 free, subperigynous, clawed, unequal ; disk unilateral, lining the inside of the calyx ; stamens 4, inserted within the

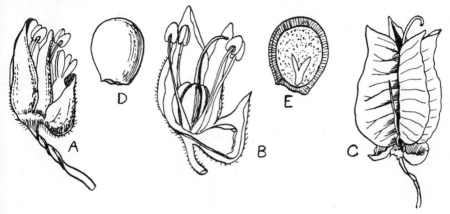

FIG. 202.—Melianthus major *L*. (Melianthaceae).   A, flower.   B, vertical section of same.   C, fruit.
D, seed.   E, vertical section of same.

disk, free or variously connate, often declinate ; anthers 2-celled, opening lengthwise ; ovary 4-5-celled, superior ; style central, dentate or truncate ; ovules 1-4 in each cell, axile ; fruit a papery or woody capsule, loculicidally 4-5-valved or opening only at the apex ; seeds with copious endosperm and straight embryo.   B.H. 1 : 411 (under *Sapindaceae*).   E.P. 3, 5 : 374.   Tropical and Subtropical Africa.—Melianthus, Bersama.

203. Didiereaceae

Trees with the habit of *Euphorbia*, very spiny ; leaves alternate ; flowers unisexual, dioecious ; male flower : sepals 2, decussate, petaloid, persistent ; petals 4, imbricate ; stamens 8-10, slightly united at the base, inserted outside an annular disk ; female flower : sepals and petals as in the male ; sterile anthers sometimes present ; ovary superior, 3-celled, only 1 cell fertile with 1 erect ovule ; style single, with an expanded irregularly 3-4-lobed stigma ; fruit 3-angled, not dehiscent ; seed with folded embryo and fleshy cotyledons. Engl. and Gilg, Syllab. eds. 9 and 10 : 269 (1924).   Madagascar.—Didierea (Fig. 203).

204. Staphyleaceae

Trees or shrubs ; leaves *opposite, trifoliolate* or *pinnate* ; stipules paired ; flowers ♀ or ♂ ♀, actinomorphic ; sepals imbricate ; petals imbricate, inserted on or below the hypogynous disk ; stamens 5, inserted with the petals and alternate with them, free ; anthers 2-celled, opening lengthwise ; carpels 2-3,

FIG. 203.—Didierea mirabilis *Baill.* (Didiereaceae).   A, female flower.   B, vertical section of same.
C, ovary in vertical section.   D, fruit.   E and F, male flower.   G, stamen.—After Drake.

more or less united into a 2-3-celled and lobed ovary ; styles free or coherent.
at length free ; ovules numerous, in 1-2 series on the ventral suture ; fruit a
membranous *inflated capsule* opening at the top, or a berry ; seeds few, truncate

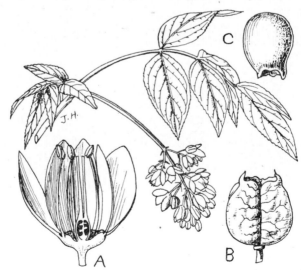

FIG. 204.—Staphylea pinnata *L.* (Staphyleaceae).   A, vertical section of flower.   B, fruit.
C, seed.—After Baill.

at the base, with scanty endosperm and straight embryo ; cotyledons flat.
B.H. 1 : 412 (under *Sapindaceae*).   E.P. 3, 5 : 258.   N. Hemisphere, S. America.
—STAPHYLEA, EUSCAPHIS, TURPINIA.   Some garden shrubs.

205. ANACARDIACEAE

Trees or shrubs, often with *resinous bark* ; leaves alternate, very rarely opposite, simple or *compound* ; stipules absent, very rarely present but obscure ; flowers ⚥ or ♂♀, mostly actinomorphic ; calyx variously divided, sometimes semisuperior in fruit ; petals 3-7 or absent, free or rarely connate and adnate to the torus ; disk present ; stamens often double the number of the petals, rarely equal or numerous ; filaments free among themselves ; anthers 2-celled, opening lengthwise ; ovary superior, *1-celled*, rarely 2-5-celled, or very rarely carpels free ; styles 1-3, often *widely separated* ; ovule solitary, pendulous from the apex or adnate to the ovary wall, or pendulous from a basal funicle ;

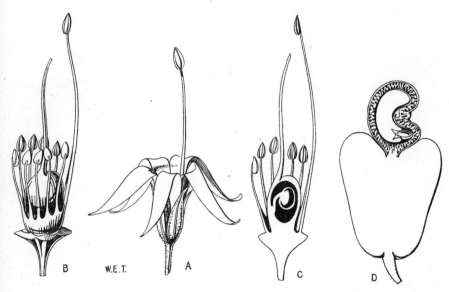

FIG. 205.—Anacardium occidentale *L.* (Anacardiaceae).   A, flower.   B, same with petals removed.
C, same in vertical section.   D, fruit in vertical section.—After Baill.

fruit mostly drupaceous ; seed without or with very thin endosperm ; cotyledons fleshy.   B.H. 1 : 415.   E.P. 3, 5 : 138.   Mainly Tropics.—RHUS, PISTACIA, SORINDEIA, MANGIFERA, ANACARDIUM, BUCHANANIA, SCHINUS, ODINA, SEMECARPUS, SPONDIAS, DRACONTOMELON, SCLEROCARYA, etc.

USEFUL PRODUCTS : *Lacquer Tree* (Rhus vernicifera *D.C.*), Japan ; [*Poison Ivy*, Rhus Toxicodendron *L.* ;] *Sumach* (Rhus Coriaria *L.*), Mediterranean ; *Chian Turpentine* (Pistacia Terebinthus *L.*), Mediterranean, etc. ; *Pistachio Nuts* (Pistacia vera *L.*), Mediterranean, West Asia ; *Mastic* (Pistacia Lentiscus *L.*), Greece ; *Quebracho Colorado Wood* (Quebrachia Lorentzii *Griseb.*), Argentine ; *Mango* (Mangifera indica *L.*), Tropics ; *Cashew Nut* (Anacardium occidentale *L.*), Tropics , *Burmese Lacquer Tree* (Melanorrhoea usitata *Wall.*) ; *Kaffir Date* (Harpephyllum caffrum *Bernh.*), S. Africa ; *Hog Plum* (Spondias mangifera *Willd.*), India, etc.

S

206. CONNARACEAE

Erect trees or shrubs or scandent ; leaves alternate, compound, *impari-pinnate* or 1-3-*foliolate* ; stipules absent ; flowers ♀, rarely ♂ ♀, actinomorphic or slightly zygomorphic ; calyx imbricate or valvate ; petals 5, free or some-times slightly connate, imbricate or rarely valvate ; stamens hypogynous to perigynous, often declinate, 5 or 10 ; filaments often united at the base ; anthers

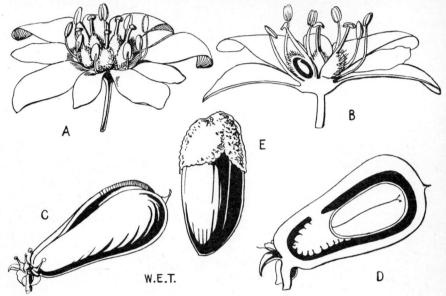

FIG. 206.—Connarus Patrisii *Planch.* (Connaraceae). A, flower. B, same in vertical section. C, fruit. D, same in vertical section. E, seed.—After Baill.

2-celled, opening lengthwise ; disk absent or thin ; carpels 1-5, *free*, 1-celled ; ovules 2, collateral, ascending from the inner angle ; fruit a capsule, sessile or stipitate, usually 1-seeded ; seeds *often arillate*, with or without endosperm. B.H. 1 : 430. E.P. 3, 3 : 61. Tropics.—BYRSOCARPUS, AGELAEA, ROUREA, CONNARUS, CNESTIS, etc.

USEFUL PRODUCTS : *Zebra Wood* (Connarus guianensis *Lamb.*), British Guiana.

Order 58. JUGLANDALES

Trees, often resinous ; leaves pinnate, alternate ; stipules absent ; flowers monoecious or dioecious, the male often in catkin-like spikes, much reduced ; calyx very small or absent ; stamens 3-40 ; anthers 2-celled, opening by slits ; ovary inferior, 1-celled ; ovule 1, erect ; seeds without endosperm.—Mostly Temperate Regions.

207. JUGLANDACEAE

Trees, often resinous and aromatic, with handsome durable dark-coloured wood ; leaves deciduous, alternate, *imparipinnate* : stipules absent ; flowers

♂♀, *monoecious*, the male often in catkin-like pendulous spikes, rarely erect, the female spikes erect ; calyx of the male flower adnate to the bract, 3-6-lobed and imbricate or absent ; stamens ∞ (3-40), attached to the torus in 2 or more series ; filaments short ; anthers erect, 2-celled, opening lengthwise ; rudimentary ovary rarely developed ; female flowers sessile on the axis, variously bracteate and often 2-bracteolate ; calyx adnate to the ovary, free at the apex, 4-toothed or shortly 4-lobed ; ovary *inferior*, 1-celled ; style short, with two

Fig. 207.—Engelhardtia nudiflora *Hook. f.* (Juglandaceae).   A, leaf and inflorescence.   B, portion of inflorescence.   C, female flower and transverse section of ovary.   D, vertical section of ovary. E, fruit.

short or elongated branches, often *plumose* ; ovule 1, erect from the base, orthotropous ; fruit a drupe or rarely a nut, often adnate to the enlarged bracts or bracteoles ; exocarp succulent, endocarp mostly hard, bony, intrusive at the base, imperfectly dividing the fruit into 2-4 cells ; seed solitary, without endosperm ; cotyledons often much contorted. B.H. 3 : 397.   E.P. 3, 1 : 19. N. Temperate Hemisphere and mountains of N. Tropics.—CARYA, JUGLANS, PTEROCARYA, ENGELHARDTIA, PLATYCARYA.

USEFUL PRODUCTS : *Hickory Nuts* (Carya alba *Nutt.*, C. tomentosa *Nutt.*), N. America ; *Peccan Nuts* (C. olivaeformis *Nutt.*) ; *Walnut Wood* and *Nuts* (Juglans regia *L.*) ; *Butternut* (Juglans cinerea *L.*), N. America.

208. JULIANIACEAE

Trees or shrubs abounding in resin ; leaves deciduous, alternate, pinnate ; stipules absent ; flowers dioecious, small, the male racemose-paniculate, the female crowded in an involucre ; calyx of the male 3-9-lobed, thin ; petals absent ; stamens the same number as the calyx-lobes and alternate with them ; anthers 2-celled, opening by a longitudinal slit, hairy ; no rudimentary ovary ; female flower : calyx and petals absent ; no staminodes ; ovary 1-celled, 1-ovuled ; style 3-parted ; ovule ascending from the base of the cell, half anatropous ; fruits enclosed in the enlarged involucre ; seeds without endosperm.   Hemsl. in *Phil. Trans. Roy. Soc.* 199 : 169 (1908).   Mexico and Peru.— JULIANIA, ORTHOPTERYGIUM.

FIG. 208.—Juliania adstringens *Schl.* (Julianiaceae).   A, male flower.   B, female flowers.
C, same in section.—After Hemsl.

Order 59. UMBELLIFLORAE

Woody to herbaceous ; leaves often compound or much divided, stipulate or not ; flowers mostly small and often arranged in umbels or heads ; stamens definite ; ovary inferior ; seeds mostly with copious endosperm.—World-wide distribution.

209. CORNACEAE

Trees, shrubs or rarely perennial herbs ; leaves opposite or alternate, simple ; stipules absent or branched-ciliate (*Helwingia*) ; flowers small, in dichotomous panicles or racemes of panicles, ♂ or dioecious, actinomorphic ; calyx-tube adnate to the ovary, 4-5-lobed or subtruncate ; petals 4-5, rarely absent, valvate or imbricate ; stamens the same number as the petals and *alternate* with them ; anthers short, 2-celled, opening lengthwise ; disk cushion-shaped, central in the ♂ flower, epigynous in the ♀ flower ; ovary *inferior*, 1-4-celled ; style simple or lobed ; ovules solitary and pendulous in each cell, anatropous, with 1 integument ; fruit a drupe or berry, 1-4-celled ; seeds pendulous ; embryo often small in copious endosperm. B.H. 1 : 947, partly. E.P. 3, 8 : 250. Scattered distribution.—HELWINGIA, COROKIA, CORNUS, AUCUBA, GRISELINIA.

USEFUL PRODUCTS : Ornamental garden shrubs. *Cornelian Cherry Wood* (Cornus Mas *L.*).

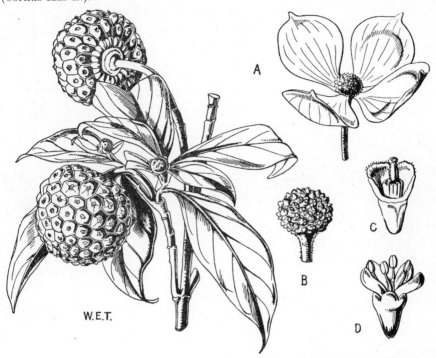

W.E.T.

FIG. 209.—Cornus capitata *Wall.* (Cornaceae). A, flower. B, flowers in bud. C, pistil. D, flower.

210. ALANGIACEAE

Trees or shrubs, sometimes spiny ; leaves alternate, simple ; stipules 0 ; flowers ♀, in axillary cymes ; pedicels *articulated* ; calyx *truncate* or with 4-10 teeth ; petals 4-10, mostly linear, *valvate*, at length recurved, sometimes coherent at the base ; stamens the same number as and alternate with the petals or 2-4 times as many, free or slightly connate at the base, more or less *villous inside* ; anthers 2-celled, linear, opening lengthwise ; disk cushion-like ; ovary *inferior*, 1-2-celled ; style simple, clavate or 2-3-lobed ; ovule solitary, pendulous, with 2 integuments ; fruit a drupe crowned by the sepals and disk, 1-seeded ; seeds with the embryo about equal to the endosperm. B.H. 1 : 949 (under *Cornaceae*). E.P. 3, 8 : 260. Tropical Old World.—ALANGIUM.

211. NYSSACEAE

Trees or shrubs with alternate, simple leaves ; stipules 0 ; flowers dioecious or ♀, capitate, racemose or umbellate, rarely solitary ; male flowers : calyx *obsolete* or of very small teeth ; petals 5 or more, *imbricate*, or absent ; stamens up to double the number of the petals, often 2-seriate ; anthers 2-celled, opening

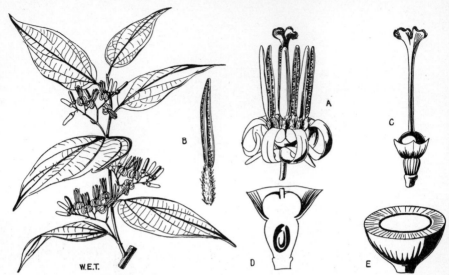

FIG. 210.—Alangium*begoniifolium *Roxb.* (Alangiaceae). A, flower. B, stamen. C, pistil. D, vertical section of ovary. E, cross section of ovary.—Orig.

lengthwise; disk central, fleshy; female flowers: calyx *adnate to the ovary*; petals 5 or more, imbricate, small; ovary *inferior*, 1-celled or 6-10-celled (*Davidia*); ovules solitary, pendulous from the apex, anatropous, with 2 integuments; disk pulvinate or absent; style simple or divided into as many lobes as ovary cells; fruit drupaceous or subsamaroid, 1-5-celled, cells 1-seeded; endosperm thin with fairly large embryo. B.H. 1 : 952 (under *Cornaceae*). E.P. 3, 8 : 257. Eastern Asia to N. America.—NYSSA, CAMPTOTHECA, DAVIDIA.

USEFUL PRODUCTS : Handsome garden trees. *Ogeechee Lime Fruits* (Nyssa capitata *Walt.*), N. America.

212. ARALIACEAE

Mostly woody, sometimes climbing by means of aerial roots; leaves alternate or rarely opposite, simple, pinnate or digitate, often with *stellate indumentum*; stipules either adnate to and scarcely distinguishable from the base of the petiole, or intrapetiolar, rarely absent; flowers ☿, polygamous or dioecious, actinomorphic, racemose, umbellate or capitate, rarely epiphyllous; calyx superior, small, entire or toothed; petals 3 or more, often 5, *valvate* or slightly imbricate, free or united; stamens free, alternate with the petals and mostly the same number; anthers 2-celled, opening lengthwise; disk on top of the ovary, often confluent with the style in the middle; ovary *inferior*, 1- or more-celled; styles free or connate; ovule solitary in each cell, pendulous from the apex, anatropous, raphe ventral; fruit a berry or drupe; seeds with copious endosperm and very small embryo. B.H. 1 : 931. E.P. 3, 8 : 1. Mainly Tropics.—ARALIA, HEDERA, PANAX, ACANTHOPANAX, FATSIA, DIDYMO-PANAX, HELWINGIA, SCIADOPHYLLUM, POLYSCIAS, HEPTAPLEURUM, DENDRO-PANAX, CUSSONIA, OREOPANAX, etc.

USEFUL PRODUCTS : *Virginian Sarsaparilla* (Aralia nudicaulis *L.*); *Ginseng Root* (Aralia quinquefolia var. Ginseng), N. China; *Ivy* (Hedera Helix *L.*).

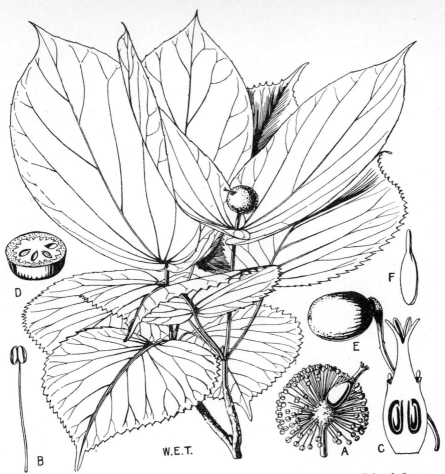

FIG. 211.—Davidia involucrata *Baill.* (Nyssaceae). A, inflorescence. B, stamen. C, female flower·
D, transverse section of fruit. E, fruit. F, embryo. (Flowers pendulous in nature.)

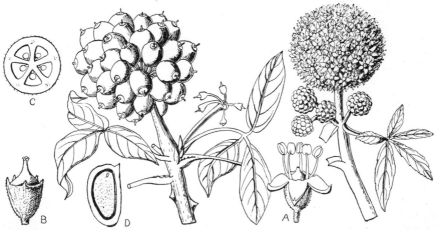

FIG. 212.—Acanthopanax Henryi *Harms* (Araliaceae). A, flower. B, ovary. C, same in transverse
section. D, seed.—After Bot. Mag.

213. Umbelliferae

Herbaceous, very rarely somewhat woody, with *furrowed stems* and wide *soft pith* ; leaves alternate, mostly *much divided, sheathing* at the base ; flowers ☿, rarely unisexual, in simple or compound *umbels* or rarely capitate ; calyx *adnate to the ovary,* 5-lobed ; petals 5, *valvate* or slightly imbricate, epigynous, free, soon falling off, mostly inflexed in bud ; stamens 5, alternate with the petals ; filaments *inflexed* in bud ; anthers 2-celled, opening lengthwise ; ovary inferior, 2-celled ; styles 2, thickened at the base and capping the ovary ; ovules solitary in each cell, pendulous ; fruit inferior, dry, 2-celled, dividing into 2 mericarps, these often remaining suspended at the top by the divided thread-like central axis (carpophore) ; carpels mostly *prominently ribbed* and often

Fig. 213.—Foeniculum vulgare *L.* (Umbelliferae).   A, flower.   B, schizocarp.   C, section of same showing vittae.

with parallel *resinous canals* (vittae) ; seeds with copious endosperm and minute embryo. B.H. 1 : 859. E.P. 3, 8 : 63. Temperate Regions mainly, in the Tropics mostly on the mountains.—Hydrocotyle, Azorella, Eryngium, Alepidea, Astrantia, Sanicula, Smyrnium, Bupleurum, Apium, Ammi, Carum, Pimpinella, Conopodium, Chaerophyllum, Scandix, Anthriscus, Seseli, Oenanthe, Ligusticum, Aciphylla, Selinum, Pleurospermum, Angelica, Perula, Peucedanum, Heracleum, Daucus, Laserpitium, etc.

Useful Products : *Celery* (Apium graveolens *L.*) ; *Carrots* (Daucus Carota *L.*), Europe to India ; *Parsnips* (Peucedanum sativum *Bth. & Hk. f.*) ; *Caraway Seeds* (Carum Carvi *L.*), Europe to Himalayas ; *Gum Ammoniacum* (Dorema Ammoniacum *Don*), Orient ; *Anise* (Pimpinella Anisum *L.*), S.E. Europe ; *Dill Seed* (Peucedanum graveolens *Bth. & Hk. f.*), S. Europe to Abyssinia ; *Coriander Seeds* (Coriandrum sativum *L.*), Mediterranean ; *Fennel* (Foeniculum capillaceum *Gilibert*), S. Europe ; *Common Hemlock* (Conium maculatum *L.*), Europe, etc. ; and many minor products.

Division II. METACHLAMYDEAE.

Order 60. ERICALES

Shrubs, rarely herbs or trees, sometimes parasitic or epiphytic ; leaves simple, sometimes scaly, alternate to rarely opposite ; stipules absent ; flowers ♀, rarely ♂ ♀, actinomorphic ; petals united (rarely free) ; stamens hypogynous or epigynous, usually double the number of the corolla-lobes ; anthers often opening by terminal pores ; ovary superior to inferior, with axile placentation ; seeds with copious endosperm and small embryo.— Mainly temperate and mountainous regions of the Tropics.

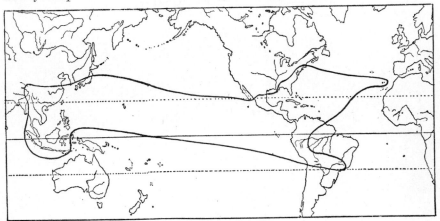

Range of Clethra (Clethraceae).

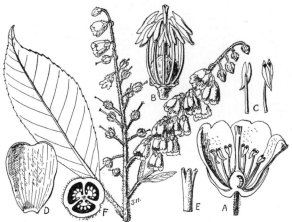

FIG. 214.—Clethra arborea *L.* (Clethraceae).   A, vertical section of flower.   B, flower with sepals and petals removed.   C, stamens.   D, petal.   E, style.   F, transverse section of ovary.—Orig.

214. Clethraceae

Shrubs or trees ; leaves alternate, simple ; stipules 0 ; flowers ♀, fragrant, in terminal racemes or panicles ; calyx deeply 5-lobed, lobed *imbricate, persistent* around the fruit ; corolla of 5 *free* imbricate petals ; stamens 10-12, *hypogynous*, free ; filaments hairy or glabrous ; anthers extrorsely *inflexed in bud*, sagittate, opening by *apical pores* ; disk obsolete ; ovary superior, hairy, 3-celled, 3-lobed ; style 1, 3-lobed at the apex ; ovules numerous on axile placentas ; fruit a sub-globose 3-lobed loculicidally 3-valved capsule ; seeds numerous, compressed or trigonous, often winged ; endosperm fleshy, with a cylindric embryo. B.H. 2 : 603 (under *Ericaceae*). E.P. 4, 1 : 2. Subtropical and Tropical Asia, Madeira, S.E. United States, Central and Tropical S. America.—CLETHRA.

USEFUL PRODUCTS : Evergreen and deciduous garden shrubs.

215. ERICACEAE

Shrubs or undershrubs, rarely trees ; leaves mostly alternate, simple, mostly evergreen ; stipules absent ; flowers ⚥, symmetric or slightly asymmetric ;

FIG. 215.—Rhododendron cinnamomeum *Wall.* (Ericaceae).   A, stamen.   B, section of ovary.— After Hook. f.

calyx persistent ; corolla hypogynous, mostly *gamopetalous*, inserted below a fleshy disk, lobes contorted or imbricate ; stamens mostly *double the number of the corolla-lobes,* rarely the same number and then alternate, *hypogynous,* inserted on the disk ; filaments free or rarely somewhat connate ; anthers 2-celled, often with tails, *opening by pores* ; ovary *superior,* several-celled, with numerous ovules on axile placentas which often protrude into the cells, rarely ovule 1 ; style simple ; fruit a capsule, berry or drupe ; seeds with fleshy endosperm and straight embryo, sometimes winged (incl. *Pyrolaceae*). B.H. 2 : 577.

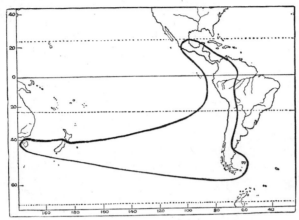

Range of Pernettya (Ericaceae).

E.P. 4, 1 : 15. Generally distributed ; great concentration of species in S. Africa (*Erica*) and Western China (*Rhododendron*).—Arbutus, Arctostaphylos, Pernettya, Gaultheria, Cassiope, Leucothoe, Agarista, Andromeda, Pieris, Enkianthus, Calluna, Erica, Philippia, Blaeria, Grisebachia, Simocheilus, Scyphogyne, Loiseleuria, Bryanthus, Daboecia, Kalmia, Elliottia, Ledum, Rhododendron (Azalea), Pyrola, Moneses, etc.

Useful Products : Many beautiful outdoor shrubs and rock-garden plants ; *Rhododendron, Erica,* etc. *Bear-Berry* (Arctostaphylos Uva-ursi *Spreng.*), N. cool Temperate Zone; *Heather* (Calluna vulgaris *Salisb.*); *Briar Root Wood* (Erica arborea *L.*), S. Europe, etc. ; *Labrador Tree* (Ledum latifolium *Jacq.*), N. America.

216. Vacciniaceae

Shrubs ; leaves alternate, simple ; stipules absent ; flowers ⚥ ; calyx deciduous or persistent ; corolla gamopetalous, *epigynous,* lobes *imbricate* ; stamens *twice as many* as the corolla-lobes, epigynous ; anthers 2-celled, opening by *terminal pores* ; ovary *inferior,* 4-10-celled ; ovules usually many, on axile placentas ; fruit a berry or drupe ; seeds with copious fleshy endosperm and straight embryo. B.H. 2 : 564. E.P. 4, 1 : 15 (under *Ericaceae*). Mountainous regions of Tropical America and Asia ; absent from Trop. Africa, rare in Temperate Regions.—Psammisia, Ceratostemma, Cavendishia, Agapetes, Pentapterygium, Gaylussacia, Vaccinium, Oxycoccus, etc.

Useful Products : *Cranberry* (Oxycoccus palustris *Pers.*) ; *Whortleberry* or *Bilberry* (Vaccinium Myrtillus *L.*) ; *Cowberry* (V. Vitis-Idaea *L.*) ; *Broussa Tea* (V. Arctostaphylos *L.*).

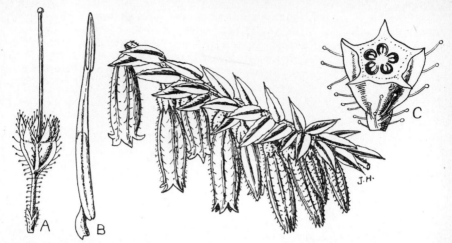

FIG. 216.—Vaccinium serpens *Wight* (Vacciniaceae). A, flower with corolla and stamens removed. B, stamen. C, ovary in transverse section.—After Hook. f.

217. EPACRIDACEAE

Shrubs or small trees; leaves alternate, rarely opposite, often crowded; stipules absent; flowers ♂, rarely ♂♀, bracteate; calyx 4-5-lobed, persistent; corolla gamopetalous, hypogynous, lobes imbricate or valvate, rarely the lobes

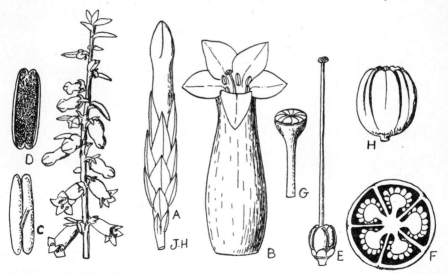

FIG. 217.—Epacris nivalis *Lodd.* (Epacridaceae). A, flower in bud. B, open flower. C and D, anthers. E, pistil. F, section of ovary. G, stigma. H, fruit.—After Le Maout & Decne.

coherent and then the tube opening transversely near the persistent base; stamens usually 4-5, *hypogynous* or *epipetalous*, alternate with the corolla-lobes, sometimes alternating with bunches of *hairs* or *glands*; *anthers 1-celled*, opening lengthwise ; ovary superior, often surrounded at the base by hypogynous disk-glands, 1-10-celled ; style simple ; ovules 1 to many, on axile or apical placentas, rarely erect ; fruit a capsule or drupe ; seeds with straight embryo in the middle of fleshy endosperm. B.H. 2 : 608. E.P. 4, 1 : 66. Mainly extratropical Australia, New Caledonia, New Zealand.—Astroloma, Leuco-pogon, Epacris, Andersonia, Richea, Dracophyllum, etc.

Useful Products : Ornamental greenhouse shrubs.

218. Monotropaceae

Leafless herbs *parasitic* on the roots of trees, never green ; stem scaly, ·scales alternate, the upper ones becoming bracteate or involucrate ; flowers ⚥,
actinomorphic, solitary to capitate,
often dull-coloured ; sepals 2-6, erect,
imbricate, often not distinguishable
from the bracts ; petals 3-6, free or
united into a lobed corolla, subcontorted or imbricate, very rarely absent;
stamens 6-12, *hypogynous* ; filaments
free or connate at the base ; anthers
2-celled, *opening lengthwise* ; pollen
mostly in a *mass* ; disk present or
absent ; ovary superior, 1-6-celled ;
style various, with a mostly *capitate,
indusiate* stigma ; ovules very numerous, minute, in the 1-celled ovaries on
parietal placentas, axile in the ovaries
with more cells ; capsule often membranous, loculicidally 4-6-valved; seeds
minute, with copious endosperm and
minute undivided embryo. B.H. 2:604.
E.P. 4, 1 : 15 (under *Pyrolaceae*). N.
Temperate Hemisphere.—Monotropa,
Hypopithys, Cheilotheca, etc.

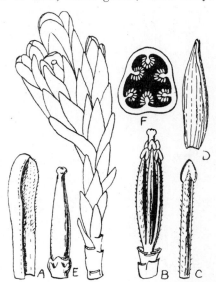

FIG. 218.—Cheilotheca malayana *Scort.* (Monotro-paceae). A, sepal. B, flower with perianth removed. C, stamen. D, petal. E, ovary. F, transverse section of same.—After Hook. Ic. Pl.

219. Diapensiaceae

Small shrublets ; leaves simple, small and imbricate or few and larger ; flowers ⚥, actinomorphic, solitary to subcapitate, white, rose or purple ; calyx 5-lobed, persistent, lobes imbricate ; corolla gamopetalous, 5-lobed, lobes imbricate ; stamens 5, *inserted on the corolla* and *alternate* with the lobes, free, or connate into a ring with as many *staminodes* ; anthers 1-2-celled, mostly *opening lengthwise* ; staminodes when present either scale-like or spathulate ; disk none ; ovary superior, 3-celled ; ovules few to numerous on *axile placentas* ; fruit a capsule, loculicidally 3-valved ; seeds minute with copious fleshy endo-sperm and cylindric central embryo. B.H. 2 : 618. E.P. 4, 1 : 80. N. Temperate and cold Hemisphere.—Diapensia, Pyxidanthera, Shortia, Schizocodon, Galax, Berneuxia,

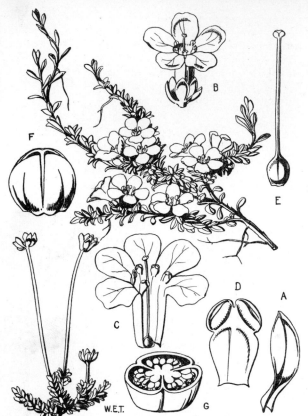

FIG. 219.—Diapensia himalaica
Hk. f. & Thoms. A, sepal.
B, flower. C, same opened.
D, stamen. E, ovary. F,
fruit. G, same in transverse
section.—After Hook. f.

220. LENNOACEAE

Parasitic leafless herbs
destitute of chlorophyll;
flowers ☿, actinomorphic,
spicate, cymose or capi-
tate; calyx 6-10-lobed,
lobes linear or subulate;
corolla gamopetalous,
5-8-lobed, lobes imbri-
cate; stamens inserted
below the apex of the
tube, 1-2-seriate, the
same number as the
corolla-lobes and *alter-
nate* with them; fila-
ments short; anthers
2-celled, *opening lengthwise*; disk absent;
ovary superior, *10-15-*

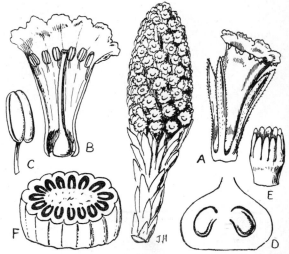

FIG. 220.—Pholisma arenarium *Nutt.* (Lennoaceae). A, flower. B,
same opened. C, stamen. D, vertical section of ovary. E, stigmas.
F, transverse section of ovary.

celled, cells surrounding the *thick central axis*, each cell *spuriously divided*; style simple; stigma subcapitate; ovules paired in each carpel, axile; fruit at length irregularly circumscissile; seeds small, with copious endosperm and small subglobose undivided embryo. B.H. 2 : 621. E.P. 4, 1 : 12. Mexico and California.—PHOLISMA, AMMOBROMA, LENNOA.

Order 61. EBENALES

Trees or shrubs; leaves alternate, entire; stipules absent; flowers ♀ or ♂ ♀, actinomorphic; petals united, imbricate; stamens epipetalous or rarely hypogynous, 1-4 times as many as the corolla-lobes; petaloid staminodes often present; anthers opening lengthwise; ovary superior; cells 1-2-ovuled; ovules axile; seeds with copious or scanty endosperm.— Mainly Tropics.

221. EBENACEAE

Trees or shrubs with often hard and black wood; leaves alternate, entire; stipules absent; flowers mostly ♂ ♀, often *dioecious*, the ♂ with a rudimentary ovary, the ♀ with imperfect or no stamens; female flowers usually solitary;

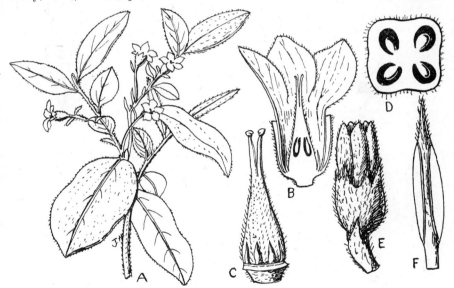

FIG. 221.—Royena lucida *Lim.* (Ebenaceae).   A, habit.   B, female flower in vertical section.   C, ovary. D, transverse section of same.   E, male flower.   F, stamen.

calyx 3-6-lobed, persistent and often accrescent in fruit; corolla 3-7-lobed, lobes imbricate; stamens *hypogynous* or on the bottom of the corolla, *2-4 times the number* of the corolla-lobes, rarely equal and alternate; filaments free or united in pairs; anthers 2-celled, introrse, opening lengthwise; ovary superior, 3- or more-celled; style often divided; ovules 1-2 in each cell, pendulous from the inner angle; berry more or less succulent; seeds with a thin testa; embryo about half as long as the endosperm; cotyledons about equal to the radicle, foliaceous. B.H. 2 : 662. E.P. 4, 1 : 153. Tropics and Subtropics of the Old World and N. America.—Royena, Euclea, Maba, Diospyros, etc.

Useful Products : Heavy and valuable timbers, including *Calamander Wood* (Diospyros quaesita *Thw.*), Ceylon ; *Andaman Marble* or *Zebra Wood* (Diospyros Kurzii *Hiern*), Indian Archipelago ; *Ebony* (Diospyros Ebenum *Koenig*), S. India, Ceylon ; *Gaub Fruits* (D. Embryopteris *Pers.*), India to Malaya ; *Date Plum* (D. Lotus *L.*), Italy and Orient ; *Persimmon* (Diospyros virginiana *L.*), United States ; *Kaki Plum* (D. Kaki *L. f.*), Japan.

Fig. 222.—Butyrospermum Parkii *Kotschy* (Sapotaceae). A, flower opened. B, stamen and staminodes. C, calyx. D, vertical section of ovary. E, transverse section of same. F, stamen. G, fruit. H, seed.—After Kotschy.

222. SAPOTACEAE

Trees or shrubs with *milky juice*, often cauliflorous ; leaves simple, alternate, entire, leathery ; *stipules absent* ; flowers ⚥, actinomorphic, usually rather small ; calyx 4-8-lobed ; corolla 4-8-lobed, lobes 1-2-seriate, imbricate ; stamens *epipetalous*, the fertile ones equalling the corolla-lobes and *opposite* to them, or more numerous and 2- or more-seriate ; *staminodes sometimes present* ; anthers opening lengthwise ; ovary several-celled, superior ; style simple ; ovules solitary in each cell, ascending from the inner axil ; fruit 1-many-celled, often a rather hard berry, rarely a capsule ; seeds with a bony, often shining, testa, and a large broad hilum ; endosperm mostly scanty ; embryo large, with small radicle and broad foliaceous cotyledons.   B.H. 2 : 650.   E.P. 4, 1 : 126.   Mainly Tropics and Subtropics.—CHRYSOPHYLLUM, LUCUMA, SIDEROXYLON, ACHRAS, DICHOPSIS, BASSIA, BUMELIA, BUTYROSPERMUM, MIMUSOPS, IMBRICARIA.

USEFUL PRODUCTS : *Shea Butter Tree* (Butyrospermum Parkii *Kotschy*), N. Tropical Africa ; *Balata* or *Bully Tree* (Mimusops globosa *Gaertn.*) ; *Gutta Percha* (Palaquium Gutta *Burck.*), Malay Peninsula ; *Mahwa* or *Mowa Tree* (Bassia latifolia *Roxb.*), India ; *Sapodilla Plum* (Achras Sapota *L.*), Tropical America and cultivated ; *Star Apple* (Chrysophyllum Cainito *L.*), Tropical America, West Indies ; *Mammee Sapote Plum* (Lucuma mammosa *Gaertn.*), S. America, West Indies.

Order 62. MYRSINALES

More or less as in *Ebenales*, but leaves mostly gland-dotted, and flowers small ; petals united, rarely free, usually contorted or imbricate ; stamens the same number as and *opposite* the corolla-lobes, usually epipetalous ; anthers opening lengthwise or by apical pores ; ovary superior to half - inferior, with numerous ovules on a free-basal placenta.

223. MYRSINACEAE

Trees, shrubs, rarely subherbaceous ; leaves alternate, rarely sub-opposite or subverticillate, simple, *punctate* or with schizogenous lines; flowers small, ⚥ or rarely dioecious, in racemes or panicles ; sepals free or connate, often *punctate*, *valvate*, *imbricate* or

FIG. 223.—Ardisia humilis *Vahl.* (Myrsinaceae).   A, bud.   B, vertical section of same.   C, stamens.   D, ovary.   E, transverse section of same.—After De Wild.

T

contorted, persistent ; corolla rotate or tubular, rarely the petals free ; lobes contorted, imbricate or rarely valvate ; stamens *opposite the petals* and the same number ; filaments adnate to the corolla or rarely almost free ; anthers introrse, opening lengthwise or by *apical pores*, rarely septate ; ovary *superior or half-inferior, 1-celled* ; style simple, sometimes capitate ; ovules numerous on a *free-central placenta* ; fruit a berry or drupe, rarely irregularly dehiscent ; seeds with smooth or rarely ruminate endosperm (rarely absent), with the embryo sometimes placed transversely, straight or arcuate ; incl. *Theophrastaceae.* B.H. 2 : 639. E. P. 4, 1 : 84. Mainly Tropics.—MAESA, MYRSINE, CYBIANTHUS, EMBELIA, CONOMORPHA, ARDISIA, AEGICERAS, THEOPHRASTA, CLAVIJA, JACQUINIA, etc.

Order 63. STYRACALES

Trees or shrubs ; leaves simple, alternate ; stipules absent ; flowers actinomorphic ; sepals valvate ; petals free to united, imbricate or valvate ;

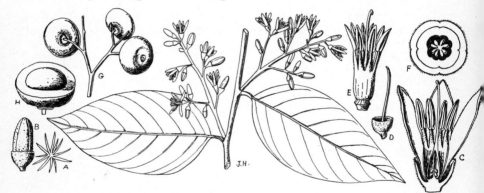

FIG. 224.—Styrax Benzoin *Dryand.* (Styracaceae). A, hair. B, bud. C, flower in vertical section. D, calyx. E, flower with perianth removed. F, transverse section of ovary. G, fruits. H, same showing stone.—Partly after Pierre.

stamens free from or adnate to the corolla-tube, few and alternate with the lobes or more numerous ; anthers opening lengthwise ; ovary superior to inferior, with axile placentation ; seeds with copious endosperm. Warmer regions.

224. STYRACACEAE

Trees or shrubs often with *stellate or lepidote* indumentum ; leaves alternate, simple ; *stipules absent* ; flowers actinomorphic, ☿, racemose, axillary or terminal ; calyx tubular, more or less *adnate to the ovary* ; lobes or teeth *valvate* or open ; corolla gamopetalous or rarely of free petals, lobes 4-7, valvate or imbricate ; stamens equal and alternate with or double the number of the corolla-lobes, adnate to the corolla-tube or rarely free ; anthers 2-celled, opening lengthwise ; ovary superior to inferior, 3-5-celled ; style slender, 3-5-lobed ; ovules 1 to many in each cell, axile, anatropous ; fruit drupaceous or capsular, calyx persistent ; seed with copious endosperm and straight or slightly curved embryo. B.H. 2 : 667. E.P. 4, 1 : 172. Warmer parts of N. Hemisphere ; very rare in

Africa. — Pamphilia, Styrax, Bruinsmia, Alniphyllum, Halesia, Pterostyrax, Afrostyrax.

Useful Products : *Storax* (Styrax officinale *L.*), S. Europe, Asia Minor ; *Gum Benzoin* (Styrax Benzoin *Dry.*), Malaya, Indo-China. Some ornamental garden shrubs.

225. Symplocaceae

Trees or shrubs ; leaves alternate, simple ; *stipules absent* ; flowers axillary or terminal, solitary or in spikes, racemes or fascicles, actinomorphic, ☿, rarely polygamous ; sepals 5, connate, *valvate* ; petals 3-11, more or less connate ;

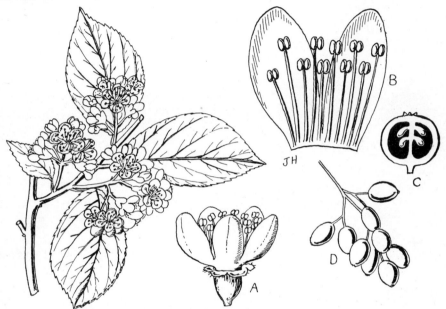

Fig. 225.—Symplocos crataegoides *Buch.-Ham.* (Symplocaceae). A, flower. B, petals and stamens. C, ovary in vertical section. D, fruits.

stamens *inserted on the corolla*, 4 to numerous, free or variously united, in 1-4 series ; anthers subglobose, 2-celled, opening lengthwise ; ovary *inferior* or *semi-inferior*, 2-5-celled ; ovules 2-4, pendulous ; style slender ; fruit baccate, or drupaceous, crowned by the calyx-lobes, 1-5-celled ; seeds solitary in each cell, with copious endosperm ; embryo straight or curved ; cotyledons very short. B.H. 2 : 668 (under *Styracaceae*). E.P. 4, 1 : 165. Warmer parts of Asia, Australia and America ; absent from Africa.—Symplocos.

Useful Products : *Lodh Bark* (Symplocos racemosa *Roxb.*), India.

226. Diclidantheraceae

Trees or shrubs with hard wood ; leaves alternate, exstipulate, entire ; flowers in axillary or terminal racemes or panicles ; calyx-tube campanulate, lobes 5, imbricate ; corolla-tube elongated, cylindric, lobes 5, imbricate ; stamens 10 in a single series near the apex of the corolla-tube ; anthers opening by a transverse slit ; ovary superior, 5-celled ; style simple ; ovule solitary in each cell, pendulous ; fruit globose, indehiscent ; seeds with some endosperm and straight embryo. B.H. 2 : 671 (under *Styracaceae*). Engl. and Gilg, Syllab., eds. 9 and 10 : 323. Brazil.—DICLIDANTHERA.

FIG. 226.—Diclidanthera lamifolia *Mart.* (Diclidantheraceae).   A, flower.   B, stamen.   C, ovary in transverse section.   D, seed.   E, same in vertical section.—After Martius.

227. LISSOCARPACEAE

Small trees ; leaves alternate, entire ; stipules absent ; flowers cymose ; calyx-tube shortly adnate to the base of the ovary, campanulate, lobes 4, im-

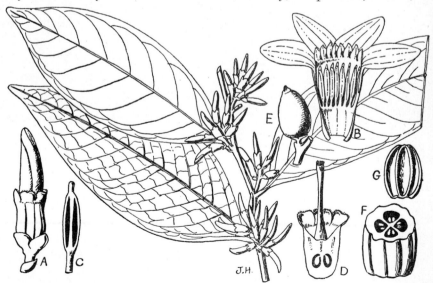

FIG. 227.—Lissocarpa Benthami *Gürke* (Lissocarpaceae).   A, bud.   B, flower opened.   C, stamen. D, ovary in vertical section.   E, fruit.   F, same in transverse section.   G, seed.—After Hook. Ic. Pl.

bricate ; corolla-tube 4-lobed, lobes contorted ; stamens 8, inserted near the base of the corolla, the filaments connate into a tube ; anthers linear, adnate within the middle of the tube, opening lengthwise ; ovary nearly completely superior, 4-celled ; style club-shaped ; ovules 2 in each cell, pendulous ; fruit indehiscent, 1-2-seeded ; seed 3-ribbed, with copious endosperm and straight embryo about half as long. B.H. 2 : 671 (under *Styracaceae*). Engl. and Gilg, Syllab., eds. 9 and 10 : 324. Tropical S. America.—LISSOCARPA.

Order 64. LOGANIALES

Mostly trees and shrubs with opposite, simple or rarely compound leaves ; stipules present or absent ; sepals mostly valvate ; petals united, rarely free or absent ; stamens epipetalous, alternate with the corolla-lobes or fewer ; ovary superior, 2-4-celled ; ovules mostly numerous ; seeds with endosperm and straight embryo.—Tropics and Temperate Regions.

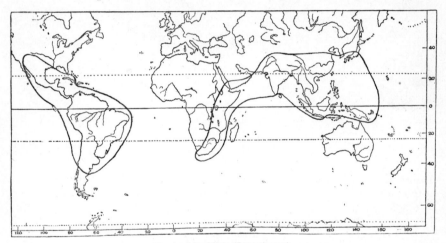

Range of Buddleia (Loganiaceae).

228. LOGANIACEAE

Stem usually woody ; leaves *opposite*, simple ; stipules present or absent, free or cohering in a sheath ; flowers ♀, actinomorphic, sometimes corymbose or in globose heads ; calyx *valvate*, rarely imbricate ; corolla tubular, lobes 4-10, contorted, imbricate or valvate ; stamens *epipetalous, as many as* the corolla-lobes and alternate with them or rarely reduced to 1 ; anthers 2-celled, opening lengthwise ; *ovary superior*, 2-4-celled ; style single ; ovules numerous, rarely solitary, axile or ascending from the base of each cell ; fruit a capsule, berry, or drupe ; seeds sometimes winged ; embryo straight in the middle of fleshy or cartilaginous endosperm ; incl. *Desfontaineaceae*. B.H. 2 : 786. E.P. 4. 2 : 19. Tropics and Subtropics.—GELSEMIUM, MOSTUEA, SPIGELIA, MITRA-SACME, LOGANIA, GENIOSTOMA, NUXIA, CHILIANTHUS, BUDDLEIA, DESFONTAINEA, FAGRAEA, ANTHOCLEISTA, USTERIA, STRYCHNOS, GAERTNERA, etc.

USEFUL PRODUCTS : *False Jasmine Root* (Gelsemium sempervirens *Ait.*),
N. America ; *Indian Pink Root* (Spigelia marilandica *L.*), S. United States ;

FIG. 228.—Buddleia Colvillei *Hk. f. & Thoms.* (Loganiaceae). A, flower opened. B, stamens.
C, flower with corolla and stamens removed. D, ovary. E, transverse section of same. F and F₁,
ovules. G, section of ovule. H, embryo. I, fruits. J, seed. K, same in vertical section.—After Hook. f.

Nux-vomica (Strychnos Nux-vomica *L.*), Tropical Asia, also yielding *Strychnine* ;
St. Ignatius' Beans (Strychnos Ignatii *Berg.*), Philippines ; *Wourali Poison Bark*
(S. toxifera *Schomb.*), Guiana.

229. OLEACEAE

Trees, shrubs or climbers ; leaves *opposite* or very rarely alternate, simple
or *pinnate* ; stipules absent ; flowers hermaphrodite or rarely unisexual,
actinomorphic ; calyx lobed or dentate, rarely absent ; petals present or absent,
free or connate, often 4, imbricate or induplicate-valvate ; stamens hypogynous
or epipetalous, *usually 2*, rarely 4 ; anthers apiculate, 2-celled, *cells back to back*,
opening lengthwise ; disk absent ; ovary superior, *2-celled* ; style simple with a
capitate or bifid stigma ; ovules usually 2 in each cell, axile, pendulous or
ascending ; fruit capsular, baccate or drupaceous ; seeds usually with endosperm ;
embryo straight, the radicle sometimes hidden within the base of the cotyledons.
B.H. 2 : 672. E.P. 4, 2 : 1. Temperate and Tropical Regions.—JASMINUM,
SCHREBERA, FORSYTHIA, SYRINGA, FRAXINUS, PHILLYREA, OSMANTHUS, CHION-
ANTHUS, LINOCIERA, NOTELAEA, OLEA, LIGUSTRUM, etc.

USEFUL PRODUCTS : *American Ash* (Fraxinus americana *L.*) ; *Manna Ash*
(F. Ornus *L.*), S. Europe ; *Common Ash* (F. excelsior *L.*), Europe ; *Iron Wood*
(Notelaea ligustrina *Vent.*), Australia, Tasmania ; *Black Iron Wood* (Olea

laurifolia *Lam.*), S. Africa ; *Olive Tree* (Olea europaea *L.*), S.E. Europe, Asia Minor, widely cultivated, yields *Olive Oil.* Several ornamental trees and shrubs : *Lilac* (Syringa).

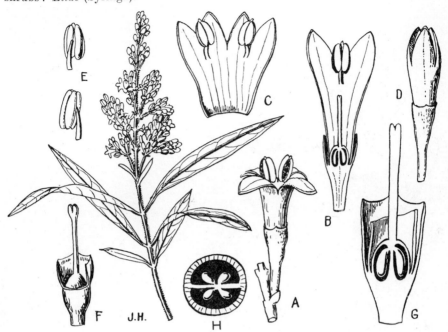

FIG. 229.—Ligustrum Massalongianum *Vis.* (Oleaceae). A, flower. B, same in vertical section. C, same opened. D, bud. E, stamens. F, ovary. G, same in vertical section. H, same in transverse section.—After De Wild.

Order 65. APOCYNALES

Woody or herbaceous ; leaves opposite, simple, without stipules ; petals united ; stamens the same number as the corolla-lobes ; pollen granular or glutinate ; corona often present ; carpels 2, often free, or becoming free in fruit ; styles united above, with a common stigma ; seeds usually with endosperm and straight embryo.—Mainly Tropics.

230. Apocynaceae

Trees, shrubs or climbers, rarely perennial herbs ; leaves *opposite* or *verticillate*, rarely alternate, simple, entire ; *stipules absent* ; flowers ☿, actinomorphic ; calyx often *glandular inside* ; lobes 5 or rarely 4, *imbricate* ; corolla tubular, variously shaped ; lobes *contorted-imbricate*, very rarely valvate ; stamens 5 or rarely 4, inserted in the tube ; filaments free or rarely united ; anthers often *sagittate*, free or connivent around the stigma, rarely adherent to the latter, 2-celled, opening lengthwise, connective often *produced at the apex* ; pollen *granular* ; disk usually present, annular, cupular or of separate glands ; ovary superior, 1-celled with 2 *parietal* placentas or 2-celled with the placentas adnate to the septa, or carpels 2 and free or connate only at the base with ventral placentas in each carpel ; style 1, split at the base or entire, thickened and stigmatose below the apex ; ovules 2 or more in each carpel ; fruit entire and indehiscent or of 2 separate carpels, baccate, drupaceous or follicular ;

FIG. 230.—Allamanda Aubletii *Pohl.* (Apocynaceae).—After Bot. Mag.

seeds mostly with endosperm and large straight embryo, often winged or appendaged with long silky hairs. B.H. 2 : 681. E.P. 4, 2 : 109. Mainly Tropics and Subtropics.—ALLAMANDA, LANDOLPHIA, MELODINUS, CARISSA, ACOKANTHERA, RAUWOLFIA, ALYXIA, CERBERA, ASPIDOSPERMA, VINCA, PLUMERIA, ALSTONIA, TABERNAEMONTANA, PRESTONIA, FORSTERONIA, PARSONSIA,

NERIUM, STROPHANTHUS, APOCYNUM, BAISSEA, FUNTUMIA, ECHITES, DIPLA-
DENIA, MANDEVILLA, etc.

USEFUL PRODUCTS : *Landolphia Rubbers* (Landolphia Heudeloti *A.D.C.*
and L. owariensis *P. Beauv.*, W. Africa ; L. Kirkii *Dyer*), E. Africa ; *Karaunda
Fruits* (Carissa Carandas *L.*), India ; *Arrow Poisons* from Acokanthera Schimperi
Schweinf., E. Tropical Africa, and A. venenata *G. Don*, S. Africa ; *Paddle
Wood* (Aspidosperma excelsum *Bth.*), Guiana ; *Kombe Seeds* (Strophanthus
Kombe *Oliv.*), Tropical E. Africa ; *Silk Rubber Tree* (Funtumia elastica *Stapf.*),
Tropical Africa.

231. ASCLEPIADACEAE

Perennial herbs, undershrubs or shrubs, sometimes climbing ; leaves opposite
or verticillate, very rarely alternate, simple ; stipules absent ; flowers mostly
cymose, ♂, actinomorphic ; calyx-lobes imbricate or open ; corolla 5-lobed,
lobes contorted or valvate ; corona simple or of 5 or more scales, either adnate
to the corolla-tube or the stamens or to both ; stamens 5, mostly inserted at
the base of the corolla ; filaments separate or connate in the tube ; anthers

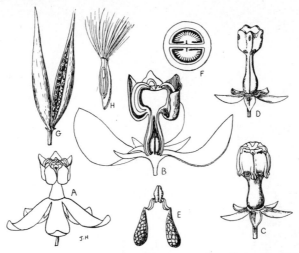

FIG. 231.—Asclepias curassavica *L.* (Asclepiadaceae). A, flower. B, vertical section of same. C, staminal
column. D, pistil. E, pollinia. F, transverse section of ovary. G, fruit. H, seed.—After Baill.

connivent around the stigma and often adnate to it, 2-celled ; pollen granular
or glutinose in masses ; disk absent ; ovary of 2 distinct carpels, superior,
with ventral placentas ; styles 2, distinct, but united at the apex in a common
stigma, the latter thick and often disk-like ; ovules mostly numerous in each
carpel, pendulous in several series ; fruit of 2 often widely divergent follicles ;
seeds often crowned with a beard of long silky hairs, with rather thin endosperm
and large embryo. B.H. 2 : 728. E.P. 4, 2 : 189. Mainly warmer regions,
very numerous in S. Africa, rare in cool countries.—CRYPTOLEPIS, RAPHION-
ACME, PERIPLOCA, SECAMONE, PHILIBERTIA, OXYPETALUM, XYSMALOBIUM,
SCHIZOGLOSSUM, GOMPHOCARPUS, ASCLEPIAS, METASTELMA, DITASSA, VINCE-
TOXICUM, CYNANCHUM, DAEMIA, GONOLOBUS, GYMNEMA, TYLOPHORA, MARS-

DENIA, STEPHANOTIS, PERGULARIA, HOYA, DISCHIDIA, CEROPEGIA, BRACHY-
STELMA, HOODIA, STAPELIA, etc.

USEFUL PRODUCTS : *Indian Sarsaparilla* (Hemidesmus indicus *R. Br.*) ;
Yercum or *Madar Fibre* (Calotropis gigantea *R. Br.*), India ; *Condurango Bark*
(Marsdenia Cundurango *Nichols.*), S. America ; *Rajmahal Hemp* (Marsdenia
tenacissima *W. & A.*), India.

Order 66. RUBIALES

Trees, shrubs or herbs ; leaves opposite, usually stipulate, mostly entire ;
stipules inter- or intra-petiolar ; petals united ; stamens epipetalous,
alternate with the corolla-lobes ; ovary inferior, syncarpous ; placentation
axile ; style 1 ; ovules numerous to one ; seeds mostly with endosperm.—
Mainly Tropics.

232. RUBIACEAE

Trees, shrubs or more rarely herbs ; leaves *opposite* or *verticillate, entire*
or rarely toothed, simple ; stipules often *inter-* or *intra-petiolar*, free or connate,
sometimes *leafy* and indistinguishable from the leaves ; flowers mostly ☿, very
rarely slightly zygomorphic, solitary to capitate ; calyx adnate to the ovary ;

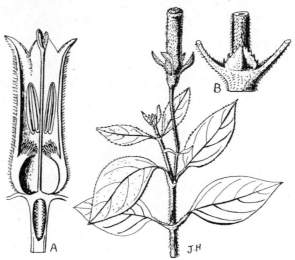

FIG. 232.—Manettia bicolor *Paxt.* (Rubiaceae). A, vertical section of flower. B, stipule.—Orig.

corolla epigynous, more or less tubular ; lobes 4-10, contorted, imbricate or
valvate ; stamens as many as corolla-lobes and *alternate with them*, inserted in
the tube or at its mouth ; anthers mostly free, 2-celled, opening lengthwise ;
ovary inferior, 2- or more-celled with axile, apical or basal placentation, rarely
1-celled with parietal placentas ; style often slender, variously lobed ; ovules
1 to many ; fruit a capsule, berry or drupe ; seeds rarely winged, mostly with
endosperm ; embryo straight or curved. B.H. 2 : 7. E.P. 4, 4 : 1. Generally
distributed, but mostly Tropical.—NAUCLEA, UNCARIA, CINCHONA, CASCARILLA,
BOUVARDIA, MANETTIA, EXOSTEMMA, LUCULIA, BIKKIA, RONDELETIA, WEND-

LANDIA, ARGOSTEMMA, PENTAS, HEDYOTIS, OLDENLANDIA, HOUSTONIA, OPHIOR-
RHIZA, MUSSAENDA, UROPHYLLUM, SABICEA, BERTIERA, ALIBERTIA, POSOQUERIA,
BURCHELLIA, WEBERA, RANDIA, GARDENIA, OXYANTHUS, GUETTARDA, PLEC-
TRONIA, VANGUERIA, IXORA, PAVETTA, COFFEA, MORINDA, FARAMEA, PSYCHOTRIA,
PALICOUREA, CEPHAELIS, LASIANTHUS, LEPTODERMIS, PLOCAMA, NERTERA,
COPROSMA, PHYLLIS, SPERMACOCE, RUBIA, GALIUM, ASPERULA, etc.

USEFUL PRODUCTS : *Quinine* (Cinchona spp.), S. America, much cultivated
in Eastern Tropics ; *Coffee* (mainly Coffee arabica *L.*), E. Tropical Africa,
Arabia ; *Ipecacuanha Root* (Psychotria Ipecacuanha *Stokes*), Tropical S. America ;
Gambier (Uncaria Gambier *Roxb.*), Malaya.

233. CAPRIFOLIACEAE

Shrubs, mostly with rather soft wood and broad pith, rarely herbs ; leaves
opposite, simple or deeply divided ; *stipules absent* or very small ; flowers ⚥,
actinomorphic or zygomorphic, mostly cymose ; calyx *adnate to the ovary*,

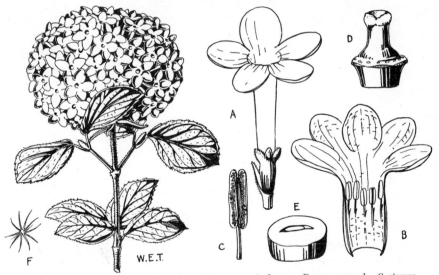

FIG. 233.—Viburnum Carlesii *Hemsl.* (Caprifoliaceae). A, flower. B, same opened. C, stamen.
D, ovary. E, same in transverse section. F, hair.—Orig.

5-fid or toothed ; corolla epigynous, gamopetalous, sometimes *2-lipped*, lobes
imbricate ; stamens inserted on the corolla-tube and alternate with its lobes ;
anthers free, 2-celled, opening lengthwise ; *ovary inferior*, 2-5-celled ; style
terminal, often slender ; ovules 1 or more, pendulous or axile ; fruit a fleshy
berry ; seeds often with bony testa, copious endosperm and often small or
linear straight embryo. B.H. 2 : 1. E.P. 4, 4 : 156. Generally distributed.—
SAMBUCUS, VIBURNUM, SYMPHORICARPUS, ABELIA, LINNAEA, LONICERA, LEYCES-
TERIA, DIERVILLA (*Weigelia*), etc.

USEFUL PRODUCTS : Beautiful ornamental shrubs and climbers. *Common
Elder* (Sambucus nigra *L.*), Europe, etc. ; *American Elder* (S. canadensis *L.*) ;
Snow-berry (Symphoricarpos racemosus *Michx.*) ; *Honeysuckle* (Lonicera Peri-
clymenum *L.*), Europe, etc.

Order 67. ASTERALES

Woody or herbaceous ; leaves various ; no stipules ; flowers mostly crowded into heads surrounded by an involucre of bracts ; anthers mostly united around the style ; ovary inferior, mostly 1-celled with 1 ovule.— World-wide distribution.

234. ADOXACEAE

Small herbs from a perennial rhizome ; stem-leaves 2, opposite, 3-foliolate ; radical leaves variously divided ; flowers small, green, capitate, about 5 in each head, the terminal one often 4-merous, the others 5-6-merous ; calyx 2-3-

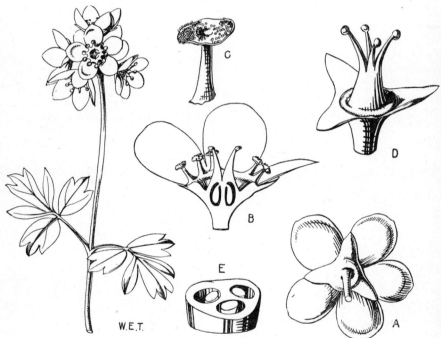

FIG. 234.—Adoxa Moschatellina *L.* (Adoxaceae). A, flower showing 3 calyx-lobes. B, same in vertical section. C, stamen. D, ovary. E, transverse section of same.—Orig.

lobed ; corolla rotate, 4-6-lobed ; disk none ; stamens on the corolla, 4, 5 or 6 (apparently double this number owing to the splitting of the filaments) ; anthers 1-celled ; ovary subinferior, 3-5-celled ; style 3-5-lobed ; ovules solitary in each cell, pendulous ; fruit a drupe of 1-5 pyrenes ; seeds with endosperm and minute embryo. B.H. 2 : 2 (under *Caprifoliaceae*). E.P. 4, 4 : 170 Temperate and cold regions of N. Hemisphere.—ADOXA.

235. VALERIANACEAE

Perennial or annual herbs, often with strong smelling rhizomes ; leaves *opposite* or radical, often much divided ; *stipules absent* ; flowers ♀ or ♂♀,

mostly cymose, often somewhat zygomorphic ; calyx epigynous, various,
sometimes the lobes plumose ; corolla
gamopetalous, tubular ; tube often
saccate or spurred at the base ; lobes
imbricate ; stamens on the corolla-tube,
alternate with the corolla-lobes, usually
4 ; anthers 2-celled, opening lengthwise ; ovary inferior, 3-celled, *only 1
cell fertile* ; style simple, slender ; ovule
solitary, *pendulous* from the top ; fruit
dry and indehiscent, 1-seeded ; embryo
straight ; endosperm absent. B.H.
2 : 151. E.P. 4, 4 : 172. Generally
distributed, but very rare in Africa and
absent from Australasia. — PATRINIA,
PHYLLACTIS, VALERIANA, CENTRANTHUS,
VALERIANELLA, etc.

USEFUL PRODUCTS : *Spikenard* (Nar-
dostachys Jatamansi *D.C.*), Himalayas ;
Valerian Roots (Valeriana officinalis *L.*),
Europe to Japan.

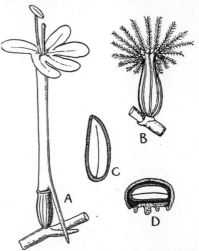

FIG. 235.—Centranthus ruber *L.* (Valerianaceae).
A, flower.   B, achene.   C, longitudinal
section of same.   D, transverse section of
same.

236. DIPSACACEAE

Perennial or annual herbs ; leaves opposite or verticillate ; *stipules absent* ;
flowers ⚥, zygomorphic, often capitate ; calyx epigynous, cupular or divided

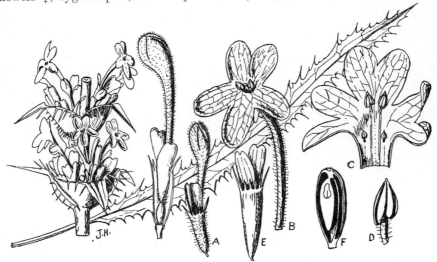

FIG. 236.—Morina longifolia *Wall.* (Dipsacaceae).   A, flower.   B, corolla.   C, corolla opened to show
insertion of stamens.   D, stamen.   E, achene.   F, same in vertical section.—After De Wild.

into *pappus-like segments* ; corolla epigynous, gamopetalous ; lobes imbricate ;
stamens *usually 4*, rarely 2-3, alternate with the corolla-lobes and inserted at
the *bottom of the tube* ; filaments free or *united in pairs* ; anthers 2-celled, opening

lengthwise ; ovary inferior, *1-celled*, mostly adnate to the receptacle ; style slender ; ovule solitary, *pendulous* from the top ; embryo large, straight in scanty endosperm. B.H. 2 : 157. E.P. 4, 4 : 182. Old World ; absent from Australasia, Polynesia, and America except as introductions.—Triplostegia, Morina, Dipsacus, Cephalaria, Scabiosa.

Useful Products : *Fuller's Teazle* (Dipsacus fullonum *L.*), Europe.

237. Calyceraceae

Annual or perennial herbs ; leaves radical or alternate, entire or pinnately lobed ; stipules absent ; flowers *capitate* on a common receptacle surrounded by 1-2 series of *bracts*, ♀ or rarely subunisexual, actinomorphic ; calyx-tube adnate to the ovary, angled and dentate ; corolla tubular, with 4-6 valvate

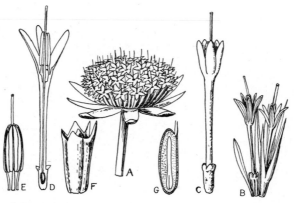

Fig. 237.—Calycera balsamitaefolia *Rich.* (Calyceraceae). A, capitulum. B, flowers showing relation to bracts. C, flower. D, vertical section of same. E, stamens and pistil. F, calyx. G, vertical section of seed showing embryo.—After Le Maout & Decne.

lobes; stamens the same number as and alternate with the corolla-lobes, inserted towards the *top of the tube* ; filaments more or less *connate* ; anthers more or less *connate around the style*, 2-celled, opening lengthwise ; ovary inferior, 1-celled ; style undivided, slender ; ovule solitary, pendulous ; fruits (achenes) sometimes becoming connate ; seed solitary, pendulous, with thin or copious endosperm ; embryo straight. B.H. 2 : 161. E.P. 4, 5 : 84. Temperate and Subtropical S. America.—Boopis, Calycera, Acicarpha.

238. Compositae

Herbs, shrubs or rarely trees or climbers ; leaves alternate or opposite, simple or variously divided ; *stipules absent* ; flowers *crowded into heads* (capitula) surrounded by an *involucre* of one or more series of free or connate bracts ; sometimes the head compound and the partial heads reduced to a single flower ; receptacle bracteate amongst the flowers, honeycombed or nude, usually conical, rarely elongated or hollowed out ; flowers ♀ or ♂ ♀, rarely dioecious, the outer ones often *ligulate* (rayed), the inner ones *tubular* (discoid) ; calyx usually much modified and thread-like (*pappus*), rarely dry and chaffy, epigynous ; corolla epigynous, gamopetalous, 4-5-fid, *valvate*, actinomorphic or zygomorphic, rarely bilabiate ; stamens 5 or rarely 4, epipetalous, mostly included in the corolla-tube ; filaments free from each other ; anthers *connate* (syngenesious) into a tube, very rarely free, 2-celled, opening lengthwise ; ovary *inferior*, 1-celled, 1-ovuled ; style of the ♂ flowers mostly 2-fid or 2-lobed with various forms of collecting hairs which serve to brush out the pollen ; ovule erect from the base ; fruit (achene) sessile, sometimes beaked ; seed without endosperm ; embryo straight with plano-convex cotyledons. B.H. 2 : 163. E.P. 4, 5 : 87. Distribution world-wide.—SPARGANOPHORUS, ERLANGEA, VERNONIA, STOKESIA, ELEPHANTOPUS, AGERATUM, STEVIA, EUPATORIUM, MIKANIA, SOLIDAGO, PTERONIA, BELLIS, ASTER, OLEARIA, CELMISIA, ERIGERON, BACCHARIS,

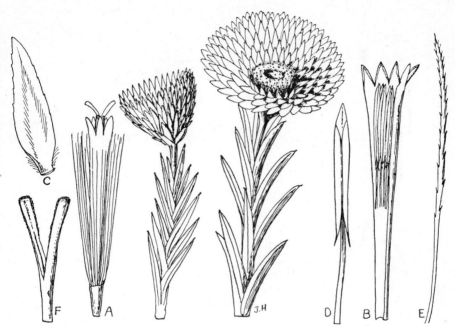

FIG. 238.—Helichrysum leucopsideum *D.C.* (Compositae).   A, disk floret.   B, same opened to show stamens.   C, involucral bract.   D, stamen.   E, pappus bristle.   F, style.—After Hook.

TARCHONANTHUS, SPHAERANTHUS, ANTENNARIA, LEONTOPODIUM, ANAPHALIS, GNAPHALIUM, RAOULIA, HELICHRYSUM, HUMEA, INULA, PULICARIA, BUPHTHAL-MUM, ZINNIA, XANTHIUM, MONTANOA, RUDBECKIA, COREOPSIS, BIDENS, DAHLIA, COSMOS, TAGETES, ACHILLEA, SANTOLINA, ANTHEMIS, CHRYSANTHEMUM, MATRI-CARIA, ARTEMISIA, TUSSILAGO, SENECIO, OTHONNA, CALENDULA, URSINIA, ARCTOTIS, ECHINOPS, CARDUUS, SERRATULA, CENTAUREA, BARNADESIA, MUTISIA, GERBERA, CICHORIUM, CREPIS, HIERACIUM, SONCHUS, LACTUCA, etc.

USEFUL PRODUCTS : *Jerusalem Artichoke* (Helianthus tuberosus *L.*), United States ; *Globe Artichoke* (Cynara Scolymus *L.*) ; *Santonin* (Artemisia Cina *Berg.*), Turkestan ; *Chicory* (Cichorium Intybus *L.*) ; *Lettuce* (Lactuca Scariola *L.*), and numerous minor medicinal products and dyes, besides a great number of ornamental garden plants.

Order 68. GENTIANALES

Herbs with opposite leaves; corolla actinomorphic; stamens epipetalous, the same number as and alternate with the corolla-lobes; disk
often present; ovary
superior, 1 - celled with
parietal placentation; ovules
numerous; seeds with copious
endosperm and small em-
bryo. — Temperate Regions
and Subtropics mainly.

239. GENTIANACEAE

Annual or perennial herbs,
very rarely woody; leaves
opposite, rarely alternate,
often *connate at the base* or
connected by a transverse
line; *stipules absent*; flowers
☿, rarely polygamous, actinomorphic, mostly showy and
bright-coloured; calyx tubular
or of separate sepals, imbricate; corolla gamopetalous,
lobes 4-12, *contorted* or very
rarely imbricate or induplicate-valvate (*Menyantheae*);
stamens the same number as
the corolla-lobes and *alternate
with them,* inserted on the
corolla; anthers 2 - celled,
opening lengthwise; disk
absent or annular or of 5
glands below the ovary;
ovary superior, mostly 1-celled
with *2 parietal placentas,* sometimes 2 - celled with the
placentas adnate to the septa;
style simple; ovules often
numerous; fruit often capsular;
seeds with copious endosperm
and small subterete or conical
embryo. B.H. 2 : 799. E.P.
4, 2 : 50. Mainly Temperate

FIG. 239.—Sabbatia campestris *Nutt.* (Gentianaceae). A, flower
opened. B, stamen. C, transverse of ovary.—After Bot.
Mag.

and Subtropical Regions.—EXACUM, SEBAEA, CHIRONIA, VOYRIA, LEIANTHUS,
BLACKSTONIA (CHLORA), CENTAURIUM (ERYTHRAEA), SABBATIA, CANSCORA,

A   B   C

W.E.T.

FIG. 240.—Primula calciphila *Hutch.* (Primulaceae).   A, vertical section of thrum-eyed flower.
B, same of pin-eyed flower.   C, vertical section of ovary.—Orig.

U

Schultesia, Eustoma, Lisianthus, Gentiana, Swertia, Halenia, Meny-anthes, Villarsia, Limnanthemum, etc.

Useful Products : Bitter properties. *Gentian Root* (Gentiana lutea *L.*), S. Europe, etc. ; *Chiretta* (Swertia Chirata *Hamilt.*), N. India. Many beautiful plants suitable for rock gardening.

Order 69. PRIMULALES

Herbs or rarely climbers ; no stipules ; flowers often subumbellate ; petals united, imbricate ; stamens epipetalous, the same number as and opposite the corolla-lobes ; ovary superior, 1-celled, with free-basal placenta and numerous to solitary ovules ; seeds with or without endosperm.—Mainly mountains of N. Hemisphere and maritime shores.

240. Primulaceae

Perennial or annual herbs, rarely undershrubs ; leaves all basal or some-times cauline, alternate, opposite or verticillate, simple or variously lobate ; flowers from solitary to paniculate or umbellate, bracteate, actinomorphic, very rarely zygomorphic, ♂, often heterostyled ; calyx persistent, often rather foliaceous ; corolla tubular, sometimes split nearly to the base, lobes usually 5, imbricate ; stamens inserted *opposite the petals*, rarely with alternating staminodes ; ovary superior, rarely semi-superior, 1-celled, with a *free-basal* sessile or stipitate placenta ; style simple ; ovules numerous, with 2 integuments ; fruit a capsule, variously dehiscent, usually many-seeded ; seeds angular, with small straight embryo immersed in copious endosperm. B.H. 2 : 628. E.P. 4, 1 : 98. Mostly mountain regions of the N. Temperate Zone, rare in the Tropics and S. Hemisphere.—Hottonia, Primula, Androsace, Cortusa, Soldanella, Dodecatheon, Cyclamen, Lysimachia, Trientalis, Glaux, Anagallis, Coris, Samolus.

Useful Products : Value mainly horticultural.

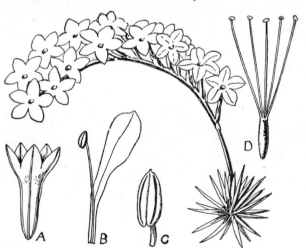

FIG. 241.—Acantholimon venustum *Boiss.* (Plumbaginaceae). A, calyx. B, stamen and petal. C, anther. D, ovary and styles.

241.

Plumbaginaceae

Herbs, under-shrubs or climbers ; stipules absent ; flowers ♂, actinomor-phic, often in uni-lateral inflorescences or subumbellate ; bracts often sheath-ing, dry and mem-branous ; calyx inferior, gamosepal-ous, often conspicu-ously *ribbed*, often *membranous between the lobes* or teeth ; corolla mostly gamo-petalous, imbricate, often persistent; stamens 5, *opposite* to the petals or corolla-lobes and more or less adnate to the tube; anthers 2-celled, opening lengthwise; disk absent; ovary superior, mostly sessile, *1-celled*; styles 5, free or variously connate; ovule 1, pendulous from a *basal funicle*; fruit indehiscent or at length calyptrately dehiscent, rarely valvate from the base upwards; seed with or without endosperm, and straight fairly large embryo. B.H. 2 : 623. E.P. 4, 1 : 116. Mainly maritime shores and mountains; numerous around the Mediterranean.—ACANTHOLIMON, LIMONIUM (STATICE), ARMERIA, PLUMBAGO, CERATOSTIGMA, etc.

USEFUL PRODUCTS : Some of medicinal use, but chiefly of horticultural value.

Order 70. PLANTAGINALES

Characters of the family, below.

242. PLANTAGINACEAE

Herbs; leaves all radical, alternate or opposite, simple, sometimes reduced, often *sheathing at the base*; flowers usually ⚥ and spicate, actinomorphic;

FIG. 242.—Plantago Lagopus *L.* (Plantaginaceae).   A, flower.

calyx herbaceous, *4-lobed* or parted, sometimes the abaxial sepals more or less united ; corolla gamopetalous, scarious, 3-4-lobed, lobes imbricate ; stamens 4 (rarely 1-2), inserted on the corolla-tube and alternate with the lobes or hypogynous ; anthers 2-celled, opening lengthwise ; ovary superior, 1-4-celled ; style simple ; ovules 1 or more in each cell, axile or basal ; fruit a circumscissile capsule or a bony nut ; seeds peltately attached ; embryo straight, in the middle of fleshy endosperm, rarely curved. B.H. 2 : 1223. E.P. 4, 3b : 363. Widely dispersed.—PLANTAGO, BOUGUERIA, LITTORELLA.

USEFUL PRODUCTS : *Ispaghul* or *Spogel Seeds* (Plantago ovata *Forsk.*), N.W. India.

Order 71. CAMPANALES

Herbaceous to somewhat woody ; corolla actinomorphic to zygomorphic, epigynous ; stamens free from or inserted low down on the corolla ; anthers free to connivent ; ovary inferior ; ovules usually numerous, axile.—Mainly Temperate Regions.

243. CAMPANULACEAE

Herbs, rarely small shrubs to small trees, nearly always with *milky juice* ; leaves alternate, rarely opposite, simple ; *stipules absent* ; flowers often showy, ♀, actinomorphic ; calyx-tube adnate to the ovary, 3-10-lobed, lobes imbricate or valvate ; corolla gamopetalous, tubular or campanulate, lobes *valvate* ; stamens as many as the corolla-lobes and alternate with them, inserted towards the *base* of the corolla or on the disk ; filaments usually free from each other ; anthers free, 2-celled, opening lengthwise ; ovary *inferior* or rarely superior, 2-10-celled, with *axile placentas*, rarely the placentas basal or apical ; ovules mostly numerous ; fruit capsular and variously dehiscent or baccate, often crowned by the persistent calyx-lobes. B.H. 2 : 541. E.P. 4, 5 : 40. Widely distributed.— JASIONE, LIGHTFOOTIA, WAHLENBERGIA, PLATYCODON, CODONOPSIS, CYANANTHUS, CANARINA, ROELLA, PRISMATOCARPUS, PHYTEUMA, CAMPANULA, SPECULARIA, ADENOPHORA, TRACHELIUM, etc. Value mainly horticultural.

FIG. 243. — Campanula Allionii *Vill.* (Campanulaceae). A, vertical section of flower. B, ovary. C, transverse section of same. D, stamen.—After Bot. Mag.

244. LOBELIACEAE

Herbaceous, sometimes woody below, rarely entirely woody ; juice often *milky* ; leaves alternate, simple ; stipules absent ; flowers ☿, rarely ♂♀, *zygomorphic* ; calyx adnate to the ovary, 5-lobed ; corolla *zygomorphic*, epigynous, 1-2-lipped, of 5 variously united petals, *valvate* ; stamens 5, alternate with the corolla-lobes, epipetalous or free ; filaments free from each other at the base ;

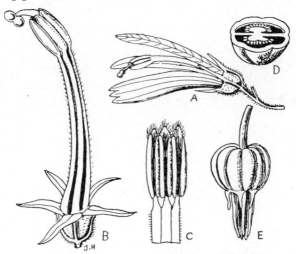

FIG. 244.—Pratia physaloides *Hemsl.* (Lobeliaceae). A, flower. B, same with perianth removed.
C, stamens. D, transverse section of ovary. E, fruit.

anthers *cohering into a tube* around the style ; ovary more or less inferior, 2-3-celled (rarely sub-1-celled) ; style simple, or 2-lobed and girt with a ring of hairs ; ovules numerous, axile ; fruit fleshy or capsular and variously dehiscent ; seeds numerous, small, with small straight embryo in copious endosperm. B.H. 2 : 545. E.P. 4, 5 : 40 (under *Campanulaceae*). Mainly Tropics and Subtropics.—CENTROPOGON, SIPHOCAMPYLUS, ISOTOMA, LAURENTIA, PRATIA, LOBELIA, CYPHIA, etc.

Value mainly horticultural. *Indian Tobacco* (Lobelia inflata *L.*), N. America.

245. GOODENIACEAE

Herbs or undershrubs, rarely spinescent ; leaves alternate or rarely opposite, sometimes all radical ; stipules absent ; flowers from solitary to paniculate, ☿, zygomorphic ; calyx tubular, adnate to the ovary, rarely free ; lobes mostly 5 ; corolla gamopetalous, 5-merous, *bilabiate* or rarely *1-lipped*, lobes *valvate*, often induplicate ; stamens 5,

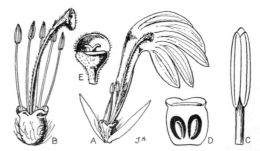

FIG. 245. — Scaevola gracilis *Hook. f.* (Goodeniaceae).
A, flower. B, same with corolla removed. C, stamen.
D, vertical section of ovary. E, stigma.

alternate with the corolla-lobes, free or rarely shortly adnate to the corolla-tube ; anthers free or connivent around the style, 2-celled, opening lengthwise ; ovary mostly inferior, 1-2- (rarely 4-) celled ; style simple or fid ; *stigma indusiate* at the apex ; ovules 1 or more in each cell, mostly erect or ascending ; fruit drupaceous or nut-like, or capsular ; seeds small, flat, with straight embryo in the middle of copious endosperm, incl. *Brunoniaceae.* B.H. 2 : 536. E.P. 4, 5 : 70. Mainly Australian ; a few in New Zealand, Antarctic America, and Tropical Asia.—LESCHENAULTIA, VELLEIA, GOODENIA, SELLIERA, SCAEVOLA, DAMPIERA, BRUNONIA, etc.

USEFUL PRODUCTS : *Taccada Pith* (Scaevola Koenigii *Vahl*), E. Tropics.

246. STYLIDIACEAE

Herbs or rarely undershrubs ; leaves radical or fasciculate on the stems, simple ; stipules absent or rarely scaly ; flowers ♀ or ♂ ♀, mostly zygomorphic, in racemes or corymbs ; calyx-tube adnate to the ovary ; lobes 5-7, free or

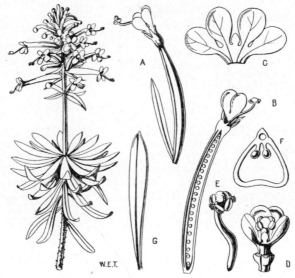

FIG. 246.—Stylidium adnatum, var. abbreviata *De Wild.* (Stylidiaceae). A, flower. B, same in vertical section. C, corolla. D, flower with calyx removed. E, style and stamens. F, transverse section of fruit. G, bract.—After De Wild.

connate and 2-lipped ; corolla gamopetalous, 5-lobed, lobes imbricate, mostly unequal, the lowermost forming a lip ; *stamens 2* ; filaments *connate into a column around the style* but free from the corolla ; disk present or absent, sometimes glandular ; ovary inferior, 2-celled, or 1-celled at the base ; style divided at the apex of the staminal column ; ovules numerous in each cell, axile ; capsule 2-celled or 1-celled by the disappearance of the septum, rarely fruit indehiscent ; seeds small, with fleshy endosperm and minute embryo. B.H. 2 : 534. E.P. 4, 5 : 79 (as *Candolleaceae*). Australia, Tropical Asia, New Zealand, Antarctic S. America.—STYLIDIUM, LEVENHOOKIA, FORSTERA, PHYLLACHNE.

Order 72. POLEMONIALES

Herbs or rarely climbers ; corolla actinomorphic ; stamens epipetalous, alternate with the corolla-lobes ; ovary superior, entire, with numerous or few ovules on parietal or axile placentas.—Mostly American.

247. POLEMONIACEAE

Annual to perennial herbs or rarely small trees or climbing shrubs ; leaves alternate or opposite, entire or palmately or pinnately partite ; flowers ♂, actinomorphic, rarely sub-bilabiate, ter-minal, rarely axillary, often crowded into corymbs or heads ; sepals 5, ± connate ; corolla of 5 united petals, tubular, lobes contorted ; stamens 5, inserted on the corolla and alternate with the lobes, free from one another, included or ex-serted ; anthers 2-celled, opening length-wise ; ovary superior, *inserted on a disk*, 3- (rarely 2-) celled, sessile ; ovules 1 or more in each cell, inserted on the inner angle of the cells ; style 1, filiform ; stigmas 3 or rarely 2 ; fruit a capsule or rarely indehiscent, mostly loculicidal ; seeds mostly with copious endosperm and straight or slightly curved embryo. B.H. 2 : 820. E.P. 4, 3a : 40. Mostly N. America and the Andes ; rare in the Old World.—PHLOX, COLLOMIA, GILIA, POLE-MONIUM, LOESELIA, BONPLANDIA, CANTUA, COBAEA. Value mainly horticultural.

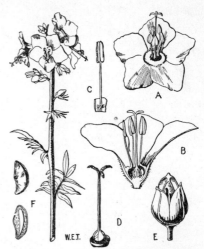

FIG. 247.—Polemonium coeruleum *L.* (Pole-moniaceae). A, flower. B, vertical section of same. C, stamen. D, ovary. E, fruit. F, seeds.—After Le Maout & Decne.

248. HYDROPHYLLACEAE

Annual or perennial herbs, rarely subshrubby, often hairy or scabrid, some-times spiny ; leaves radical or alternate, rarely opposite, entire to pinnately or palmately lobed ; flowers often cymose, ♂, actinomorphic ; calyx-segments mostly 5, imbricate, often with *appendages* between ; corolla gamopetalous, mostly 5-lobed, lobes imbricate or rarely contorted ; stamens the same number as the corolla-lobes and alternate with them, often inserted towards the base of the tube ; anthers 2-celled, opening lengthwise ; disk hypogynous or absent ; ovary superior, 1-celled with *2 parietal placentas* or spuriously or completely 2-celled with the placentas adnate to the septa ; styles 1 or 2 ; ovules often numerous ; fruit a loculicidal capsule, rarely septicidal ; seeds with fleshy endosperm and small straight embryo. B.H. 2 : 825. E.P. 4, 3a : 54. Mainly N. America.—HYDROPHYLLUM, NEMOPHILA, PHACELIA, CODON, WIGANDIA, HYDROLEA. Some useful garden annuals.

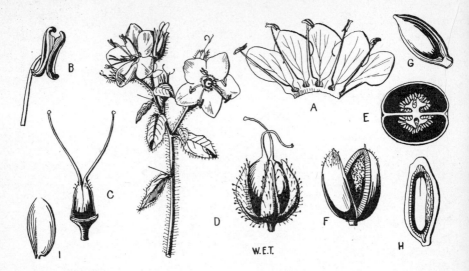

FIG. 248.—Hydrolea spinosა L. (Hydrophyllaceae). A, flower opened. B, stamen. C, ovary. D, fruit.
E, transverse section of same. F, capsule. G, seed. H, vertical section of same. I, ovule.—After
Le Maout & Decne.

Order 73. BORAGINALES

More or less as in *Polemoniales*, but sometimes woody ; ovary often
deeply lobed with gynobasic style, bicarpellate with paired ascending ovules.

249. BORAGINACEAE

Herbs, shrubs or trees, glabrous or often scabrid or hispid ; leaves *alternate*
or very rarely opposite, simple ; *stipules absent* ; flowers often in *scorpioid
cymes*, actinomorphic or rarely oblique, mostly ♀ ; calyx-lobes imbricate or

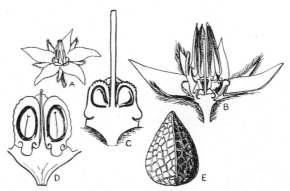

FIG. 249.—Borago officinalis L. (Boraginaceae). A, flower. B, vertical section of same. C, vertical
section of ovary. D, vertical section of fruit. E, seed.

rarely valvate ; corolla with contorted or imbricate lobes ; stamens the same number as the corolla-lobes and alternate with them, inserted on the corolla ; anthers 2-celled, opening lengthwise ; disk present or obsolete ; ovary superior, 2-celled or 4-celled by spurious septa, entire or *deeply 4-lobed* ; style terminal or from the middle of the lobes (*gynobasic*) ; ovules paired, *erect* or spreading from the central axis ; fruit a *drupe* or of *4 nutlets* ; seeds with or without endosperm, and straight or curved embryo. B.H. 2 : 832. E.P. 4, 3a : 71. Widely dispersed, numerous in the Mediterranean region.—CORDIA, BOURRERIA, EHRETIA, COLDENIA, TOURNEFORTIA, HELIOTROPIUM, TRICHODESMA, OMPHA-LODES, CYNOGLOSSUM, RINDERA, ECHINOSPERMUM, ERITRICHIUM, AMSINCKIA, SYMPHYTUM, BORAGO, ANCHUSA, NONNEA, PULMONARIA, ALKANNA, MERTENSIA, MYOSOTIS, LITHOSPERMUM, LOBOSTEMON, ECHIUM, ONOSMA, CERINTHE, etc.

USEFUL PRODUCTS : *Sebesten Tree* (Cordia Myxa *L.*), Egypt, etc. ; *Alkanet Root* (Alkanna tinctoria *Tausch.*), Mediterranean ; *Thé de Montagne* (Lithospermum officinale *L.*), Pyrenees. Some beautiful garden plants.

Order 74. SOLANALES

Mostly herbs or twiners ; leaves alternate ; no stipules ; corolla actinomorphic; stamens the same number as and alternate with the corolla-lobes; ovary superior, 1-4-celled, often 2-celled ; ovules numerous to solitary, axile ; seeds with some endosperm and often curved embryo.—General distribution.

250. SOLANACEAE

Herbaceous or woody ; leaves *alternate*, simple ; *stipules absent* ; flowers ⚥, mostly *actinomorphic* ; calyx 4-6-lobed, persistent ; corolla gamopetalous, usually 5-lobed, lobes folded, contorted or valvate ; stamens inserted on the corolla-tube and alternate with its lobes ; anthers 2-celled, cells parallel, opening lengthwise or by apical pores ; *ovary 2-celled*, the cells sometimes again divided by a false septum ; style terminal ; ovules very *numerous*, axile ; fruit a capsule or berry ; seeds with copious endosperm and curved or annular embryo. B.H. 2 : 882. E.P. 4, 3b : 4. Generally distributed in Temperate and Tropical Regions. —SOLANUM, PHYSALIS, CAPSICUM, WITHANIA, LYCIUM, ATROPA, DATURA, HYOSCYAMUS, JUANULLOA, CESTRUM, NICOTIANA, PETUNIA, SCHIZANTHUS, SALPIGLOSSIS, BRUNFELSIA, SCHWENKIA, etc.

USEFUL PRODUCTS : *Potato* (Solanum tuberosum *L.*), Chile ; *Tomato* (Lycopersicum esculentum *Mill.*), S. America ; *Capsicums* or *Chillies* (Capsicum annuum *L.* and C. frutescens *L.*) ; *Cayenne Pepper* from same source ; *Deadly Nightshade* (Atropa Belladonna *L.*), Europe ; *Tobacco* (Nicotiana Tabacum *L.*), America.

251. CONVOLVULACEAE

Herbaceous or woody, often climbing, juice usually milky ; leaves *alternate*, simple ; *stipules absent* ; flowers ⚥, actinomorphic ; bracts often forming an *involucre* ; sepals usually free, imbricate, persistent ; corolla gamopetalous, mostly funnel-shaped, lobes 5, *contorted* ; stamens 5, inserted towards the *base*

of the corolla-tube and alternate with the lobes ; anthers 2-celled, opening
lengthwise ; ovary often surrounded by a *disk*, 1-4-celled ; ovules *solitary* or
paired, erect ; style terminal ; fruit a capsule or fleshy and indehiscent ; seeds

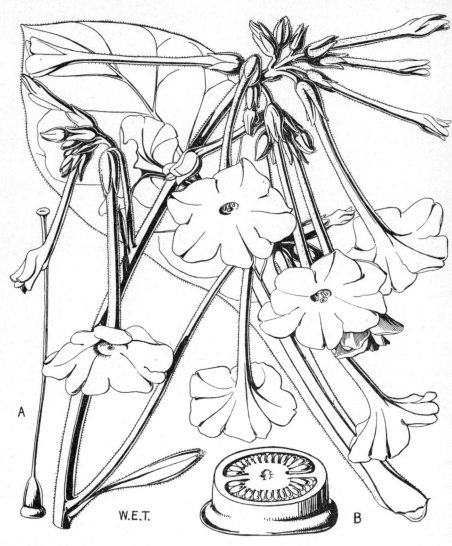

FIG. 250.—Nicotiana fragrans *Hook*. (Solanaceae).   A, ovary.   B, transverse section of same.—
After Bot. Mag.

sometimes hairy, with rather scanty endosperm and more or less *curved* embryo ;
cotyledons *folded* or *crumpled* ; incl. *Nolanaceae*. B.H. 2 : 865.   E.P. 4, 3a : 1.
Generally distributed.—IPOMOEA, HEWITTIA, CALYSTEGIA, JACQUEMONTIA,
CONVOLVULUS, EVOLVULUS, NOLANA, CUSCUTA, etc.

USEFUL PRODUCTS : *Jalap* (Ipomoea Purga *Hayne*), Mexico ; *Sweet Potato* (Ipomoea Batatas *Poir.*), Tropics ; *Scammony* (Convolvulus Scammonia *L.*), Asia Minor.

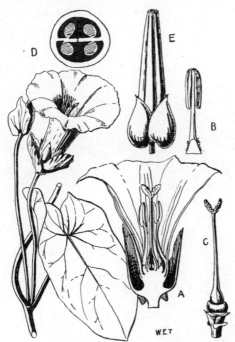

FIG. 251.—Calystegia sepium *R. Br.* (Convolvulaceae).   A, vertical section of flower.   B, stamen.
C, ovary.   D, transverse section of same.   E, bud.

Order 75. PERSONALES

More or less as in preceding ; leaves alternate to opposite ; corolla always zygomorphic ; stamens fewer than the corolla-lobes, often 4 or 2 ; placentation usually axile but some parietal ; ovules numerous.—General distribution.

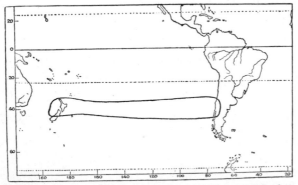

Range of Jovellana (Scrophulariaceae), formerly included in Calceolaria.

252. SCROPHULARIACEAE

Herbs or shrubs, rarely small trees ; leaves alternate, opposite or verticillate ; *stipules absent* ; flowers ♀, mostly *zygomorphic* ; calyx imbricate or valvate ; corolla gamopetalous ; limb 4-5, rarely 6-8-lobed, often more or less *2-lipped*, lobes *imbricate* ; stamens *often 4*, didynamous, or 2, inserted on the corolla-tube and alternate with the lobes, the fifth (adaxial) stamen represented by a *staminode* or absent, rarely perfect ; filaments free from each other ; anthers 2-celled, opening lengthwise or the cells confluent at the apex and opening by one continuous slit, sometimes the anthers connivent in pairs ; ovary superior, sessile,

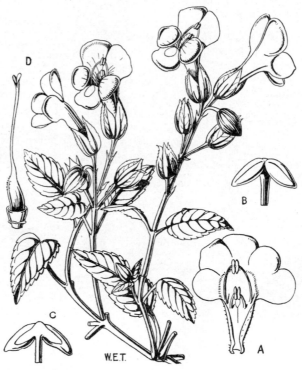

FIG. 252.—Torenia Fournieri *Linden ex Four.* (Scrophulariaceae).   A, flower opened to show insertion of stamens.   B and C, stamen.   D, ovary.—After Bot. Mag.

entire, usually perfectly *2-celled* ; style *terminal* ; ovules axile, *numerous*, rarely few ; fruit a capsule, rarely a berry ; seeds numerous, with fleshy endosperm and straight or slightly curved embryo.   B.H. 2 : 913.   E.P. 4, 3b : 39. Generally distributed.—VERBASCUM, CALCEOLARIA, NEMESIA, LINARIA, ANTIRRHINUM, SCROPHULARIA, PAULOWNIA, PENTSTEMON, SUTERA, MIMULUS, TORENIA, SIBTHORPIA, SCOPARIA, REHMANNIA, DIGITALIS, ERINUS, VERONICA, STRIGA, SOPUBIA, CASTILLEJA, EUPHRASIA, BARTSIA, PEDICULARIS, RHINANTHUS, MELAMPYRUM, etc.

USEFUL PRODUCTS : Mostly of horticultural value. *Foxglove* (Digitalis purpurea *L.*), Europe, etc.

253. OROBANCHACEAE

Herbs *parasitic* on roots, often covered with scales at the base, never green; stems with alternate, often crowded, scales; flowers solitary in the axils of bracts, often crowded, ♀, *zygomorphic*; calyx 4-5-toothed or lobed or variously split, lobes open or *valvate*; corolla gamopetalous, often curved; limb oblique or 2-lipped, lobes 5, imbricate, the adaxial 2 interior; *stamens 4*, didynamous, inserted below the middle of the corolla-tube, alternate with the lobes, the fifth (adaxial) one reduced to a *staminode* or absent; anthers often connivent

FIG. 253.—Cistanche laxiflora *Aitch. & Hemsl.* (Orobanchaceae). A, ovary. B, same in transverse section. C, corolla. D, stamen.—After Hemsl.

in pairs, opening lengthwise; ovary superior, 1-celled, with 4 *parietal* placentas; style terminal; ovules numerous; capsule often enveloped by the calyx, opening by 2 valves; seeds very numerous, small, with fleshy endosperm and minute embryo. B.H. 2 : 980. E.P. 4, 3b : 123. Rather scattered distribution.—AEGINETIA, CHRISTISONIA, PHELIPAEA, CISTANCHE, OROBANCHE, LATHRAEA, etc.

254. LENTIBULARIACEAE

Herbs of wet or damp places, sometimes epiphytic; leaves in rosettes or alternate and reduced to scales; flowers scapose, ♀, *zygomorphic*; calyx 2-5-parted, lobes open or slightly imbricate; corolla gamopetalous, *spurred* at the back; limb 2-lipped, lobes 5, imbricate; *stamens 2*, inserted at the base of the corolla, with 2 *rudimentary* stamens; anthers 1-2-celled, opening lengthwise ; disk absent ; ovary superior, 1-celled ; stigma often sessile ; ovules numerous on *basal* globose or ovoid placenta ; fruit a capsule opening irregularly

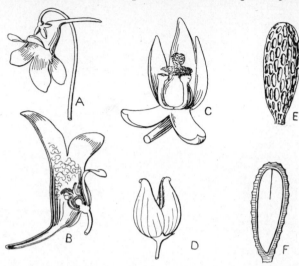

FIG. 254.—Pinguicula vulgaris *L.* (Lentibulariaceae). A, flower. B, vertical section of same. C, same with corolla removed. D, fruit. E, seed. F, vertical section of same.—After Baill.

or by 2 or 4 valves ; seeds numerous, without endosperm. B.H. 2 : 986. E.P. 4, 3b : 108. Temperate and Tropical Regions.—Utricularia, Genlisea, Pinguicula, Polypompholyx.

255. Columelliaceae

Trees or shrubs ; leaves *opposite*, simple ; stipules absent ; flowers in terminal cymes, ⚥, slightly zygomorphic ; calyx-tube *adnate to the ovary* ; lobes

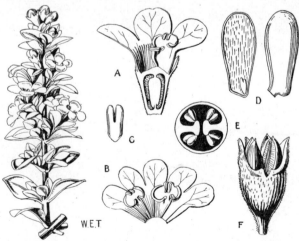

FIG. 255.—Columellia obovata *R. & P.* (Columelliaceae). A, vertical section of flower. B, flower opened. C, embryo. D, seed. E, transverse section of ovary. F, capsule.

5, scarcely imbricate ; corolla gamopetalous ; tube very short, subcampanulate ; lobes usually 5, imbricate ; *stamens 2*, inserted near the base of the corolla, alternate with the adaxial and lateral lobes ; anther-cells undulately *plicate* and *twisted* ; disk absent ; ovary almost quite *inferior*, imperfectly 2-celled ; style terminal ; ovules numerous on 2 *parietal* placentas which are subcontiguous in the middle of the ovary ; fruit a capsule ; seeds numerous, with fleshy endosperm and minute straight embryo. B.H. 2 : 989. E.P. 4, 3b : 186. Andes of S. America.—COLUMELLIA.

256. GESNERIACEAE

Herbs, shrubs or rarely trees ; leaves radical or opposite, equal or alternately large and small, sometimes the smaller one like a stipule, or the alternate one altogether reduced ; flowers ♀, usually zygomorphic, often large and showy ; calyx usually tubular, free to completely adnate to the ovary ; lobes *valvate* or rarely imbricate ; corolla with an *oblique limb*, often more or less 2-lipped,

FIG. 256.—Aeschynanthus Peelii *Hk. f. & Thoms.* (Gesneriaceae). A, flower opened to show insertion of stamens. B, ovary. C, transverse section of same. D, fruits. E, seeds.—After Hook. f.

lobes imbricate, the adaxial pair usually interior ; stamens 4 or 2, often with an additional staminode ; anthers *connate* or *connivent* in pairs, rarely free, 2-celled, opening lengthwise ; disk annular or 1-sided or of separate glands or scales ; ovary superior to inferior, 1-celled, with 2 *parietal* or *intrusive* placentas ; ovules numerous ; fruit a capsule or rarely a berry ; seeds numerous, small, with or without endosperm ; embryo straight. B.H. 2 : 990. E.P. 4, 3b : 133. Mainly Tropics and Subtropics.—GLOXINIA, ACHIMENES, ISOLOMA, GESNERIA, PENTARHAPHIA, EPISCIA, ALLOPLECTUS, COLUMNEA, CYRTANDRA, AESCHY-NANTHUS, BESLERIA, DIDYMOCARPUS, CHIRITA, STREPTOCARPUS, RAMONDIA, HABERLEA, SINNINGIA, etc.

USEFUL PRODUCTS : Mainly of horticultural value ; many beautiful green-house plants.

257. BIGNONIACEAE

Trees or shrubs, sometimes scandent, very rarely herbs ; leaves *opposite*, rarely alternate, mostly *compound*, digitate or pinnate, sometimes the terminal

Fig. 257.—Catalpa speciosa *Warder* (Bignoniaceae). A, ovary. B, stamens and staminodes. C, fruit.
D, seed.—Partly orig.

leaflet tendril-like ; stipules absent ; flowers often showy, ⚥, more or less *zygo-morphic* ; calyx campanulate, closed or open in bud, truncate or 5-toothed ; corolla with 5 imbricate lobes sometimes forming 2 lips, the upper of 2, the lower of 3 lobes ; stamens alternate with the corolla-lobes, only 4 or 2 perfect ; anthers *connivent in pairs* or rarely free, 2-celled, opening lengthwise ; staminode representing the fifth stamen often short, sometimes absent, often 3 present when only 2 stamens ; disk usually present ; ovary superior, 2-celled with 2 placentas in each cell or 1-celled with 2 *parietal* bifid placentas ; style terminal, 2-lipped ; ovules *numerous* ; fruit capsular or fleshy and indehiscent ; seeds often *winged*, without endosperm ; embryo straight. B.H. 2 : 1026. E.P. 4, 3b : 189. Tropics and Subtropics. — BIGNONIA, MACFADYENA, ADENO-CALYMNA, ANEMOPAEGMA, PITHECOCTENIUM, CATALPA, TABEBUIA, TECOMA, NEWBOULDIA, SPATHODEA, DOLICHANDRONE, STEREOSPERMUM, INCARVILLEA, ECCREMOCARPUS, JACARANDA, CRESCENTIA, KIGELIA, etc.

USEFUL PRODUCTS : *West Indian Boxwood* (Tabebuia pentaphylla *Hemsl.*). Ornamental trees (*Catalpa*, etc.).

258. PEDALIACEAE

Annual or perennial herbs ; leaves opposite or the upper alternate, simple ; stipules absent ; flowers ⚥, zygomorphic ; calyx of 5 or 4 segments or 4-fid or spathaceous ; corolla gamopetalous, often oblique ; lobes 5, imbricate ; stamens

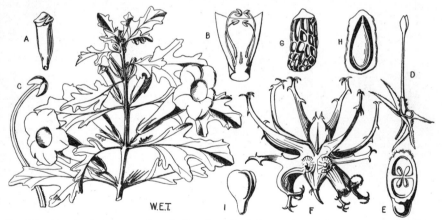

FIG. 258.—Harpagophyton procumbens *L.* (Pedaliaceae). A, bud. B, stamens and staminode. C, stamen. D, style. E, transverse section of ovary. F, fruit. G, seed. H, vertical section of same. I, embryo. —Partly orig.

4 or rarely only 2 perfect, alternate with the corolla-lobes ; anthers *connivent in pairs*, 2-celled, cells distinct, parallel or divaricate, opening lengthwise ; fifth stamen often represented by a *staminode* ; disk hypogynous, fleshy ; ovary sessile, 1-celled with 2 *intrusive parietal* placentas or 2-4-celled, the cells again often divided by spurious septa ; style terminal ; ovules solitary or numerous on each placenta ; fruit a capsule, nut, or subdrupaceous ; endocarp hardened and often *horned* or *prickly* ; seeds without endosperm ; embryo with flat cotyledons ; incl. *Martyniaceae*. B.H. 2 : 1055. E.P. 4, 3b : 253. Warm regions, most abundant in Africa.—MARTYNIA, PEDALIUM, HARPAGOPHYTUM, SESAMUM, etc.

Useful Products : *Grapple Plant* (Harpagophytum procumbens *D.C.*), S. Africa ; *Oil of Sesamum* (from Sesamum indicum *L.*), cultivated.

259. Acanthaceae

Herbaceous or climbing, rarely somewhat shrubby ; leaves opposite, often with distinct *cystoliths* ; stipules absent ; flowers ☿, *zygomorphic*, often with

B

A

W.E.T.

Fig. 259.—Thunbergia laurifolia *Lindl.* (Acanthaceae).   A, stamens.   B, ovary.—After Bot. Mag.

conspicuous bracts ; calyx-segments or lobes 4 or 5, imbricate or valvate, rarely the calyx reduced to a ring ; corolla gamopetalous, *2-lipped* or sometimes

1-lipped, lobes imbricate or contorted; *stamens 4*, didynamous or 2, inserted on the corolla-tube and alternate with its lobes; filaments free amongst themselves, or partially connate in pairs; anthers 2-celled or 1-celled by reduction, cells confluent or separated, sometimes one *much smaller* than the other, opening lengthwise; disk present; ovary superior, sessile on the disk, 2-celled; style simple; ovules axile, 2 or more in each cell; fruit a capsule, often club-shaped, mostly elastically dehiscent from the apex downwards, the valves recurved and leaving the central axis; seeds mostly with *indurated funicle*; endosperm rarely present; embryo large. B.H. 2 : 1060. E.P. 4, 3b : 274. Warm regions. —Thunbergia, Ruellia, Strobilanthes, Blepharis, Acanthus, Barleria, Asystasia, Eranthemum, Lepidagathis, Aphelandra, Justicia, Beloperone, Dianthera, Jacobinia, Thyrsacanthus, Dicliptera, Hypoestes, etc. Mainly of horticultural value.

Order 76. LAMIALES

As in preceding groups but leaves mostly opposite or whorled, rarely alternate; ovary often deeply lobed with gynobasic style; ovules mostly paired; flowers often bilabiate; stamens 4 or 2; ovules mostly paired.— General distribution.

260. Globulariaceae

Shrubs or undershrubs; leaves *alternate*, simple; stipules absent; flowers *capitate*, ☿, *zygomorphic*, arranged on a scaly receptacle and surrounded by an

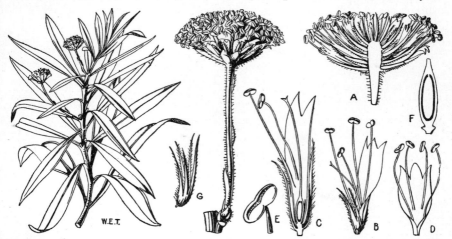

Fig. 260.—Globularia salicina *Lam.* (Globulariaceae). A, capitulum. B, flower. C, vertical section of same. D, stamens showing insertion. E, stamen. F, vertical section of ovary. G, calyx.

involucre of numerous bracts; calyx 5-lobed, actinomorphic or rarely 2-lipped; corolla gamopetalous; limb 1-2-lipped, lobes imbricate; stamens 4, inserted at the top of the corolla-tube, and alternate with the lobes; anthers *reniform*, at first 2-celled, at length the cells confluent and opening by a *single slit*; ovary superior, *1-celled*, inserted on a short disk or the latter gland-like or absent; style 1; ovule solitary, *pendulous*; fruit enveloped by the persistent calyx,

mucronate ; seeds with straight embryo in the middle of fleshy endosperm.
B.H. 2 : 1130 (under *Selaginaceae*). E.P. 4, 3b : 270. N. Temperate Old World.
—GLOBULARIA, LYTANTHUS, COCKBURNIA.

261. MYOPORACEAE

Shrubs or rarely trees ; indumentum sometimes *lepidote* or *plumose* ; leaves
alternate or rarely opposite, simple ; stipules absent ; flowers axillary, solitary

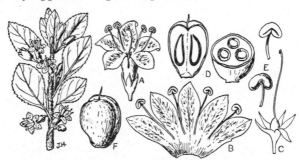

FIG. 261.—Myoporum viscosum *R. Br.* (Myoporaceae). A, flower. B, same opened. C, ovary.
D, sections of fruit. E, stamens. F, fruit.

or fasciculate, ♂, *zygomorphic* ; calyx deeply 5-lobed or 5-fid, imbricate or open ;
corolla gamopetalous, usually 5-lobed, lobes imbricate ; stamens 4 or rarely
the same number as the corolla-lobes, inserted on the corolla-tube and alternate
with the lobes ; anthers 2-celled, but the cells often *divergent* and confluent
at the apex, opening lengthwise ; ovary superior, normally 2-celled, cells
2-ovuled and ovules collateral, or 4-8-ovuled and ovules superposed in pairs,
rarely with numerous cells ; style simple ;
ovules pendulous from near the top of the
central axis ; fruit drupaceous ; seeds with
thin or scarcely any endosperm and straight
or slightly curved embryo. B.H. 2 : 1123.
E.P. 4, 3b : 354. Mascarene Islands to
Australia and Japan. — MYOPORUM, PHO-
LIDIA, EREMOPHILA, OFTIA, BONTIA.

262. SELAGINACEAE

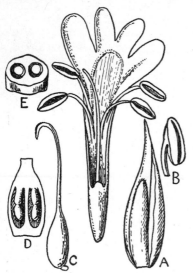

FIG. 262. — Hebenstretia comosa *Hochst.*
(Selaginaceae). A, bud. B, stamen.
C, ovary. D and E, sections of same.

Herbs or undershrubs ; leaves *alternate*
or subopposite, simple, *mostly ericoid* ;
stipules absent ; flowers ♂, zygomorphic,
often spicate ; calyx persistent, 3-5-toothed
or lobed, rarely of 2 free sepals ; corolla
gamopetalous ; tube sometimes split ; limb
4-5-lobed, lobes imbricate ; stamens on the
corolla-tube, alternate with the lobes, 2, 4
or 5 ; *anthers 1-celled*, opening lengthwise ;
ovary superior, 2-celled ; style terminal,
simple ; ovules *solitary* from the top of each
cell ; fruit of two *unequal carpels* separating

when ripe, one often *sterile* or obsolete ; seeds with straight large embryo in the middle of fleshy endosperm. B.H. 2 : 1126. E.P. 4, 3b : 80 (under *Scrophulariaceae*). S. Africa, Mascarene Islands, E. Tropical Africa.—HEBENSTRETIA, SELAGO, etc.

263. VERBENACEAE

Herbaceous or woody, often with *quadrangular* branchlets ; leaves usually *opposite* or whorled, simple or compound ; stipules absent ; flowers ☿, zygomorphic ; calyx 4-5-lobed or toothed, persistent ; corolla gamopetalous, tubular, 4-5-lobed, lobes imbricate ; stamens on the corolla, 4 or rarely 2, rarely 5 ; anthers 2-celled, cells often divergent, opening lengthwise ; ovary superior, 2-8-celled, often 4-celled ; *style terminal,* simple ; ovules solitary or paired,

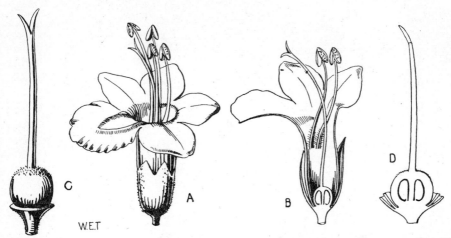

FIG. 263.—Vitex Agnus-castus *L.* (Verbenaceae). A, flower. B, vertical section of same. C, ovary. D, vertical section of same.—After Baill.

erect or rarely pendulous ; fruit a drupe or berry ; seeds with straight embryo and scanty or no endosperm ; incl. *Phrymaceae.* B.H. 2 : 1131. E.P. 4, 3a : 132. Mostly Tropics and S. Temperate.—LANTANA, LIPPIA, BOUCHEA, STACHYTARPHETA, VERBENA, PETRAEA, CITHAREXYLUM, DURANTA, CALLICARPA, AEGIPHILA, TECTONA, PREMNA, VITEX, CLERODENDRON, HOLMSKIOLDIA, AVICENNIA, etc.

USEFUL PRODUCTS : *Fiddle Wood* (Petitia domingensis *Jacq.*), West Indies ; *Teak Wood* (Tectona grandis *L.*), India to Malaya. Some beautiful garden plants.

264. LABIATAE

Herbaceous or rarely woody, often odoriferous ; stems usually *quadrangular* ; leaves *opposite* or whorled, simple ; stipules absent ; flowers ☿, zygomorphic, rarely almost actinomorphic, *axillary or whorled* ; calyx persistent, of 5 variously united sepals, often 2-lipped ; corolla gamopetalous, hypogynous, tubular ; lobes 4-5, imbricate, often forming 2 lips or rarely 1 lip ; stamens on the corolla-tube, 4 or 2 ; anthers 2-celled, cells often *divergent,* opening lengthwise ; ovary superior, of *2 deeply lobed carpels,* the style (*gynobasic*) rising from the inner base of the lobes ; stigma mostly bifid ; ovules 4 in each ovary, *erect* ; fruit of

4 achene-like *nutlets*, free or cohering in pairs; seeds with usually straight embryo without endosperm, or the latter very scanty. B.H. 2 : 1160. E.P. 4, 3a : 183. Widely distributed. — OCIMUM, ACROCEPHALUS, MOSCHOSMA, HOSLUNDIA, PLECTRANTHUS, COLEUS, HYPTIS, LAVANDULA, POGOSTEMON, ELSHOLTZIA, MENTHA, ORIGANUM, THYMUS, MICROMERIA, CALAMINTHA, SALVIA, ROSMARINUS, NEPETA, DRACOCEPHALUM, SCUTELLARIA, BRUNELLA, SIDERITIS,

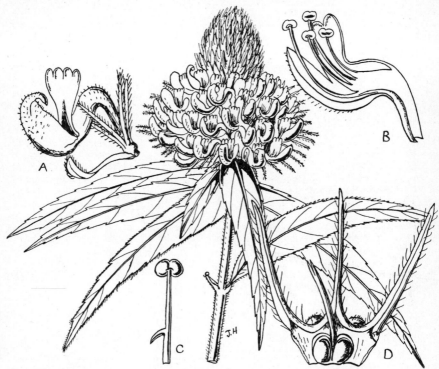

FIG. 264.—Pycnostachys Dawei *N.E.Br.* (Labiatae). A, flower. B, same in longitudinal section. C, stamen. D, fruit.—After Bot. Mag.

MARRUBIUM, STACHYS, LEONURUS, LAMIUM, BALLOTA, LEUCAS, PHLOMIS, PROSTANTHERA, TEUCRIUM, AJUGA, etc.

USEFUL PRODUCTS : *Mint* (Mentha viridis *L.*); *Lavender Oil* (Lavandula vera *D.C.*), S. Europe; *Patchouli* (Pogostemon Heyneanus *Bth.*), India; *Peppermint* (Mentha piperita *L.*).   Culinary herbs are : *Marjoram* (Origanum Marjorana *L.*), *Thyme* (Thymus vulgaris *L.*), and *Sage* (Salvia officinalis *L.*); *Rosemary* (Rosmarinus officinalis *L.*); *Chinese Artichoke* (Stachys Sieboldii *Miq.*), China.

GLOSSARY

abaxial, away from the axis.

abortion, suppression of parts usually present.

accumbent, lying against.

achene, small dry indehiscent fruit containing a single seed.

actinomorphic (*regular*), capable of vertical division into equal halves through two or more planes.

acyclic, floral parts in whorls.

adaxial, next the axis.

adnate, united to a member of another series.

aestivation, arrangement of sepals or petals in bud.

amentiferous, bearing catkins.

anemophilous, wind-pollinated.

apocarpous, separate carpels.

aril, appendage arising from the funicle and often covering the seed.

articulate, jointed.

axile, attached to the central axis.

baccate, berry-like.

bilabiate, 2-lipped.

bisexual, with two sexes in the same flower or inflorescence.

calyx, outer envelope of a flower of the *Dicotyledons*, often green or scarious.

capitate, head-like.

capsule, dry fruit (composed of more than one carpel) which opens.

carpel, a fruit leaf.

catkin, a close bracteate, often pendulous spike.

cell, compartment of an ovary or anther.

circinate, inwardly coiled upon itself, like a watch-spring.

circumscissile, opening transversely all around.

cleistogamous, fertilisation within the unopened flower.

compound, composed of several similar parts, as a leaf of several leaflets.

conduplicate, folded together lengthwise.

connate, when similar parts are united.

contorted, twisted in bud, such as sepals or petals which overlap on one side only.

corolla, the inner envelope of the flower.

corona, a ring of appendages (sometimes united) on the inside of the petals or corolla.

cotyledon, seed leaf.

cyclic, floral parts in whorls.

deciduous, not evergreen.

dehiscent, opening spontaneously.

diadelphous, in two bundles (as in *Papilionaceae*, with one stamen separate from the other nine).

digitate, diverging from the same point like the fingers of a hand.

dimorphic, of two forms.

dioecious, male flowers on one individual, females on another.

discoid, like a disk; applied to *Compositae* without ray flowers.

disk, an enlargement of the receptacle within the calyx, petals or stamens.

embryo, rudimentary plant still enclosed in the seed.

endosperm, the nutritive food material within the seed.

entomophilous, insect pollinated.

epigynous, above the pistil or gynaecium.

epipetalous, on the petals or corolla.

epiphyte, growing or supported on another plant.

exstipulate, without stipules.

extrorse, facing outwards.

follicle, a several-seeded fruit, resulting from a separate carpel opening by one suture.

free basal placentation, ovules arranged on a basal placenta in a 1-celled ovary (see Fig. 240, p. 289).

free central placentation, ovules on a central placenta reaching from the bottom to the top of a 1-celled ovary (see Fig. 53, p. 128).

gamopetalous (= sympetalous, monopetalous), a corolla with the petals partially or wholly united.

gamosepalous, sepals more or less united.

glandular, clothed with glands.

gynaecium (pistil), the female part of the flower (in the middle), consisting of free or united carpels, with style or stigma.

gynobasic, a style which arises from the base of the carpels or ovary lobes (as in Fig. 249, p. 296).

gynophore, a stalk supporting the ovary.

herb, not woody.

hermaphrodite, with stamens and pistil in the same flower.

hypogynous, parts inserted below the gynaecium or pistil.

imbricate, overlapping ; applied to sepals or petals with one or more wholly outside or inside and some half out and half in.

incumbent, lying on.

indehiscent, not opening.

indumentum, the hairy covering.

induplicate, folded inwards.

indusiate, like an indusium or small cup.

inferior, below, as the ovary below the other parts of the flower.

interpetiolar, between the petioles.

intrapetiolar, within the petiole.

introrse, facing inwards.

irregular, see *zygomorphic*.

legume, pod opening by two sutures (cf. *Papilionaceae*).

lepidote, clothed with scales.

loculicidal, opening into the cells.

monadelphous, in one bundle.

monochlamydeous, a flower with only one whorl of the perianth.

monocotyledon, a plant with only one seed-leaf.

monoecious, unisexual flowers on the same plant.

ochreate, sheathing, as the stipules in *Polygonaceae*.

opposite, inserted at the same level.

ovary, the lower part of the pistil containing the ovules.

ovule, the potential seed.

parietal placentation, ovules attached to the walls of a 1-celled syncarpous ovary (see Fig. 93, p. 161).

pellucid, translucent.

pendulous, hanging down.

perennial, lasting for more than two seasons.

perianth, the floral envelope or envelopes.

perigynous, placed around the ovary but free from it.

phalange, a bundle of stamens.

pistil, see *gynaecium*.

placenta, the part of the ovary to which the ovules are attached.

plicate, folded like a fan.

pollen, the powdery contents of an anther.

polygamous, flowers male, female and hermaphrodite on the same plants.

polypetalous, petals free from each other.

protandrous, anthers ripening before the stigmas.

protogynous, stigmas receptive before the anthers open.

punctate, dotted.

racemose, inflorescence with stalked flowers on a single axis.

radical, leaves from the base of the plant.

radicle, embryonic root.

receptacle, part of the floral axis bearing the sepals, petals, stamens and carpels.

regular, see *actinomorphic*.

ruminate, endosperm into which the inner layer of the testa protrudes.

septate, divided by partitions.

septicidal, a fruit which opens between the cells.

simple, the opposite of compound.

spike, inflorescence with sessile flowers on a single elongated axis.

spur, a hollow horn-like extension of a part of the flower.

staminode, an abortive, sometimes much modified or reduced, stamen.

stellate, star-like.

stigma, the receptive part of the style.

stipe, the stalk of a carpel or pistil.

stipitate, furnished with a stipe.

stipules, usually small appendages to the leaf or petiole.

stoma (pl. *stomata*), the breathing apparatus in the epidermis of leaves.

style, the narrow part of the pistil bearing the stigma.

superior, above, as an ovary above the other parts of the flower.

superposed, placed one above another.

syncarpous, composed of united carpels.

testa, seed coat.

tetradynamous, four long and two short.

torus, see *receptacle*.

umbel, an inflorescence the branches of which spring from the same point.

unisexual, of one sex.

valvate, margins of sepals or petals not overlapping.

valves, of anthers which open by flaps (as in Fig. 19, p. 97).

vernation, folding of leaves in bud.

zygomorphic (*irregular*), flowers which may be divided into equal halves in only one plane.

INDEX

Family names in clarendon; common names in italics.

Y

Printed in Great Britain by R. & R. CLARK, LIMITED, Edinburgh.